GENETIC EFFECTS
OF RADIATIONS

GENETIC EFFECTS
OF RADIATIONS

By

C. E. PURDOM, B.Sc., Ph.D.

1963

ACADEMIC PRESS
NEW YORK, NEW YORK

Published in U.S.A. and Canada by
ACADEMIC PRESS INC., PUBLISHERS
111 Fifth Avenue, New York 3, New York

PRINTED IN GREAT BRITAIN

PREFACE

In 1927, H. J. Muller demonstrated that the exposure of germ cells to X-rays resulted in changes in the hereditary material. This finding aroused immense interest in biological circles but received scant attention elsewhere. The situation changed rapidly, however, with the use of atomic energy for military purposes. The explosion of atomic or nuclear weapons produces widespread dispersion of radioactive debris, the radiation from which has effects on germ cells similar to the effects which Muller demonstrated for X-rays. This is not the only source of radiations harmful to Man; they also come from outer space, from radioactive materials in the earth's crust, from radiological practices in medical diagnosis and treatment, and from peaceful uses of atomic energy. But it was the sudden increase in the level of radiation dosage to which all populations are exposed following the explosions of nuclear weapons, that focused general attention on radiation hazards.

Civilized Man has always been conscious of the hereditary links binding him to his ancestors and to his descendants. Indeed, the family link, from which derives concepts of tribe, race and nationality, has been one of the most potent directive forces of social evolution. The key factor is the transmissibility of hereditary material from parents to offspring. Although insight into the nature of this transmission, which constitutes the central problem of the science of genetics, has been gained only during the last half century, its implications have been apparent throughout the course of Man's history. Any agency which can affect the hereditary transmission of human characters is obviously of prime importance for the human species as a whole.

Considerable progress has been made in the study of radiation genetics since Muller's initial discovery. Much scientific literature has been written on the subject and several reviews and reports have been sponsored by national and international bodies. Much of this literature has been written for the specialist in one or other branch of science. In this book an attempt has been made to present the essential features of radiation genetics in a form readable by persons with no specific knowledge of either biology or physics. The book is intended, therefore, in the first place for the intelligent layman, although it is hoped that it may also prove useful to students and workers in other fields of scientific research.

I am indebted to many friends and colleagues for advice and assistance with the preparation of this book. In particular I should like to record my thanks to Dr. T. C. Carter for reading the entire manuscript,

v

and to Mr. M. J. Corp, Dr. M. F. Lyon, Mr. S. Abrahams, Dr. J. R. K. Savage, Dr. J. Godfrey and Dr. A. G. Searle for reading parts of the text. Finally, I should like to express my gratitude to Mr. T.W. McSheehy for his help in the preparation of many diagrams and in the reading of proofs.

C. E. P.

Medical Research Council,
Radiobiological Research Unit,
Harwell.

1963.

CONTENTS

PLATES

(Between pages 92 and 93)

1
BASIC RADIATION PHYSICS
ATOMIC STRUCTURE

ATOMS

An *atom* is the smallest particle to which an element can be sub-divided by chemical means. Further sub-division by physical means has shown that the atom consists of a small dense *nucleus*, with a diameter of about 10^{-12} centimetres, around which one or more *electrons* orbit. The electrons have a small mass, $9 \cdot 1 \times 10^{-28}$ grammes, and carry a unit negative charge; they may occupy one or more of seven orbital shells. The number of orbital shells occupied depends on the number of electrons in the atom, normally the outer shells are not occupied unless the inner shells are already filled. The nucleus is a closely bound aggregate of *protons* and *neutrons*; a proton is a particle of mass $1 \cdot 67 \times 10^{-24}$ grammes (1843 times as heavy as an electron), carrying a unit positive electric charge; a neutron is an uncharged particle of almost the same mass as a proton.

As the protons are positively charged, and the neutrons are uncharged, an atomic nucleus has a net positive charge equal to the charge on its protons. There are as many orbiting electrons as there are protons in the nucleus, so the atom as a whole has no net charge. A helium atom, which is one of the simplest, has a nucleus consisting of two protons and two neutrons, and there are two planetary electrons which occupy one orbit. A uranium atom, one of the most complex, has 92 protons and 142 neutrons in its nucleus, and 92 planetary electrons which normally occupy seven orbits.

ISOTOPES

The chemical nature of an atom is determined by the number of planetary electrons, and therefore by the charge on the nucleus. This is called the *atomic number*. Two atoms will be chemically similar, therefore, if they have the same atomic number, i.e. the same number of protons in their nuclei, even though they may have different numbers of neutrons and therefore different atomic masses. Thus, for example, all carbon atoms have six protons in their nuclei (or they would not be atoms of carbon), but the atoms of naturally occurring carbon have three types of nuclei: 98·9 per cent have six neutrons, 1·1 per cent have seven, and a very small minority has eight. Thus the masses of the nuclei, in terms of the mass of a proton, are 12, 13 and 14, respectively. Such different forms of chemically identical atoms are called *isotopes* and may be distinguished by postfixing the atomic mass to the name of the element: carbon 12, carbon 13 and carbon 14.

RADIOACTIVITY

NATURAL RADIOACTIVITY

Almost all the atomic nuclei occurring in nature are extremely stable. A few, however, are unstable; they include carbon 14, potassium 40 and some of the heavy elements, uranium, radium and thorium. For stability the constituent protons and neutrons must be present in an approximately balanced ratio. If there are too many protons or too many neutrons the nucleus tends to eject some or all of the excess, thereby changing into a different nucleus in which the ratio of protons to neutrons approximates more closely to that required for stability. Such spontaneous change of an atomic nucleus is called *radioactivity*. The carbon 12 and carbon 13 nuclei are stable, but the carbon 14 nucleus is unstable and tends to undergo radioactive disintegration. It has too many neutrons, so one of these changes into a proton and an electron; the electron is ejected; the residual nucleus has seven protons and seven neutrons and is stable, being in fact a nucleus of the common isotope of nitrogen, namely nitrogen 14.

INDUCED RADIOACTIVITY

The number of radioactive substances occurring in nature is quite small. Artificial radioactive isotopes, however, can be produced at will. In an atomic reactor there are very large numbers of free neutrons. These, being uncharged, are not repelled by the positive charge on an atomic nucleus; they may collide, therefore, with the nuclei of any materials put into the reactor. When this happens the neutron may enter the nucleus giving rise to a heavier isotope which may be radioactive. The isotope initially formed is often very unstable and undergoes immediate radioactive disintegration, ejecting a particle which is not necessarily a neutron and thereby resulting in a nucleus which is not necessarily the same as the original. In this and other ways artificial radioactive isotopes can be made of almost all the naturally occurring elements and of some which do not occur in nature. There are artificial isotopes of carbon, for instance, with atomic masses 10, 11 and 15. The carbon 14 found in nature has also, in fact, been formed through a nuclear reaction; it arises through the reaction of nitrogen 14 in the upper atmosphere with energetic radiations from outer space; the carbon 14 being later carried to the lower atmosphere as carbon dioxide.

RADIOACTIVE DECAY

The instant at which the nucleus of a radioactive isotope will disintegrate cannot be predicted. What can be specified is the probability

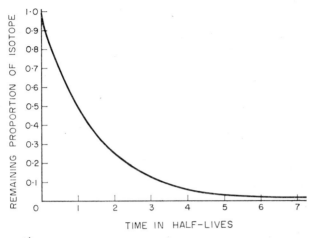

TIME IN HALF-LIVES

FIG. 1. EXPONENTIAL DIE-AWAY CURVE FOR RADIOACTIVE DECAY

that it will disintegrate in a given period of time. In a sample containing many radioactive nuclei, statistical fluctuations in the rate of disinte-

TABLE 1. HALF-LIVES OF SOME RADIOACTIVE ISOTOPES OF BIOLOGICAL INTEREST

Element	Isotope	Half-life
Thorium	Th^{232}	$1 \cdot 39 \times 10^{10}$ y
Uranium	U^{238}	$4 \cdot 50 \times 10^{9}$ y
Potassium	K^{40}	$1 \cdot 40 \times 10^{9}$ y
Carbon	C^{14}	5,700 y
Radium	Ra^{226}	1,620 y
Strontium	Sr^{90}	25 y
Hydrogen	H^{3}	$12 \cdot 5$ y
Cobalt	Co^{60}	$5 \cdot 25$ y
Thallium	Tl^{204}	$2 \cdot 7$ y
Sulphur	S^{35}	$87 \cdot 1$ d
Zirconium	Zr^{95}	65 d
Niobium	Nb^{95}	35 d
Phosphorus	P^{32}	$14 \cdot 3$ d
Iodine	I^{131}	$8 \cdot 04$ d
Radon	Rn^{222}	$3 \cdot 825$ d
Gold	Au^{198}	$2 \cdot 7$ d
Sodium	Na^{24}	$0 \cdot 625$ d

gration even out, and disintegration appears to be occurring at a steady rate. During a given period of time, a specifiable fraction of the radioactive nuclei initially present will therefore disintegrate. This fraction is independent of all environmental conditions such as temperature, pressure and the state of chemical combination of the radioactive substance. The length of time required for the disintegration of half the radioactive atoms initially present, which is characteristic for each isotope, is called its *half-value period* or less accurately, its *half-life*. The half-life of carbon 14 is 5700 years; other radioactive isotopes are known with half-lives as short as fractions of a second and as long as thousands of millions of years. After two half-lives a quarter of the radioactive nuclei is still present, after three an eighth, and so on. This exponential decay curve is illustrated in Fig. 1 and the half-lives of some isotopes of biological interest are given in Table 1.

RADIOACTIVE EQUILIBRIUM

Many radioactive nuclei do not change into stable nuclei in one step; they give rise to intermediate radioactive nuclei. One example is uranium, which gives rise to thirteen intermediate radioactive substances before becoming a stable isotope of lead; the intermediates include radium and the chemically inert gas radon. Where the parent substance has a long half-life, the daughter substances will be formed at an approximately constant rate; this is the case with uranium, which has a half-life of 4.5×10^9 years. Each daughter-product decays at its characteristic rate, and therefore comes into a state of equilibrium at which formation and decay are balanced. The number of atoms of each radioactive substance present at equilibrium is in proportion to its half-life; the long-lived intermediates are present in relatively great abundance, the short-lived in relatively small quantities. For example, the numbers of atoms of uranium, radium and radon in a sample at equilibrium are in the ratios $4.5 \times 10^9 : 1.59 \times 10^3 : 9.5 \times 10^{-3}$.

PARTICLES FROM RADIOACTIVE NUCLEI

There are several types of particles which may be ejected when a radioactive nucleus disintegrates. Two have already been mentioned, namely electrons and neutrons. By a historical accident the electrons ejected in nuclear disintegrations are commonly known by another name, β-particles; this was the name used by the early workers on radioactivity. A third type of particle which may be ejected from a radioactive nucleus was also named by the early workers in this field, namely the α-particle; it has subsequently been shown to be identical with the nucleus of a helium atom, which consists of two neutrons and two protons. An α-particle therefore has mass 4, relative to a proton, and positive electric charge 2. α-particles are emitted more especially during the disintegration of the heavy radioactive nuclei.

The particle ejected when a radioactive nucleus disintegrates has an initial speed which is characteristic of the nuclear change. In the case of carbon 14 the initial speed of the ejected β-particle (i.e. electron) is equal to the speed which an electron attains when it is accelerated from rest by an electric potential of 155,000 volts; in other words, its initial energy is 0·155 mega electron volts (MeV). Particle energies are usually expressed in terms of MeV or, if lower, kilo electron volts (keV) or electron volts (eV).

WAVE RADIATIONS FROM RADIOACTIVE NUCLEI

When a particle is ejected from a radioactive nucleus it may not carry away all the excess energy which was the cause of the nuclear instability. In that event the remaining excess energy may be emitted, simultaneously or later, as a pulse of electromagnetic radiation. This is wave-radiation of the same kind as radio, infra-red, visible and ultra-violet radiation, but of much shorter wavelength; it is known as γ-radiation, and the quantity of energy emitted is called a *photon*. The quality of γ-radiation, like that of all electromagnetic radiation, can be specified by its wave-length, λ, or its frequency, ν; the common practice, however, is to specify the energy, E, carried away by each photon; this is related to its frequency by Planck's equation

$$E = h\nu$$

where h is a constant which has the value $4·14 \times 10^{15}$ eV-seconds. The energy of a γ-ray photon is thus expressed in the same units as the energy of ejected particles.

Not all nuclear disintegrations are accompanied by the emission of γ-radiation. Where a γ-ray photon is emitted, its energy, which depends on the type of nucleus, may lie anywhere in the range from a few thousand to about 10^8 eV. γ-radiation of still higher energy is known; it constitutes the γ-ray component of the *cosmic radiation* which it is thought reaches the earth from outer space.

γ-rays are much used in biological research and in cancer therapy. Before 1950 radium was usually used as a source of γ-rays, but since then it has been largely displaced by various artificial isotopes. These include cobalt 60 which emits γ-rays of energy 1·22 MeV; and caesium 137 which emits γ-rays of energy 0·66 MeV.

Since the emission of γ-rays from a radioactive source is continuous, they are eminently suitable for work entailing long-term exposure, i.e. chronic irradiation. Their disadvantage lies in the fact that they cannot be switched off; they must therefore be surrounded by sufficient shielding material when the irradiation is to be discontinued. This limits the

2

strength of γ-ray emitting sources that can be used in laboratory or clinical work.

X-RAYS

ORIGIN OF X-RAYS

When a charged particle is moving very fast, it will suffer a momentary force of repulsion or attraction should it pass into the immediate neighbourhood of another electric charge. The moving particle will therefore be subjected to a sudden change of velocity and will yield up energy. Most of the kinetic energy is transformed into heat but if the particle was moving sufficiently fast, and the change of velocity sufficiently great, a small part of the energy will reappear as electromagnetic radiation. This will occur especially when an electron, which has a small mass and can therefore easily attain great speeds, passes close to a highly charged body such as an atomic nucleus of a heavy element. The electromagnetic radiation emitted is known as *X-radiation*. It is of exactly the same kind as γ-radiation, and covers the same range of energies, differing only in the manner of its origin.

The energy carried away by a photon of X-radiation cannot exceed the energy of the incident particle which gave rise to it. It may be less, because the particle may continue moving, though with a reduced energy. The X-radiation arising when a heavy element is bombarded by high-speed charged particles therefore covers a continuous spectrum of energies, up to but not exceeding that of the incident particle. Some energies at the low-energy end of the spectrum may, however, be favoured; these are the energies corresponding with natural frequencies of the inner-orbit electrons of the heavy atom, which may resonate when the high-speed particle passes between them and the nucleus. These favoured frequencies are therefore characteristic of the material bombarded, in contrast with the general broad spectrum, which depends mainly on the energy of the incident particles.

PRODUCTION AND USE OF X-RAYS

An X-ray tube (Fig. 2) consists essentially of a heated filament which acts as a source of electrons, and a heavy-element target which is at a high positive potential with respect to the filament; the space between the filament and target is evacuated. Electrons leaving the filament are attracted towards the target and hit it at a high speed. Much of the energy is eventually degraded to heat; the target may melt if the heat is not conducted away sufficiently fast and this limits the rate of operation of the tube. X-ray tubes usually operate at potentials between 50,000 and one million volts; the X-rays used in biological research are very often generated in machines working at about 250,000 volts. More energetic X-rays, from machines working at up to 30 million volts, are sometimes used in cancer therapy. Still more energetic X-rays can be produced from particle accelerating machines such as betatrons

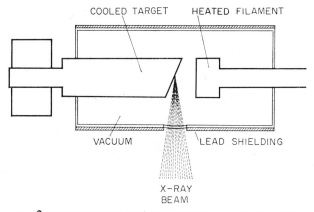

COOLED TARGET   HEATED FILAMENT

VACUUM   LEAD SHIELDING

X-RAY
BEAM

FIG. 2. DIAGRAMMATIC REPRESENTATION OF AN X-RAY TUBE

and synchrotrons. X-ray machines are eminently suitable for the production of intense beams of radiation, and have the big advantage that they can be switched off, leaving a radiation-free space; but they are ill-suited to continuous operation, partly because of the difficulty of cooling the target.

EFFECTS OF RADIATIONS ON MATTER

CHARGED PARTICLES

When a moving charged particle enters a space which is already occupied by the atoms of some material it is subjected to forces of attraction and repulsion due to the charged particles in the atoms. This will have various effects, depending on the relative speeds of the incident particle and the atomic particle, how closely they approach one another, and the magnitude of their charges.

If the charged particle is moving fairly slowly, it will be subjected to a steadily increasing force of attraction or repulsion as it approaches a planetary electron or nucleus of the material through which it is moving. It will therefore be deflected from its path. If the incident particle is one of many constituting a beam, they will then be scattered through the material. The angle of deflection, and therefore the degree of scattering, will depend on the speed of the incident particle and its mass relative to the atomic particle. Slow electrons will be scattered most of all, since they are as light as the atomic planetary electrons and much lighter than the atomic nuclei. Heavy charged particles, such as α-particles, are much heavier than planetary electrons and will therefore be deflected by atomic nuclei, most of which are heavier than α-particles. If the incident charged particle is moving faster, the force of attraction or repulsion between it and an atomic particle will be a sudden impulse rather than a steadily increasing and decreasing force. If the atomic particle is one of the planetary electrons, it will recoil relative to the rest of the atom, instead of the atom recoiling as a whole. Where the amount of energy transferred to the electron is small, it may recoil out of its orbit into a supernumerary orbit, normally unoccupied, which is slightly further away from the nucleus and in which the electron has a higher energy. The atom is then said to be in a state of *excitation*. It will subsequently revert to its normal state, the excess energy being used up in the formation of chemical bonds, or emitted as low-energy electro-magnetic radiation (*fluorescence*), or degraded to heat. If the amount of energy transferred from the incident particle to the electron is greater, the electron may recoil completely out of its atom; the atom is then left electrically charged and is said to be *ionised*. Such charged atoms, or *ions*, are chemically very reactive.

If the incident charged particle is moving very fast, and it passes near an atomic nucleus, some of its energy may be dissipated as X-radiation. This process has been described above. It occurs especially when the nucleus carries a large electric charge, i.e. when it is of a heavy element; it occurs only to a slight extent in biological tissues, which are composed mainly of light atoms.

The most important effects of charged particles on biological tissues are the chemical effects produced through ionisation and, to a lesser extent, excitation. The extent to which these occur, and their depth distribution in the tissue, depend on the nature and the initial speed of the charged particles. In general, the faster a particle is moving, and the heavier it is, relative to its charge, the less will it be deflected through proximity to an atomic particle, and the further apart will be the events at which it yields up energy. The initial part of its track will therefore tend to be straight and leave a sparse trail of ionised or excited atoms behind it; the later part of the track, where the particle is moving only slowly, will tend to have frequent changes of direction and leave a trail of densely ionised or excited material. α-particles, being much heavier than electrons, move much less rapidly than electrons of the same energy; they are therefore more densely ionising. Slow electrons are more densely ionising than fast electrons, for the same reason. Further-more, there is a limit to the depth of penetration of a beam of charged particles in matter, depending on the energy of the incident beam. This limit is usually quite low. The maximum range of the α-particles from radium, for example, is only about 4 cm. in air; in biological tissues it is very much less, about 0·07 mm; a 500,000-volt electron has a range of only about 1·7 mm in biological tissues. This severe limitation of the range of charged particles in tissues can be turned to advantage in

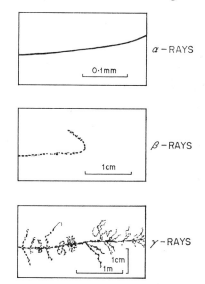

FIG. 3. IONISATION TRACKS PRODUCED BY RADIATIONS IN MATTER

some types of biological research: it makes it possible to irradiate strictly limited volumes of tissue, even down to parts of single cells.

The appearance of ionisation tracks produced by α-, β- and γ-rays are shown in Fig. 3.

NEUTRONS

Neutrons, being uncharged, are not attracted or repelled by the planetary electrons or nuclei of material through which they pass. Since they are so much heavier than planetary electrons, the main mechanism by which they yield up energy is by collision with nuclei. Such a collision usually produces one or other of two effects: first there may be recoil and, therefore, scattering; second, the neutron may enter the nucleus, i.e. it may be *captured*. Recoiling collisions are especially important where the material traversed by the neutrons is rich in hydrogen, as, for example, water and biological tissues. A hydrogen nucleus consists of only a proton and, since a proton and a neutron are of nearly the same mass, the hydrogen nucleus may recoil with any speed up to that of the incident neutron; tissue irradiated with neutrons thus has large numbers of protons moving about near the track of each neutron. Neutron irradiation is therefore densely ionising. Neutrons are always eventually captured; this may lead to the simultaneous ejection of a particle, or emission of a γ-ray photon, or both; or it may lead to the formation of a heavier isotope, which may be either radio-active or stable. In any event, neutron irradiation leads to the produc-tion of numerous charged particles and ions in the tissue, leaving it in a chemically reactive state.

The fact that neutrons are uncharged, and therefore free to pass un-hindered between atoms, being stopped only in the event of a collision with a nucleus, implies that they will penetrate far into most materials; the distance travelled between collisions is of the order of centimetres in biological tissues, and there may be many collisions before eventual capture. Just how far a neutron will penetrate before colliding with a nucleus will depend on the number of atoms per unit volume and the size of the target (i.e. the area of cross section) that each nucleus pre-sents to the neutron in its flight. For a parallel beam of neutrons of any given energy the number penetrating, i.e. the number N_x crossing a given area normal to their line of flight at a given depth x from the surface of the material, will be related to the number N_0 in the incident beam by the exponential die-away relationship

$$N_x = N_0 \, e^{-\mu x}$$

where μ is a constant called the *coefficient of absorption*. μ is not the same for neutrons of all energies, but is higher for low-energy neutrons. The neutron-stopping power of a material, therefore, progressively increases as the neutron slows down in the course of its penetration; this leads to a complex distribution of the neutrons within the material.

γ-RAYS AND X-RAYS

Photons of electromagnetic radiation are oscillating pulses of energy, without electric charge, and therefore they continue along a straight line in their passage between the atoms of a material. When a photon collides with a charged atomic particle, however, it induces the particle to oscillate and therefore yields up some or all of its energy. The effects of a collision between a γ- or X-ray photon and an atomic particle are various, and depend on the energy of the photon.

If the photon is of relatively low energy and it collides with a planetary electron, the electron may absorb the energy of the photon. This addi-tional energy may drive the electron into an alternative orbit, i.e. it may cause excitation of the atom; or it may drive the electron right out of the atom and so ionise it. The action of a low-energy photon is therefore essentially the same as that of a low-energy electron, and the later consequences are also the same, chemical action or fluorescence, and heat production.

If the photon is rather more energetic, a planetary electron may not be able to absorb all its energy. In that event the process known as *Compton scattering* may occur: the photon is scattered, the electron takes up much of its energy and recoils rapidly, and a photon of lower energy X-irradiation is emitted which carries the rest. When a narrow beam of γ- or X-rays passes through material, the material directly irradiated and its immediate neighbourhood are therefore filled with recoiling electrons; scattered lower-energy X-radiation penetrates even further. In any event, the net effect is to produce ionisation and excitation of the material.

It follows, therefore, that the net effect of ionising radiations in matter is much the same whatever the nature of the radiation. The incident radiation penetrates into the material and is attenuated through interactions with atomic nuclei and planetary electrons. These interactions eventually give rise to ionisation or excitation of atoms in the material irradiated. The distribution and relative proximity of the ionisation and excitation differ between different radiation types, however, and this has important consequences in the biological mode of action of ionising radiations: this will be described in greater detail in Chapter 6.

The depth of penetration of a beam of γ- or X-ray photons of a given energy into matter is dependent on the probability of a collision between a photon and one of the atomic charged particles of the material irradiated. The problem is similar to that of the penetration of neutrons. If the intensity of an incident parallel beam is I_0, the intensity I_x at a depth x will be given by

$$I_x = I_0\, e^{-\mu x}$$

where μ is the coefficient of absorption by the materials of X-rays of the energy in question. The absorption coefficient is not independent of photon energy, being greater for photons of low energy. High energy photons therefore penetrate further; they constitute *hard radiation*, as opposed to *soft radiation* such as X-rays generated at a potential of a few thousand volts.

Dense material, in which the atomic particles are closely packed, is more effective at stopping γ- or X-rays. For this reason lead and concrete made with barium instead of calcium compounds, are frequently used where it is desired to provide great shielding power with a reasonably thin layer of shielding material. Where very powerful sources of radioactivity are being manipulated, metallic uranium is occasionally used for shielding. Failing these, it is necessary to use great thickness of some less dense material, such as ordinary concrete or earth.

In the last few paragraphs it has been assumed that the incident radiation constitutes a parallel beam. Normally, however, it will be diverging outwards from a small source such as the target of an X-ray tube or a small piece of radioactive material. In this case, the intensity of radiation becomes progressively less at positions further removed from the source. For a given source strength, the intensity of the radiation decreases as the reciprocal of the square of the distance from the source; this is commonly called the *inverse square law*.

OTHER ELECTROMAGNETIC RADIATIONS

As we have noted, X-rays and γ-rays represent the short wavelength regions of a continuous spectrum of radiations that also includes radio, infra-red, visible and ultra-violet rays. The spectrum with the approximate limits is shown in Fig. 4.

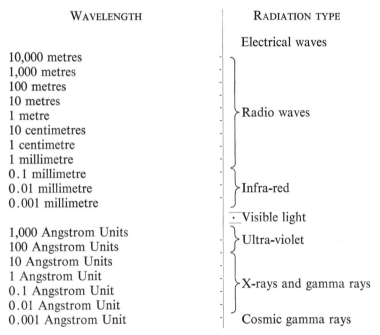

WAVELENGTH	RADIATION TYPE
	Electrical waves
10,000 metres	
1,000 metres	
100 metres	
10 metres	
1 metre	Radio waves
10 centimetres	
1 centimetre	
1 millimetre	
0.1 millimetre	
0.01 millimetre	Infra-red
0.001 millimetre	
	Visible light
1,000 Angstrom Units	Ultra-violet
100 Angstrom Units	
10 Angstrom Units	
1 Angstrom Unit	X-rays and gamma rays
0.1 Angstrom Unit	
0.01 Angstrom Unit	
0.001 Angstrom Unit	Cosmic gamma rays

FIG. 4. THE SPECTRUM OF ELECTROMAGNETIC RADIATION

In addition to X- and γ-rays, radiations from two other regions in this spectrum will be mentioned in the following chapters; these are the infra-red and ultra-violet regions. Neither of these two types of radiation produces ionisations when they pass through matter. Ultra-violet rays, however, produce excitations by the displacement of planetary electrons and this, we have noted, is also a property of the ionising radiations. The excitations produced by ultra-violet rays are not distributed in tracks, as they are in the case of ionising radiations, but are uniformly dispersed in the matter being irradiated; each excitation arises through the complete absorption of the energy of a photon. Infra-red rays are not sufficiently energetic to produce excitation; their energy is dissipated only as local heat.

ENERGY ABSORPTION IN MATTER

The usual measure of an ionising radiation in biological work is the amount of energy absorbed per unit mass of tissue. This is called the *radiation dose*; the unit of dose is the *rad*, which is defined as an energy absorption of 100 ergs per gramme of tissue. Radiation doses can be measured directly, by measuring the temperature rise; the amount of energy in a radiation beam is almost always small, however, and the temperature rise therefore also small, so other methods are normally used.

The radiation dose to a piece of material is commonly found by making measurements of the dose of radiation at its surface, or in small cavities in it, and using them to calculate the distribution of ionisation in the material. The actual measurements are therefore made in air. For γ- and X-rays (other than those of very high energy, which present special problems) the radiation dose in air is measured in terms of a unit called the *röntgen* (r); this is the quantity of γ- or X-radiation which produces in 0·00129 gramme of air (the amount of air in one cubic centimetre at normal temperature and pressure) one electrostatic unit of electricity of either sign. By a fortunate coincidence a γ- or an X-ray beam which produces 1 e.s.u. of electricity in this amount of air gives a dose of almost exactly 1 rad to soft tissue, so for many purposes the rad and the röntgen can be treated as equivalent.

Radiation produces other effects besides ionisation (e.g. fluorescence in some materials), but since the röntgen is defined in terms of static electricity, i.e. the amount of ionisation, this is the effect chosen for the primary standard of measurement. The radiation is allowed to enter a space containing two electrodes, separated by air or some other gas, which are at different electric potentials. The ions produced in the gas by the radiation, flow towards one or other electrode, according to sign, and therefore constitute an electric current. This current, although small, can be measured directly or after suitable amplification. This is called the *ionisation chamber* method of measurement and is the standard method where the *dose rate* needs to be measured with great accuracy. A simple ionisation chamber is illustrated in Fig. 5.

The total dose, integrated over a period of time, can be measured by allowing the ionisation current to discharge a capacitance. The gold-leaf electroscope was an early form of such an instrument. Nowadays pocket ionisation chambers are used, in which one plate of the capacitance is a metal-coated quartz fibre held under tension; it is attracted towards the other plate, and the distance between them is a measure of the charge. In another form of instrument the chamber consists of a wire at the axis of a tube; it is held at an electric potential, with

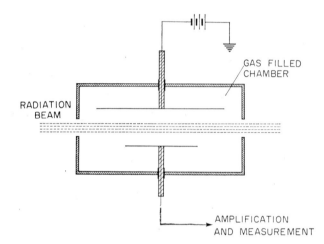

FIG. 5. SIMPLE IONISATION CHAMBER

respect to the tube, which is just not quite sufficient to cause a discharge in the gas between them. When an ionising particle or wave photon enters the space between them, the ionisation triggers a complete discharge, after which the potential builds up again. The chamber therefore discharges once per ionising particle or photon. This device is called a *Geiger counter*, its essential features are shown in Fig. 6.

Neutron dosimetry uses the same general principles, but is complicated by the fact that the neutrons themselves are not charged particles, and therefore the effect measured is more remote from the primary effect than is the case with charged particles and electromagnetic radiations. Ionisation chambers are commonly used, filled with some gas which is rich in hydrogen or boron, and the effect measured is the ionisation current due to the protons or α-particles liberated when the neutrons collide with these.

Ultra-violet and infra-red radiation, neither of which produces ionisation in matter, are measured in terms of direct energy absorption; i.e.

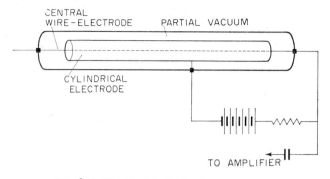

CENTRAL
WIRE-ELECTRODE   PARTIAL VACUUM

CYLINDRICAL
ELECTRODE

TO AMPLIFIER

FIG. 6. BASIC FEATURE OF THE GEIGER COUNTER

in ergs per gramme of irradiated material. Usually, a lamp with standard output is used, the total dose is calculated from the absorption co-efficient of the irradiated material, the distance the material lies from the lamp and the duration of exposure.

The particles emitted by a radioactive substance were first detected through their power of inducing a chemical action, namely blackening of a photographic plate. This method can be used quantitatively by comparing the plate with others, developed in the same solutions, which had been exposed to standard radiation sources. It is not a very accurate method, but it is admirable for use wherever a simple, light instrument is needed and great accuracy is not required, or where it is desired to have a permanent record of the exposure, or where the tracks of indi-vidual particles must be located. Its widest application is in film-badges which are small pieces of photographic film in light-proof containers worn on the lapels or fingers of workers in radiation laboratories. They are developed every week or two, together with films given standard exposures, and thereby provide an estimate of the total exposure which the worker has received during the period.

2

PRINCIPLES OF HEREDITY

MECHANISMS OF INHERITANCE

It seems probable that Man has held theories on the mechanisms of inheritance since the Neolithic age (approx. 5000 B.C.) when he first began to domesticate animals and grow crops for food. The problems of inheritance were certainly in the minds of theologians and philosophers several centuries before Christ as evidenced by passages in Hebrew scriptures referring to the inheritance of original sin, and by writings of the ancient Greeks, particularly Hippocrates, on the inheritance of a trait "longheadedness". This latter peculiarity was thought to have been produced originally by the lateral compression of the heads of the new-born. The commonly held concept was, therefore, that characters that had been developed during the lifetime of an individual were passed on to his offspring. This process has been called *the inheritance of acquited characters.*

A second concept of equal antiquity concerned the nature of the semen, the material by which characters are passed from father to offspring. The semen was thought to come from all parts of the body and to be stored in the testes. This idea, which was termed *Pangenesis*, and the inheritance of acquired characters were widely held until the nineteenth century and at this time received detailed study and widespread popularity at the hands of eminent scientists. Notably they were studied by Jean Baptiste Lamarck, who associated them with evolution by suggesting that the environment stimulated inherited adaptation, and by Charles Darwin, who showed clearly the complementary nature of the two ideas and associated them with a more reputable theory of evolution, *natural selection or survival of the fittest.*

The concepts of Pangenesis and the inheritance of acquited characters aroused considerable interest during the nineteenth century but no convincing proof of their veracity was obtained. Negative evidence was forthcoming, however, and this led to the postulation of the *germ-plasm* theory by the German biologist August Weismann. This theory was directly opposed to the idea of the inheritance of acquired characters. Weismann's theory was that the reproductive or germ cells were quite distinct from the cells that made up the rest of the body, the *soma*. The germ-plasm could not, therefore, be affected by factors which influenced the development of the soma. Subsequent embryological evidence confirmed this view: at an early stage in the development of an embryo, prior to the extensive differentiation of cells into blood, bones, nerves, etc., a small group of cells are "set aside" as the presumptive germ cells.

These new facts were diametrically opposed to the concept of Pangenesis, and, as a corollary of this, at variance with the hypothesis of the inheritance of acquired characters. The latter still retained a somewhat diminished appeal, however, since the only alternative theory was that of blending inheritance. This theory offered no explanation of the mechanism of inheritance, merely presuming that the offspring carried a mixture or blend of their parents' characters. This blend differing from that of the parents in the sense that a chemical compound differs from its constituent elements; the mechanism of transmission of material from one generation through another to a third was not clearly defined. The resolution of this problem finally came through the work of Gregor Mendel, published in 1866 in the proceedings of a little known Natural History Society. The work escaped immediate notice and its immense significance was not realised until its rediscovery in 1900.

SEGREGATION

In the first part of his work Mendel showed that the material inherited by an individual from its parents did not blend, but remained as discrete units which were passed on to the next generation in the same form as they were received from the first. Furthermore, any one character* in an individual was governed by two units, one having been received from each parent.

These conclusions, which were quickly confirmed in many species of plants and animals during the early years of the twentieth century, were finally accepted as a fundamental law of inheritance. This has been termed *Mendel's Principle of Segregation*.

We may illustrate this initially by considering a character in the golden hampster. The fur on the dorsal side of this animal is normally tan in colour but some individuals have a white band around the body. This character, white band, is inherited.If an offspring inherits a white band unit from one parent and the tan unit from the other parent, it itself shows the full banded character, not a blend of both parental characters. Subsequently the offspring of this animal show either the banded character or the non-banded; no intermediate patterns are

* The term character is rather loosely defined. In connection with Mendelian genetics it is used to indicate a structural or functional attribute of an organism which exists in two or more forms.

found. Thus the different units from the original parents did not blend
with one another in the first generation offspring but reappeared, each
in its original form in the next generation offspring. This is illustrated
in Fig. 7.

In 1906 the term *genetics* was proposed for the study of inheritance
and the inherited units, as described by Mendel, were called *genes*.

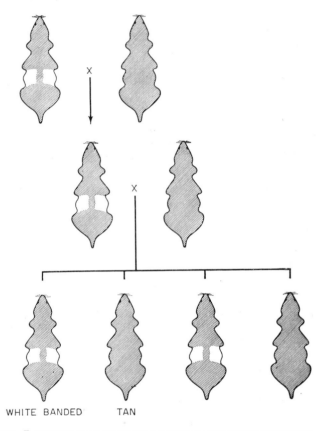

WHITE BANDED   TAN

FIG. 7. INHERITANCE OF WHITE BANDED IN THE GOLDEN HAMSTER

In Man, eye colour can be either brown or blue and one can speak,
therefore, of a gene for brown eyes and one for blue. Thus if the gene
for brown eyes is called B and that for blue eyes b, then in a race of
men having brown eyes, the genetic structure as regards eye colour
can be written BB and, similarly, in a race with blue eyes it can be

written *bb*. Offspring from a marriage between two such races will receive one *B* from the brown-eyed and one *b* from the blue-eyed parent. The genetic structure of such an individual would be *Bb*, and it is called a *heterozygote* since the gene received from one parent differs from that received from the other. The parents, which have two identical genes each, are called *homozygotes*.

The above heterozygote does not show an eye colour intermediate between brown and blue, but does, in fact, have brown eyes. Thus the presence of *B* overrides that of *b*. This phenomenon, which is very widespread, is called *dominance*; *B* is said to be dominant over *b*, and *b* is thus called the *recessive*. To return to the white band character in the golden hampster, we can now see that this was determined by a dominant gene. The names and symbols for genes showing dominant effects always start with a capital letter.

In the above example it will be seen that the character brown eye colour is shown in individuals with genes *Bb* as well as in those with *BB*. To differentiate between these, the terms *phenotype* and *genotype* are used. The phenotype describes the physical appearance of a character, individuals having *BB* or *Bb* show the same phenotype, brown eye colour. The genotype describes the genes that an individual carries. Thus the above individuals, which are identical phenotypically, are distinguished by their genotypes which are actually written *BB* or *Bb*. The phenotype is sometimes written $\underline{B}$ or $\underline{b}$ for brown or blue eyes respectively.

The complete genetic structure of an organism is made up of a very large number of different units which collectively determine, to some extent, the form and function of every part of the body. The genes *B* and *b* represent different forms of one such unit; only one, either *B* or *b*, can be received from each parent, respectively. To distinguish the relationship between *B* and *b* from that between any two genes representing different units, the former are called *alleles*: *B* is said to allelic to *b*.

Clear cut contrasting phenotypes, such as eye colour in Man, are not commonly found in any wild population of animals or plants. In actual fact, eye colour in Man is not inherited in quite such a straightforward way as described here but for the sake of simplicity the complex details have been ignored. In most respects, individuals in any wild species are remarkably similar in their outward appearances. Contrasting phenotypes do arise sporadically, however, and in these circumstances it is possible to distinguish a normal phenotype and an abnormal one. In this way one may conceive that the normal phenotype, in respect to any character, is produced by the normal allele of the gene while the abnormal phenotype is produced by a gene in some way altered from the normal.   The normal gene and its corresponding phenotype are called the *wild-type* while the abnormal gene and phenotype are described as *mutants*, following the concept that they arise by change of a wild-type gene.   The process of change is called *mutation*; it represents that property of genes which is most influenced by the action of ionising radiations and thus constitutes the main subject of this book.

We have considered the type of offspring produced by parents homozygous for different alleles.   In the next generation, that is, among the offspring from marriages between the *Bb* heterozygotes, are found both brown-eyed and blue-eyed individuals.   Thus the original characters have segregated in the second generation.   Furthermore, the numbers of such offspring are, on the average, in the ratio of 3 brown to 1 blue-eyed.   Subsequently, the blue-eyed and one third of the brown-eyed

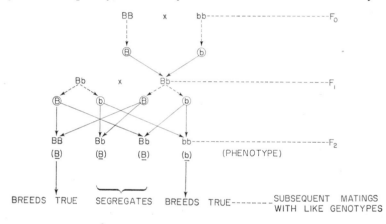

FIG. 8. SEGREGATION OF F_0 CHARACTERS IN AN F_2

individuals breed true, producing only blue-eyed and brown-eyed offspring respectively.   The other two thirds of the brown-eyed individuals produce offspring in which brown and blue eye colours segregate as in the former generation.   Those individuals which breed true are clearly homozygotes *BB* and *bb* while the rest of the browns must be heterozygotes *Bb*.   The segregation of characters in this way can only be explained by concluding that each heterozygous parent can only pass one allele to an individual in the next generation and that the probability of passing *B* is equal to that of passing *b*.

Figure 8 presents this segregation in a diagrammatic form.   The letters F_0, F_1, etc., to the right of the figure are in general use for the identification of generations.   Parents at the start of an experiment or at the beginning of a family tree are called F_0 (sometimes P_0) generation, their offspring F_1, the offspring of individuals with F_1 genotypes F_2 and so on. A mating between individuals of one generation and the individuals of the parental genotype is called a *backcross*.

Segregation was first demonstrated by Mendel in genetic experiments with the garden pea (*Pisum sativum*), his conclusions are now known as Mendel's *First Law*, or the *Principle of Segregation*. This we can formulate in the terms of modern genetics:

(i) Hereditary characters are governed by genes which are transmitted through the germ cells.

(ii) Genes may exist in alternative forms or alleles.

(iii) Individuals have their genes in pairs, one of each pair having been received from each parent.

(iv) One allele in a heterozygote may be dominant over the other.

(v) Two alleles present in a heterozygote do not blend or contaminate one another but remain distinct and separate.

(vi) When germ cells are formed, only one gene of each pair enters each germ cell.

(vii) When a heterozygote forms germ cells, half the cells contain one allele and half the other.

INDEPENDENT ASSORTMENT

Mendel's *Second Law* concerns the inheritance of two or more characters taken together. It states that the offspring of parents differing in respect of two characters, themselves produce offspring in which the two characters segregate independently. That is, that the characters found together in the grandparents may appear separately in the grandchildren.

To illustrate this, we will consider an example in the fruit fly *Drosophila melanogaster* (Plate 1). This small fly was first used in genetics research by T. H. Morgan in 1911. Since then, it has become the most commonly used organism in the study of genetics. Its principle virtues are that it is quite small, each fly weighing about 1 milligramme; it has a life cycle of less than a fortnight, in which one pair can produce over 100 offspring; it is very easy to breed in small containers and is remarkably free from disease; finally, more inherited characters are known in it than in any other single species of plant or animal. Two such characters are *dumpy* and *ebony*. In a dumpy fly, the wings appear as if truncated at about two thirds of their length. Ebony describes a variation of body colour in which the flies appear blackish as opposed to the normal grey colour. The genes in control of these characters are named after the appearance of the fly, the usual practice in *Drosophila* genetics, and are abbreviated under an international system of nomen-

3

clature to, in this case, *dp* and *e* respectively. Both *dp* and *e* are recessive to their normal alleles which may be written dp^+ and e^+. However, the fly in its normal habitat is not very variable in respect of such clear cut characters, the wild-type is clearly defined such that all normal or wild-type alleles may be written as $+$ without introducing any ambiguity in the formulation of genotypes. Furthermore, when talking of such characters, the normal phenotype is taken for granted and ignored. Thus dumpy, non-ebony and ebony, non-dumpy flies are merely called dumpy and ebony respectively.

When a dumpy male is mated to an ebony female, the offspring produced are wild-type in appearance, being heterozygous for both dumpy and ebony. When such individuals are mated together, they produce offspring among which are found wild-type flies, dumpy flies, ebony flies, and dumpy-ebony flies. These four phenotypes are found in the

	GENOTYPES				PHENOTYPES			
	EGGS							
SPERM	+ +	dp +	+ e	dp e	+	dp	e	dp e
+ +	+ + + +	+ + dp +	+ + + e	+ + dp e	4	—	—	—
dp +	dp + + +	dp + dp +	dp + + e	dp + dp e	2	2	—	—
+ e	+ e + +	+ e dp +	+ e + e	+ e dp e	2	—	2	—
dp e	dp e + +	dp e dp +	dp e + e	dp e dp e	1	1	1	1
F_2 ZYGOTES				TOTALS	9	3	3	1

FIG. 9. INDEPENDENT SEGREGATION OF *dp* AND *e* IN F_2 OFFSPRING

approximate ratio of 9 : 3 : 3 : 1. From this it can be seen that $\frac{1}{4}$ of the flies are dumpy and $\frac{1}{4}$ ebony. These are the frequencies expected on the basis of Mendel's first law, when each character is considered separately. In addition to this, however, we may note that the frequency of ebony among the dumpy flies or, conversely, the dumpy among the ebony flies is also $\frac{1}{4}$. Clearly, then, dumpy is segregating in the ebony flies in exactly the same way as in the non-ebony flies and, similarly, ebony is segregating in the dumpy as in the non-dumpy flies. Therefore, these two characters are segregating independently. This is Mendel's second law or the *Principle of Independent Assortment*; it is illustrated diagrammatically in Fig. 9.

Later on in this chapter we shall show that Mendel's second law does not hold in all cases where more than one character is under consideration. The significance of the law is that maternal and paternal gene complements in an individual do not retain such a distinction when the genes become assorted for the next generation; this principle remains essentially correct.

PHYSICAL BASIS OF INHERITANCE

Once Mendel's laws of inheritance had been shown to be universal, the physical identity of the phenomena was soon recognised.

The cellular structure of living organisms had been understood since the early part of the nineteenth century. A characteristic structure in the cell was the *nucleus* and in the latter part of the nineteenth century this was shown to be firmly implicated in the process of cell division. The nuclei of all cells contain thread-like structures called *chromosomes*. Weismann first suggested that the genetic material might be carried in these bodies and this concept was strengthened by the observations of W. S. Sutton that chromosomes were inherited in just the way that Mendel had postulated for genes.

The nucleus in any cell contains a certain number of chromosomes. This number is constant for the cells of individuals from any one species but varies widely between different species of animal or plant. The chromosome number is made up of a set of similar pairs, one of each pair being maternal in origin, the other paternal. Thus the fertilised egg cell nucleus contains a full set of paired chromosomes. This paired state is called the *diploid* condition and any one chromosome of a pair is said to be *homologous* to the other.

CELL DIVISION

The development of an organism from the fertilised egg consists of a continuous series of nuclear and subsequent cellular divisons followed by an ever increasing rate of differentiation of cells, tissues and organs, until the adult is formed. In the nuclear divisions each chromosome divides longitudinally into two. These daughter chromosomes move apart to opposite ends of the cell and re-form two nuclei identical in chromosome content with each other and with the original nucleus. This process, illustrated in Fig. 10, is called *mitosis*. By it, the functional potentialities of the egg nucleus are transmitted to all cells that finally make up the body or *soma* of the adult organism. The germ cells also undergo mitosis in their early development, but before they become functional for reproduction, they undergo a reduction division in which the diploid set of chromosomes is reduced to a single or *haploid* set. This cycle of division is called *meiosis*; it takes place in two

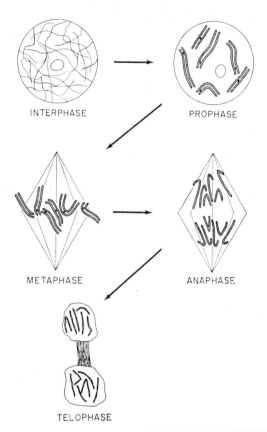

INTERPHASE   PROPHASE

METAPHASE   ANAPHASE

TELOPHASE

FIG. 10. SUCCESSIVE STAGES IN THE MITOTIC CYCLE OF NUCLEAR DIVISION

distinct phases (Fig. 11). In the first meiotic division, homologous chromosomes pair and come to lie one along the other. They each divide, as in mitosis, but with the important difference that the division is not complete, the incomplete daughter chromosomes or *chromatids* remaining attached at the *centromere*. This is a recognisable structure found in all chromosomes, its function seems to be to represent a point at which forces for moving the chromosome act. Since the chromatid pairs remain attached by their centromeres, the separation of the latter results in a reductional division; both chromatids derived from the paternal chromosome move to one end of the cell, both from the maternal chromosome move to the other. This division occurs simultaneously in all the chromosome pairs in the nucleus and since there is no mutual orientation of chromosomes with regard to their parental origin, each daughter product of the division contains an assorted set of maternal and paternal chromosomes. In the second meiotic division, no further chromosome replication occurs. The centromere divides,

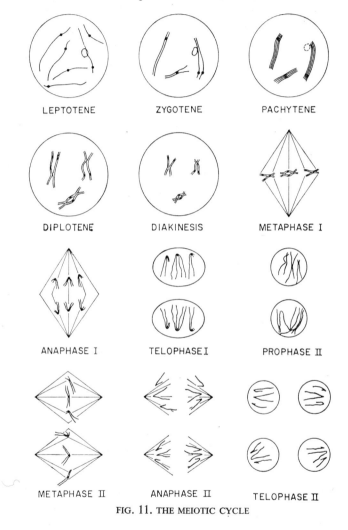

FIG. 11. THE MEIOTIC CYCLE

however, and the two chromatids now separate to produce, from one original diploid nucleus, four haploid nuclei. In the male these meiotic products form four spermatozoa. In the female only one nucleus remains functional, the remainder of the nuclear material being extruded from the egg cell as the *polar bodies*.

Mendel's first law is a natural consequence of the meiotic process; parental units do not lose their individuality in the offspring and are sorted out such that one, and only one, is passed on to the third generation; each parental gene having an equal probability of being passed to an offspring. Similarly, Mendel's second law follows from the non-assortative segregation of parental chromosomes during the first meiotic division.

GENES AND CHROMOSOMES

As mentioned earlier, Mendel's second law is not strictly true. From the above paragraph it will be seen that to relate this law with the mechanics of meiosis is to equate genes with chromosomes. From early in the twentieth century, however, it was recognised that the number of genes far exceeded the chromosome number in any organism. This observation presented a strong barrier to the general acceptance of the chromosomal theory of heredity. The problem was finally resolved in the light of two later observations, *genetic linkage*, first described by W. M. Bateson and R. C. Punnett in 1906, and a process by which homologous chromosomes exchange parts at meiosis, called *crossing-over*, described by F. A. Janssens in 1909. In 1910, T. H. Morgan also postulated that the phenomena observed by Bateson and Punnett were the effects of a linkage between two genes which are located on the same chromosome. He also postulated that the breakdown of such linkage resulted from an exchange of parts in chromosomes and that the frequency with which the breakdown occurred was related to the distance apart of the genes on the chromosome.

Genetic linkage constituted the breakdown of Mendel's second law: the following data illustrate this. In the mouse, a dominant gene White (Mi^{wh}) produces a light coat colour. Another dominant gene Lurcher (Lc) produces a behavioural abnormality. A White Lurcher was crossed with a normal mouse, the White Lurcher offspring were again mated to normal mice and, in the second generation, the following numbers of offspring in the four possible phenotypes were observed:

$Mi^{wh}Lc$	Lc	Mi^{wh}	Normal
102	10	11	99

It is clear that both Mi^{wh} and Lc individually show the one-to-one

Mendelian segregation expected from a cross between a heterozygote and the homozygous recessive individual. The frequency of Mi^{wh}, however, is considerably higher among the Lc offspring than among the non-Lc offspring. The two genes are not segregating independently. Among the 223 F_2 offspring 21 show only one character. In the remaining 202 the genes may be said to have remained linked or conversely, and perhaps more properly, the genes in the 21 individuals with but one character may be said to have recombined. The percentage of offspring in which this is observed is called the *recombination frequency*.

When three genes are linked together, their recombination frequencies show a simple relationship. If the genes are A, B and C, the recombination frequency between A and C will be equal to the sum or the difference of the recombination frequencies of A with B, and B with C. In the cross just described, there was also a third gene segregating which shows linkage with both Mi^{wh} and Lc: this was the recessive gene, Waved (wa-1), which produces a wavy fur texture. The F_0 mice were White-Lurcher-waved and wild-type, respectively. The triple heterozygous F_1 offspring were mated to homozygous wa-1 mice. The full segregation observed in the F_2 was:

	$Mi^{wh}Lc$	Lc	Mi^{wh}	*Normal*
wa–1	102	3	4	0
non-wa–1	0	7	7	99

Thus wa-1 recombined with the wild-type allele of Mi^{wh} in 10 (0 + 3 + 7 + 0) out of 223 offspring and with the wild-type allele of Lc in 11 (0 + 7 + 4 + 0) to give recombination frequencies of 4·5 per cent and 5·0 per cent respectively. The sum of these is equal to the recombination frequency between Mi^{wh} and Lc.

Thus the genes in question can be represented as three points along a straight line, or, as postulated by Morgan, along a chromosome. The distance between any pair being proportional to their recombination frequencies. In this way, *linkage-group maps* can be constructed. This was first done in 1913 by A. H. Sturtevant for six genes in a linkage group in *Drosophila melanogaster*. Such maps have been built for many animals and plants and also for lower organisms such as moulds, bacteria and viruses. A start has been made on the construction of linkage maps in Man.

The explanation of the phenomena of linkage and recombination was found in Janssen's observations on the behaviour of chromosomes during meiosis. As each pair of chromatids moved apart during the last stage of the first meiotic division, they occasionally remain attached at the same point, not separating completely until the centromeres had moved sufficiently far apart to make this contact physically impossible. The partially attached chromatid pairs appear, sometime during the division cycle, in the form of crosses with centromeres on one axis, they are called *chiasmata*. This is shown in Fig. 12. Janssen realised that

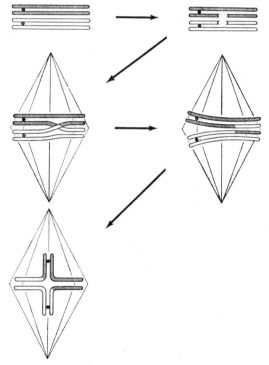

FIG. 12. CHIASMATA FORMATION

the laterally attached portions, that is, those on the axis not containing the centromeres, must be parts of daughter chromatids and that since they were now joined to different centromeres an actual exchange of sections must have occurred. This supplied, therefore, a physical explanation of crossing-over. While the four chromatids, derived from the paired homologous chromosomes, lie alongside one another, a "break" occurs at identical points on two separate chromatids. The distal piece of one chromatid joins with the proximal piece of the other, and *vice versa*, producing chromatids containing new arrangements of alleles. In actual fact, it is probable that breakage is not the primary agency in the formation of such crossing-over: breaks are unlikely to occur randomly at exactly the same point in two chromatids and yet, during crossing-over, one chromatid does not gain material at the expense of the other.

Conclusive evidence for the theory of the chromosomal basis of heredity and also for the concept of linkage maps came from a study of a unique type of chromosome found in some cells, notably those of the larval salivary glands, in *Drosophila* and other insects of the order *Diptera*. In these cells the chromosomes are very large and can easily be studied microscopically. They are formed by repeated chromosome divisions unaccompanied by any separation of daughter chromatids. This process, which, of course, does not involve cell division, is called *endomitosis* and the resultant bundle of threads or *chromonemata* is called a *polytene chromosome*. After suitable staining these chromosomes appear as long threads with very numerous transverse bands. (Plate II.) These bands vary in their thickness, staining ability, texture and distance apart; the arrangement of the bands is constant in the cells of any individual or between individuals of a given strain. Furthermore, the pattern varies very little between unrelated individuals of any species of *Diptera* and such variation that is found is usually simple such as the presence of an extra band, absence of a band or the simple inversion of a block of bands. Even between related species many similarities of band pattern may be observed.

The striking constancy of detail in the fine structure of the polytene chromosomes is immediately suggestive of a fundamental relationship between genes and bands. This approach was first made by T. S. Painter in 1934, when he discovered that the salivary gland chromosomes, although in the form of a five-armed cross, were in fact derived from the set of four pairs of chromosomes as observed during meiosis (Fig. 13). The possibility that certain mutations were actually losses of parts of chromosomes was suggested many years before Painter's discoveries. These mutations were recessive lethals; that is, the expression of the mutant character was inviability in individuals homozygous for the mutation. The peculiarity about these lethals was that some of them appeared to be allelic to two or more closely linked genes. The heterozygote between either of these genes and the lethal mutation showed the phenotype of whichever gene was used. The hypothesis was then, that the lethal represented a loss of a piece of chromosome containing the wild-type alleles of those genes with which it appeared to be allelic. These lethals were called *deficiencies* and a microscopical examination of the salivary gland chromosomes of the lethal heterozygotes confirmed that they were, in fact, actual losses of chromosomal material. This is relatively easy to observe because of the band to band pairing of the parental chromosomes; normal and abnormal chromosomes in the heterozygote are ideally placed for comparison. When genes are known, by genetic analysis, to be covered by a deficiency, then their location on the chromosome can be deduced by observation of

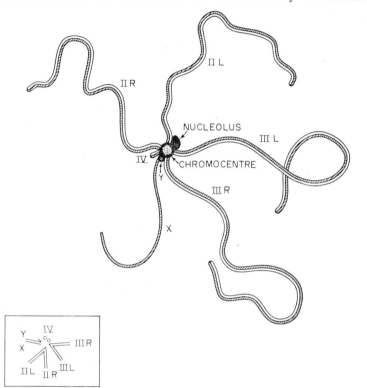

FIG. 13. DIAGRAMMATIC REPRESENTATION OF SALIVARY GLAND CHROMOSOMES OF *Drosophila melanogaster* WITH METAPHASE CHROMOSOMES INSERT. MATERNAL COMPLEMENT IN BLACK, PATERNAL IN WHITE

the position of the deficiency. In this way many chromosome maps have been made and these agree closely with the comparable linkage group maps. This presents the final link in the proof of the chromosomal basis of heredity.

CHROMOSOME ABNORMALITIES

It was mentioned earlier that the chromosomal fine structure of an individual may differ to a variable extent from that characteristic of most individuals of the species. These visible chromosome changes are called *aberrations*. They may be losses, duplications or rearrangements of chromosomal material. The commonest form of loss is the deficiency as described above in relation to chromosome maps. They may vary in size from one band of a polytene chromosome up to a whole chromosome. In *Drosophila* only the smaller deficiencies, involving up to a dozen bands or so, are viable, and then only in the heterozygous condition: homozygous deficiencies are almost always non-viable. Larger losses, sometimes called *deletions*, are usually lethal in the heterozygous condition; these changes belong to the class called *dominant lethals*. This principle is generally true in animals but in plants whole chromosome losses are frequently viable. This is thought to be possible because of the polyploid nature of many plant chromosome sets, the loss of one chromosome being less serious in a plant with several homologous chromosomes than in an animal with only two; polyploidy in animals is very rare.

SEX DETERMINATION

In animals, and some plants, one very important natural phenomenon is associated with what is virtually chromosomal deficiency. This is sex determination. It is frequently found that the chromosome contents of the sexes are unequal. This phenomenon is observed in an extreme case in the *Hymenoptera* (bees), where fertilised eggs develop into females, unfertilised eggs into males which are consequently haploid. More frequently, only one pair of chromosomes is concerned in sex determination and the sex determining mechanism may involve the absence of a whole chromosome or only part of it. Furthermore, the *heterogametic sex*, the one with unequal sets of chromosomes, may be either the male as in *Drosophila*, the mouse and Man, or the female as

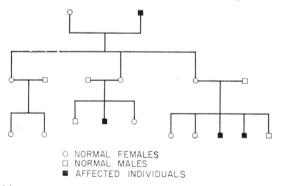

○ NORMAL FEMALES
□ NORMAL MALES
■ AFFECTED INDIVIDUALS

FIG. 14. SIX-LINKED INHERITANCE IN MAN: A PEDIGREE SHOWING INHERITANCE OF HAEMOPHILIA

in birds and some moths. The chromosomes concerned in this sex determination are called the *sex-chromosomes*, the one found in the homogametic sex is called the *X*-chromosome, the abnormal one in the heterogametic sex the *Y*-chromosome. The latter may, as in *Drosophila*, carry almost no genetic material at all.

The inheritance of genes on the sex-chromosomes differ, in some respects, from that of genes on the other chromosomes or *autosomes*. In the heterogametic sex the *X*-chromosome is, to all intents and purposes, in the haploid condition; it is called the *hemizygous* state. There is, of course, no dominance or recessiveness and genes must pass from the heterogametic sex to the opposite sex in the next generation. This gives rise to a criss-cross inheritance within the sexes which is called *sex-linkage* (Fig. 14); genes on the *X*-chromosome are linked, in their inheritance, to sex.

CHROMOSOME STRUCTURAL ABNORMALITIES

To return to genuine chromosome aberrations, the remaining category, rearrangement, may be divided into two classes: *inversions*, in

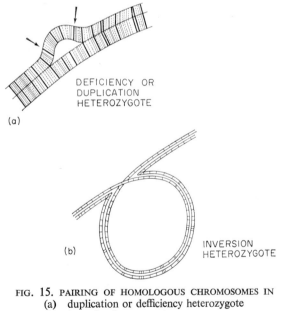

DEFICIENCY OR
DUPLICATION
HETEROZYGOTE

(a)

INVERSION
HETEROZYGOTE

(b)

FIG. 15. PAIRING OF HOMOLOGOUS CHROMOSOMES IN
(a)   duplication or defficiency heterozygote
(b)   inversion heterozygote

which a segment of a chromosome is found inverted and *translocation*, in which non-homologous chromosomes have exchanged parts. Both phenomena upset the normal occurrence of linkage. Inversions greatly reduce crossing-over in the area of chromosome in which they appear. This is thought to be due to mechanical stresses produced during pairing in meiosis (Fig. 15). Use can be made of this effect to retain unchanged the structure of any given chromosome. If the chromosome in question is kept as a heterozygote with an inverted chromosome, then the latter protects the former from any disruption by crossing-over.

The genetic effects of translocations are to make the genes on the two different chromosomes appear to be linked. If the genes on two normal chromosomes are *ABCD* and *EFGH* a translocation between them may be represented as *A'B'G'H'* and *E'F'C'D'*. The translocation heterozygote will have the genetic structure *ABCD, A'B'G'H'; EFGH, E'F'C'D'*. When these chromosomes segregate during meiosis, the only

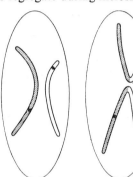

TRANSLOCATION   VIABLE   GAMETES
HETEROZYGOTE

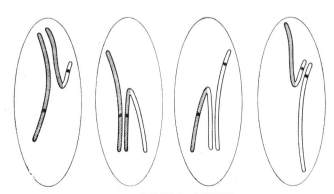

INVIABLE   GAMETES

FIG. 16. TRANSLOCATION HETEROZYGOTE AND POSSIBLE GAMETIC PRODUCTS

balanced gametic genotypes will be *ABCD*, *EFGH* and *A'B'G'H'*, *E'F'C'D'*. The others, *ABCD*, *A'B'G'H'*; *EFGH E'F'C'D'* etc., all contain either deficiencies or duplications and they will be unbalanced and therefore inviable; this leads to semi-sterility which is sometimes used for the detection of translocations. The surviving gametes must contain the linked genes *ABCDEFG* or *A'B'G'H'E'F'C'D'*. Figure 16 shows these genetic properties of translocations and describes diagrammatically the cytological appearance of translocations. Some crossing-over can occur in the translocation heterozygote, and if the arms of the tetrad are long, this gives rise to incomplete linkage of the genes on the chromosomes involved.

ABNORMAL CHROMOSOME SEGREGATION DURING DIVISION

We noted that the division cycles ensured an equal and constant

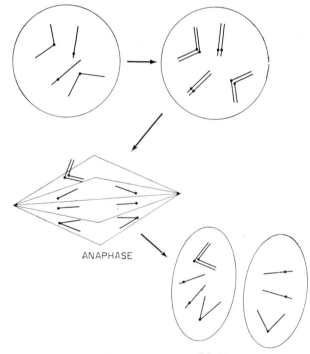

ANAPHASE

TELOPHASE

FIG. 17. SCHEMATIC REPRESENTATION OF NON-DISJUNCTION IN A ϒ-SHAPED CHROMOSOME IN A HYPOTHETICAL CHROMOSOME SET

distribution of chromosomes to resultant daughter cells. This process occasionally breaks down. One example, namely the origin of polytene chromosomes, has already been described. Similar failures in separation of replicated chromosome sets during mitosis also give rise to doubling of the diploid conditions, tetraploidy, or even higher multiples, polyploidy. This is common only in plant material, but some somatic tissues in mammals, for example the liver, are tetraploid.

A more important genetical phenomenon is the non-separation of a single pair of daughter chromosomes. This is called *non-disjunction*; one daughter cell receives both replicates of one original chromosome. This cell, therefore, has three homologous chromosomes while the other daughter cell has only one, as illustrated in Fig. 17. Such genetically unbalanced genotypes are usually inviable but when they involve the sex-chromosome this may not be the case. The consequences of non-disjunction in *Drosophila* are illustrated in Fig. 18. The resultant F_1 genotypes are XXX and XXY. The first is almost inviable but some individuals survive and appear as rather abnormal females; they are

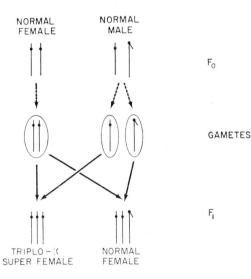

FIG. 18. PRIMARY NON-DISJUNCTION IN THE X-CHROMOSOME OF *Drosophila*

called *super females* and are sterile. The XXY genotype, on the other hand, produces a normal, fully fertile female.

The non-disjunctional X chromosomes in the XXY females may continue to be inherited together in subsequent generations; the non-disjunction has become a permanent attribute of the chromosome pair. Such permanent associations are described as *attached-X* chromosomes and are written $\widehat{XX}$. It will be seen from Fig. 19 that the presence of attached-X chromosomes in females reverses the normal pattern of

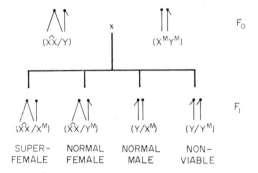

FIG. 19. SEX-LINKAGE IN ATTACHED-X STOCK IN *Drosophila*

sex-linked inheritance; paternal X-chromosomes are passed to F_1 sons while the attached-X chromosomes always, of course, go to the F_1 females.

3

GENES: THE MATERIAL OF HEREDITY

THE CHEMICAL NATURE OF THE GENETIC MATERIAL

It is beyond the scope of this book to enter into a detailed account of the chemical structure of chromosomes; although much is known on this subject, the structure of the genes themselves remains unknown and consequently the chemical nature of the mutation process is still a mystery.

The basic constituents of chromosomes are proteins and nucleic acids. The latter are complex polymers containing sugars and the nitrogenous bases adenine, guanine, cytosine, thymine and uracil. Two types of nucleic acids are found in living organisms. These are desoxyribonucleic acid (DNA) and ribonucleic acid (RNA). As their names suggest they differ principally in the nature of the sugar moiety; a desoxypentose in the former and a ribose sugar in the latter. They also differ, however, in that DNA contains the base thymine which is replaced, in RNA, by uracil.

DNA and RNA are found together in all living organisms with the exception of the viruses; two groups of these organisms are known which differ in containing either one or other of the nucleic acids, respectively. In organisms other than the viruses the nucleic acids are both present in nuclei but RNA alone may also be found in the cytoplasm. A further difference between the nucleic acids is that the DNA content of cells is constant and characteristic for any given species of living organism; RNA, on the other hand, may be present in variable amounts at different times within even one single cell. These facts have led to the view that DNA constitutes the hereditary material and hence represents the chemical nature of the gene. Additional evidence for this comes from the discovery of the remarkable processes of *transformation* and *transduction* in the bacteria. By transferring DNA from one genetic strain of bacteria to another it is possible to incorporate in the recipient, genetic characters of the donor. Transformation involves the transfer of purified DNA extract from one strain to the other; in transduction the transfer is done by a vector, a bacterial virus, which is first cultured in the donor strain and then in the recipient. It is thought that both processes involve the substitution of recipient genes by genes from the donor. This then appears to be clear evidence for the DNA composition of genes.

4 37

Further evidence supporting the view that DNA constitutes the hereditary matter comes from a consideration of the structure of DNA in relation to the presumed properties of the genetic material. The bases and sugars in DNA are arranged in long chains in which sugar-base complexes are linked together by phosphate bonds. Two such chains are linked along their length by hydrogen bonds between the bases. In this respect, the linked bases comprise either of the pairs adenine-thymine or cytosine-guanine. The chemical structure of DNA is shown diagrammatically in Fig. 20. The chains are not

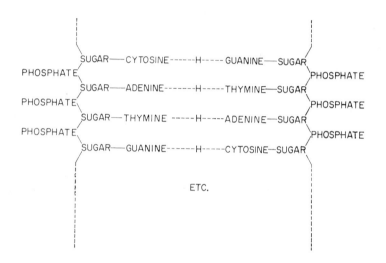

FIG. 20. DIAGRAMMATIC ARRANGEMENT OF SUGARS AND BASES IN DNA

arranged in one plane, however, but exist in the form of a double helix or spiral. This model of the structure of DNA was proposed by J. D. Watson and F. H. C. Crick; it is called the *Watson-Crick* model.

Two obvious characteristics of the hereditary material are, first, that it must be infinitely variable in its chemical structure and, second, that it must be self-replicating. The Watson-Crick model for DNA can encompass both these requirements. If genes are constructed of DNA molecules, the number and linear arrangement of the different base pairs within a molecule can be infinitely variable. An explanation of the second requirement, self-replication, follows from the paired helical structure of DNA. The two helices separate, each then acts as a template for the construction of the complementary helix necessary to reconstitute the original double structure; this is shown diagrammatically in Fig. 21. Some recent studies on DNA synthesis, using radioactive tracer methods, support this view of replication.

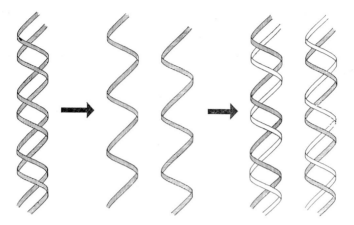

FIG. 21. POSSIBLE MODE OF REPLICATION OF DNA

Less is known of the structure of RNA, but it seems unlikely to be implicated in the chemical structure of the genes except in the case of the viruses which contain no DNA. It is thought probable that RNA may function as some sort of intermediate between the genic material and the metabolic processes which take place in the cell.

GENE ACTION

The principles governing the transmission of genes from parent to offspring, discussed in the previous chapter, involve phenomena which are generally applicable to all living organisms. These phenomena are basically concerned with one of the functions of the genetic material, that of self-replication. They also ensure a balanced, though variable, distribution of the genetic material to the next generation. The second property of the genes, the control of form and function of the organism, is infinitely complex, although here again the basic principles apply to the majority of animals and plants.

The development of an organism from the zygote is an extremely complex affair; the control exerted by the genes in this, and also in the continued existence of the mature organism, is very imperfectly known. What knowledge there is, is concerned with the effects of a small proportion of the genes carried by a few organisms selected because they are themselves easy to handle for genetic studies. This restricted sample of genes represents those loci at which some functional change has led to gross change at the phenotypic level. It must be remembered that the following facts do not represent an all embracing picture of the action of genes, but that of a small group of selected genes. Furthermore, it must be remembered that the existence of a gene-controlled process can be known only in the presence of gene changes that lead to contrasting phenotypes.

BIOCHEMICAL DEFICIENCIES

In micro-organisms, such as the mould *Neurospora*, the type of mutants most commonly studied are those that make the organism dependent on an external source of some biochemical entity such as an amino-acid or a vitamin. The wild-type organism is able to synthesise most of its metabolic requirements if grown in a medium containing a source of inorganic nitrogen and a source of energy such as sugar. A mutant is unable to synthesise a particular specific substance and requires this to be present in the growth medium (Plate III). Such mutant genes are called *biochemical deficiency* mutants; they illustrate one of the simplest types of gene action, namely the control of basic biochemical synthesis. In micro-organisms very many such mutants are known which affect the syntheses of many amino-acids, vitamins and other biochemical groups. This type of mutant is not found only in micro-organisms, many examples may be cited in *Drosophila*, Man and in the higher plants; their study is facilitated, however, by the straightforward way in which micro-organisms may be grown on simple, chemically defined, media. Frequently, several non-allelic mutants all require the same biochemical substance for normal growth. For example in *Neurospora* there are seven arginineless mutants (arg 1 to arg 7). It was found that four of them (arg 4, 5, 6 and 7) would grow normally if either of the amino-acids ornithine or citrulline were used

TABLE 2.   RESPONSE OF ARGININELESS MUTANTS TO SUPPLEMENTED MEDIA
(Plus sign indicates normal growth)

Mutant	Amino-acid Supplement in Medium		
	Ornithine	Citrulline	Arginine
arg 4, 5, 6, 7	+	+	+
arg 3, 2		+	+
arg 1			+

to supplement the medium in place of arginine. A further pair of mutants (arg 2 and arg 3) could use citrulline as well as arginine while the remaining mutant (arg 1) would grow only on medium supplemented with arginine itself.   The growth requirements of the arginineless mutants are summarised in Table 2.

Apart from the chemical relationship between the three amino-acids, ornithine, citrulline and arginine, the pattern of their utilisation by the arginineless mutants suggests that they are all involved in one basic metabolic process. It would appear that arginine is the end product of this synthesis since this alone of the three amino-acids is present in proteins and in addition, it was the only amino-acid which allowed growth in all the mutants. Citrulline was the next most effective supplement, only arg 1 failed to grow in its presence, and therefore, it must come just prior to arginine in the metabolic process. The order of the amino-acids in the synthesis is therefore:

$$\xrightarrow{A} \text{ornithine} \xrightarrow{B} \text{citrulline} \xrightarrow{C} \text{arginine}$$

with the steps *A*, *B* and *C* being controlled by the wild-type alleles of arg 4 to arg 7, arg 2 and arg 3, and arg 1 respectively.

The conversion of citrulline to arginine, the step marked *C* in Fig. 22,

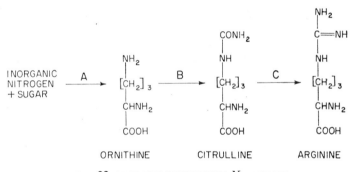

FIG. 22. ARGININE SYNTHESIS IN *Neurospoxa*

is controlled by one gene. Very many genetically determined biochemical syntheses are known and it is frequently found that one step in the process is controlled by one gene. Where two or more genes appear to control a part of the metabolic pathway, it is usually discovered that the step is not simple but involves additional intermediates such that the one gene/one step principle is retained. In the case of step *B* in Fig. 22, biochemical evidence suggests that there is an intermediate in the conversion of ornithine to citrulline; clearly, in the synthesis of ornithine from inorganic substances, step *A*, more than one step must be involved.

In this way genetic studies have been used by biochemists in the analysis of biochemical syntheses.

A step in any biochemical synthesis, such as the conversion of citrulline to arginine, involves the catalytic action of a specific enzyme. It has been postulated, therefore, that a gene controls a synthesis by the production of the necessary enzyme; a mutant gene blocks the synthesis by failing to produce the enzyme or by producing one of a different specificity. Several cases are known in micro-organisms, and also in Man, in which genetically determined biochemical blocks can be demonstrated to be related to the absence of a specific enzyme.

Figure 23 summarises the biochemical relationships of four diseases

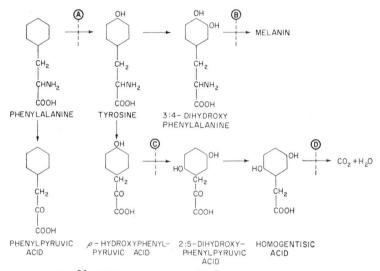

FIG. 23. PHENYLALANINE–TYROSINE METABOLISM IN MAN
Interruption at **A** gives rise to phenylketonuria, at **B** to albinism, at **C** to tyrosinosis and at **D** to alkaptonuria

in Man—phenylketonuria, albinism, tyrosinosis and alkaptonuria. All are concerned with the metabolism of the amino-acid phenylalanine and related compounds. In the normal individual phenylalanine is converted into tyrosine by the addition of an –OH group to the benzene ring. Formation of the enzyme responsible for this hydroxylation is controlled by a gene; when this is replaced by an inactive allele, tyrosine formation is interrupted. The phenylalanine then finds an alternative biochemical outlet through oxidation to phenylpyruvic acid, which is excreted in the urine; this is the condition known as phenyl-ketonuria. In the normal individuals tyrosine is metabolised through at least two paths. One leads by way of 3 : 4-dihydroxyphenylalanine to the hair and skin pigment, melanin; this path is interrupted in homozygotes for the recessive gene which causes albinism. The other involves the oxidation of tyrosine, in a series of steps, to carbon dioxide and water. This chain is interrupted immediately after *p*-hydroxyphenylpyruvic acid in individuals suffering from tyrosinosis, and after homogentisic acid in those suffering from alkaptonuria: in each case the substance last formed before the block, *p*-hydroxyphenylpyruvic acid or homogentisic acid, appears in the urine.

Since one gene controls one step, the hypothesis has been advanced that there is a one-to-one relationship between genes and enzymes, and that this forms a fundamental basis for gene action in determining not only certain metabolic syntheses, but all the ways in which the structural and functional attributes of an organism are genetically controlled. This, however, is almost certainly too simple a view.

When a mutation prevents an organism such as *Neurospora* from synthesising a particular biochemical compound, the phenotype is usually simple and straightforward. If the mutant blocks the synthesis of an amino-acid then the proteins which incorporate this particular compound are not formed and the cell dies. If the amino-acid is supplied "ready made" then the organism utilises this and growth is normal. Biochemical mutants are known in *Neurospora*, however, which produce more than one phenotypically observable effect. For example, one mutant blocks the synthesis of two amino-acids, isoleucine and valine. It is now known that the mutant locus controls only the synthesis of isoleucine. When this synthesis is blocked, a precursor of isoleucine builds up in the cell and this, in its turn, inhibits the production of valine. The latter is, therefore, a secondary effect of the isoleucine mutant. Such multiple effects of mutant genes are called *pleiotropisms*.

COMPLEX EFFECT OF GENES—PLEIOTROPISM

Neurospora is a simple fungus and to all intents and purposes it can be regarded as a unicellular organism. The possibility of pleiotropic effects exists mainly at the level of cellular metabolism and, consequently, they are not frequently observed. In the higher plants, and more particularly in animals, development is complex and highly coordinated, involving not only growth of cells but that of tissues, organs and all the many aggregates of these. The initial effect produced by a mutant may subsequently influence many of these developmental processes and can lead to a phenotype exhibiting numerous pleiotropic effects.

The most extensive studies on pleiotropic effects in relation to development, the study of developmental genetics, have been concerned with the mouse. In this organism many mutants are known which lead to complex phenotypes in which several parts of the body are affected. In some of these many of the abnormalities, which together make up a syndrome of effects of the mutant, have been shown to be linked by a common causative factor. As an example we will consider the mutant, grey lethal (gl).

The grey lethal phenotype comprises a grey coat colour; a complex syndrome of skeletal abnormalities; defections in the shape and eruption of teeth; and a general debility leading to poor growth during suckling, degeneration of the thymus gland, and death just before weaning. The skeletal effects offer an excellent example of causally related pleiotropic effects. The syndrome consists of a series of abnormalities of bone shape in which most of the bones are affected. The defects are all due to the inability of the mouse to re-absorb bone. The skeleton of an animal is continually remodelled, during growth, to suit changing conditions of stress and strain. This remodelling is brought about by the combined action of bone absorption and re-deposition. In the grey lethal mouse this remodelling cannot occur, new growth of bone takes place but the bone originally present cannot be re-absorbed.

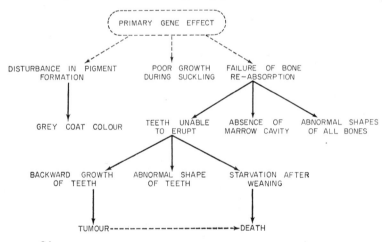

FIG. 24. PEDIGREE CAUSES OF THE GREY LETHAL SYNDROME OF THE MOUSE
(Postulated relationships)

This leads to the formation of clumsy limb bones in which the non-growing shaft remains as thick as the growing ends. In addition, no marrow cavity is present since this is formed late in development by bone re-absorption. Thus in the grey lethal mouse the bone consists of spongy material in which the marrow is diffusely spread.

The lack of bone re-absorption leads also to the dental defects. The teeth fail to erupt since for this it is necessary that overlying bone is re-absorbed. Similarly, since the teeth are confined to restricted bone cavities, their shape and calcification are abnormal. A further dental complication arises which, together with starvation due to the inability to feed after weaning, is probably the major cause of death of the grey lethal. The strongly growing lower incisors are unable to grow forward in the usual way, but succeed in pushing their way out backwards through a hole in the lower jaw. This base of the tooth then forms a tumour which compresses certain nerves and blood vessels. It is thought likely that this produces an extreme neuralgia.

The link between the failure to re-absorb bone and the effect on coat colour and growth rate during suckling are not known. The latter is a very unspecific phenomenon and can be expected to occur with any major metabolic upset. The former should be more amenable to experimental study but it is significant that the only other known mutant in the mouse which affects bone re-absorption, also produces a grey coat colour. A diagrammatic representation of the "pedigree of causes" of the grey lethal mouse is given in Fig. 24.

Mutant genes are almost always found to exhibit some degree of pleiotropism. Where one particular pleiotropic effect is very striking, the mutant gene is frequently named after this. In *Drosophila*, for example, a mutant gene on the second chromosome prevents the expansion of the wings which normally occurs just after the fly has emerged from the pupa. The wings remain rudimentary and, because of this, the mutant is called *vestigial*. In addition to the wing effect there are also many, but less striking, effects on legs, bristles, body size, viability and so on. The gene in question cannot be called a "wing gene", the normal development of many attributes of the fly depend upon the presence of the wild-type allele. This principle is of almost universal application, the phenotypic expression of a gene normally depends on factors many times removed from the primary action of the gene.

INTERDEPENDENCE OF GENES

Since any given gene can have widespread effects upon the form of an organism, it is axiomatic that any particular character of the organism may depend for its normal development on the action of many genes.

We have already considered the problem of dominance. This is gene interaction at the allelic level. One allele may suppress the action of another. The degree of dominance shown by one allele to another varies considerably between genes. The recessive gene black in *Drosophila*, for exa nple, produces a very dark body colour in the homozygote;

in the heterozygote too, some degree of darkening is noticeable. In the Andalusian fowl a pair of alleles produce in the homozygotes black and white plumage colour respectively, but the heterozygote is almost intermediate in colour, having "blue" plumage. An extreme case, where there is no dominance relationship, is found in the inheritance of the *ABO* blood group system in Man. Individuals can be *A*, *B*, *AB*, or *O*, and these phenotypes derive from the genotypes *AA* or *AO*; *BB* or *BO*; *AB*; and *OO* respectively. Thus while *A* and *B* are both dominant to *O*, neither is dominant to the other. All graduations can be found from complete dominance of one allele over another to complete independence between alleles. In general, it would appear that some degree of dominance is almost always found between pairs of alleles. This relationship need not involve all pleiotropic effects of a gene, indeed it frequently does not involve that part of the syndrome that is most noticeable in the mutant homozygote. Thus genes with clear cut visible effects may, in the heterozygous condition, have an effect only on viability.

Some gene pairs show a form of dominance phenomenon although they are not alleles. Thus in the fowl there is a gene for white plumage which prevents the expression of any other colour gene. Birds carrying this gene are always white, irrespective of colour genes at any other *loci*. This is called *epitasis*; a gene producing a clear cut phenotypic effect suppresses the expression of other genes which would normally affect the same character. Some genes, which themselves have no observable effect on a character, may suppress the expression of a second gene which normally would have an effect on that character. These genes, which are called *suppressors*, are usually specific in their action. They suppress the expression of only one gene or locus or, at the most, the expression of a small group of genes. In *Drosophila* the gene *su-b* (suppressor-black) on the *X*-chromosome has itself no phenotypic effect except to prevent the expression of black. Similar genes which act in the reverse way (*enhancers*) are also known.

More subtle forms of expression are shown by genes called *modifiers*. These can be viewed as rather mild suppressors. They merely reduce or slightly enhance the abnormal expressions of a mutant allele. This type of gene effect is very common; modifiers can be found for almost any kind of mutant gene and there may be very many of them for any one particular gene. Cumulative effects are possible producing, for example, complete suppression of a mutant genotype.

More complex types of gene interaction are observed when the genetic control of specific characters is considered. One such character that has been studied particularly thoroughly is coat colour in rodents.

Characteristically, rodents in the wild are of an indeterminate greyish brown colour, somewhat paler on the ventral surface than on the dorsal. This neutral appearance, which tends to make animals inconspicuous, is called *agouti*. Two types of pigment are detectable in agouti hairs, black pigment or *eumelanin*, and yellow pigment, *phaeomelanin*. They are found together in the hairs but are distributed in a characteristic way; the bases and tips of the hairs are black with eumelanin, the middle regions yellow with phaeomelanin. Both pigments are present in the hairs in the form of granules. This banded appearance of individual hairs produces the rather nondescript appearance of rodent hair. The development of the agouti hair character is dependent, therefore, on the following factors:

(*a*) The ability to produce pigment;

(*b*) The potentiality for producing both eumelanin and phaeomelanin;

(*c*) The type of eumelanin produced;

(*d*) The distribution of the pigment granules;

(*e*) The uniformity of pigment synthesis in the skin as a whole.

In the mouse the ability to synthesise melanin is influenced by many genes. Of particular importance is the *albino locus* at which there are five known alleles. The wild-type (symbol *C*) produces the full coat colour, the remaining alleles progressively reduce the ability of the animal to synthesise, first phaeomelanin and then both the melanins. The most extreme allele (*c*) suppresses synthesis entirely. Whether the animal produces phaeomelanin or eumelanin is determined by another five alleles at the *agouti locus*, the phenotypes ranging from yellow, absence of eumelanin (A^y), through wild-type (A^+) to black, absence of phaeomelanin (*a*). As a further modification of the chemical composition of melanin, the gene brown (*b*) produces a different type of eumelanin which, as the name implies, is brown in colour in contrast to the normal black produced by the allele *B*.

The distribution of the pigment granules can be modified in two ways, first, by aggregation of the granules into clumps, and second, by restriction of the pigment to the tips of the hairs. The result of both of these phenomena is to produce a lightening of the coat colour. The first effect is produced by the genes, blue dilution (*d*) and leaden (*ln*), the second by a mutant called misty (*m*).

Abnormalities in the uniformity of the pigment synthesis over the skin as a whole, lead to the phenomenon of spotting. Innumerable mutants are known which produce or influence spotting, but as an example, we will take the gene for piebald spotting (*s*) which occurs commonly in fancier's stocks. Mice homozygous for this gene show clearly defined patches of white fur distributed over the body in a roughly symmetrical way.

For normal development of agouti fur colour in the mouse it is necessary that the wild-type alleles of all the above loci are present. A mutant allele at any one will produce a coat colour which may deviate widely from the normal. Furthermore, the different alleles interact to give combination and addition effects covering a wide range of possible coat colour characteristics. Some major interactions are described in Table 3.

TABLE 3. COAT COLOUR INTERACTIONS IN MOUSE

Genes					Gametic genotype	Phenotypes (where recessive alleles are homozygous)
C	A+	B	D	S	CA+BDS	Agouti.
				s	CA+BDs	Piebald.
			d	S	CA+BdS	Dilute agouti.
				s	CA+Bds	Dilute agouti piebald.
		b	D	S	CA+bDS	Cinnamon.
				s	CA+bDs	Cinnamon piebald.
			d	S	CA+bdS	Dilute cinnamon.
				s	CA+bds	Dilute cinnamon piebald.
	a	B	D	S	CaBDS	Black.
				s	CaBDs	Black piebald.
			d	S	CaBdS	Blue dilution.
				s	CaBds	Blue dilution piebald.
		b	D	S	CabDS	Chocolate.
				s	CabDs	Chocolate piebald.
			d	S	CabdS	Dilute chocolate.
				s	Cabds	Dilute chocolate piebald.
c	With anything					Albino.

The control of the character coat colour in the mouse requires then the interaction of many genes. Each locus is itself concerned with only a simple step in the process and the complexity of the final character is determined by the integration of all of these. Few characters in either animals or plants are so amenable for study as coat colour, but it is generally accepted that they all depend on the existence of balanced interactions between groups of genes.

The association of genes at the phenotypic level is not reflected in their location in the chromosome set; the many genes that may influence a character are randomly dispersed over all the chromosomes. The obvious explanation of this is that, as with pleiotropic effects, the interactions are usually many times removed from the primary gene action. Certain observations on apparently unstable genes in *Drosophila* have indicated, however, that the location of a gene in the chromosome is of importance with respect to its normal functioning.

In one type of instability the gene appears to mutate sporadically during the development of the fly, producing a mosaic phenotype. In a heterozygote for white eye colour, for example, the phenomenon results in a mottled appearance of the eye; some parts are red, as expected in the heterozygote, others are white as expected in a homozygote for the recessive gene white. Cytological examination has shown that in many instances this effect is associated with a chromosomal aberration involving the removal of the wild-type allele of the gene in question, this time white, to another location on the chromosome. The phenomenon is called *position effect*; the altered position of the wild-type allele affects its normal functioning. If the gene is replaced in its original position, by a further chromosome structural change, its normal functioning is re-established. In the example of white-mottling the transposed allele may or may not function normally. More rarely, the change of function is permanent. Thus the wild-type allele of "hairy", a bristle character, has been observed to lose its dominance over recessive alleles when involved in a chromosome structural change. It is possible that many apparent mutations associated with structural change are really position effects. Experimental proof of this is very difficult to obtain; it remains possible that the chromosome breaks are associated with true mutations.

ADDITIVE GENE ACTION

One category of gene action that deserves particular attention is that concerned with the genetic control of quantitative characters, that is, characters that are assessed by measurement. These characters are of considerable importance in the study of population genetics.

Let us assume that there are two strains of some organism which differ in respect of two genes; one is homozygous for genes A and B, the other for the alleles a and b. A cross between the strains would produce the heterozygous F_1 offspring $AaBb$. If A and B loci segregate independently of one another then the mating between the F_1 offspring would produce an F_2 in which $1/16$ of the offspring were $AABB$, $1/16$

AABb and so on. Altogether 9 different genotypes would be formed since some of the 16 possible ways in which zygotes could arise would be identical; for example *AaBb* is the same as *aABb*, *aAbB* and *AabB* as shown in Fig. 25.

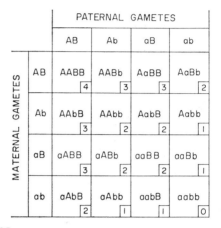

FIG. 25. SEGREGATION OF GENES AT ADDITIVE GENE LOCI
The value, in hypothetical units, for each genotype is included in the lower right-hand corner of each square.

Now suppose *A* and *B* were additive genes which increase some quantitative character such as stature, and assume further that there is no dominance and that *Aa* or *Bb* individuals are taller than *aa* or *bb*, by one unit of measurement. An individual with genes *AABB* will be four units taller than one with genes *aabb*; one with *AaBB* three units and so on: each capital letter in the genotype giving the individual a stature of one unit of measurement greater than *aabb*, which is the smallest. If the stature of *aabb* is x units then in the F_2 generation genotypes, only one has no capitals and its height is, therefore, x units, two genotypes (*Aabb* and *aaBb*) have one capital letter and each of these appears twice in Fig. 25, such that four individuals have a height of $x + 1$ units. Similarly, six individuals have a height of $x + 2$ units, four $x + 3$ units and finally, one with $x + 4$ units. In a large F_2 one would expect the proportions of the individuals in each height-category to be $1/16$ x units, $\frac{1}{4}$ $x + 1$ units, $\frac{3}{8}$ $x + 2$ units, $\frac{1}{4}$ $x + 3$ units and $1/16$ $x + 4$ units. This array is called a *frequency distribution* and is illustrated, in Fig. 26, in the form of a histogram. With two genes segregating there are five steps in the frequency histogram; with three genes segregating the range of dimensions extends from $x + 0$ to $x + 6$ units and there are seven steps; with four genes there are nine

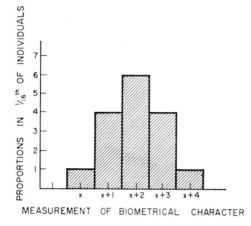

FIG. 26. DIAGRAM OF THE FREQUENCY ARRAY OF INDIVIDUALS IN WHICH
TWO PAIRS OF ADDITIVE ALLELES ARE SEGREGATING

steps and so on. With increasing number of steps the difference between
the numbers of individuals in successive steps decreases. Consequently,
when a large number of genes are segregating the individual steps merge
into one another to give a continuous line, forming a bell-shaped
frequency-distribution curve as illustrated in Fig. 27.

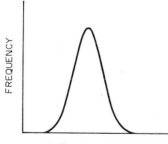

FIG. 27. FREQUENCY DISTRIBUTION MOST COMMONLY FOUND IN RESPECT
OF MEASURABLE CHARACTERS

This type of frequency distribution is characteristic of those attributes
of animals and plants that are assessed by measurement. The genetic
control of these characters is vested in large numbers of genes each
having only a small effect. These have been termed *polygenes* to distinguish them from genes with marked phenotypic effects which are
called *major genes.*

It is now thought that there is no fundamental difference between polygenes and major genes since, of the latter, many have small pleiotropic effects on biometrical characters. In any case, we have seen that genes carry out their normal functioning in an intimate relationship with the rest of the genetic make up of an individual, not as isolated entities. The terminology nevertheless remains useful in a descriptive sense.

GENES AND ENVIRONMENT

The degree of genetic diversity is such that no two organisms ever have identical genotypes except in two particular instances. Plants can be propagated by taking cuttings from an existing plant or by allowing the plant itself to bud off new individuals. In this way the descendants of one plant have the same genetic make up, they constitute a clone. A similar effect is produced in animals when a fertilised egg divides into two producing a pair of offspring, called identical or monozygotic twins, again with identical genotypes. Such individuals are not, however, identical; although much more alike than members of a population generally, they always show some distinguishing characters. These differences are due to non-genetic causes which are covered by the term *environmental*; they include, in addition to the normal components of the physical environment, less obvious factors such as diet, uterine conditions in the mother, and all the many aspects of learning involved in social contact.

The degree to which any character is dependent on environmental factors is very variable. Some may be completely independent as, for example, blood group characters; others may be almost entirely dependent on environment as is the case with the language spoken by any human being. Generally, however, both genetic and environmental factors are recognisable in the development of a character.

The effect of environment is most frequently observed in relation to biometrical characters. It is to be expected that a poor diet leads to smallness in size and *vice versa*, it is almost traditional that the village blacksmith has powerfully developed muscles. These reflect only extreme effects of environmental variation. Even when every effort is made to make an environment uniform, and to study genetically identical organisms in it, some variation is observed. There are, therefore, many small intangible ways in which environments may differ between organisms; the effect of this multiplicity, like that of polygenes, is to produce smooth frequency distribution curves of the bell-shaped type. With the exception of clones, such frequency distributions in populations are in fact the result of both genetic and environmental effects working together.

Environmental effects are not, of course, confined to biometrical characters. Of particular interest are the effects called *phenocopies*. These are exact replicas of mutant phenotypes induced in developing organisms by the action of abnormal environmental conditions. They have been observed in many organisms but a particular study of them has been made in rats and mice. Various agencies, such as ionising radiations, deficiency diets and toxic chemicals, can produce, in particular stages of the foetus, many abnormalities mimicking the effects of certain mutant genes.

The action of genes and that of environment cannot, therefore, be separated. They co-operate or not, as the case may be, in the moulding of form and function of the organism. Each is dependent on the other; the genotype responds differently according to environmental circumstances but even the best of these may prove ineffective where the genotype is poor. The problems of unravelling the effects of genotype and environment to determine their relative merits, remains one of the most important and difficult aspects of modern genetics, having deep implications on the mode by which we grow animals and plants for food.

To summarise, genes probably act by producing specific enzymes and other simple proteins. These initiate secondary chain reactions which, as development proceeds, become more and more diversified and interrelated. In higher organisms the process, when completed, involves an infinite complexity of interdependent cells, tissues and organs. The whole process is supplemented and modified throughout by stimuli from the surrounding environment.

4

THE PRODUCTION OF MUTATIONS BY RADIATIONS

RECESSIVE MUTATIONS

Geneticists in the early part of the twentieth century recognised that the existence of different alleles at a locus probably arose through a process of change or alteration in genetic material. This process was first called mutation by H. De Vries in 1910, and although the mutations observed at that time were called spontaneous, it was realised that external causative factors might be involved. This led to a search for means of producing mutations artificially. These attempts were initially unsuccessful: in 1927, however, H. J. Muller published results of experiments which showed conclusively that X-rays were highly effective in the induction of mutations. Muller was able to demonstrate that X-irradiation of *Drosophila* produced a dramatic increase in the frequency at which mutant genes appeared in subsequent generations. These mutations were induced in spermatozoa of the irradiated flies but were revealed when they had been inherited by the offspring of these flies. This demonstration of the mutagenic properties of X-rays represented a major advance in the study of genetics; it initiated the field of radiation genetics which has expanded very rapidly since 1927, to embrace the effects of various radiations on a wide diversity of organisms. In addition, by promoting the collection of various types of mutations, the mutagenic action of ionising radiations has been of great value in general genetic studies.

RECESSIVE LETHAL MUTATIONS IN DROSOPHILA

Since Muller's classical studies on the mutagenic effect of X-rays in *Drosophila*, this organism has continued to play a leading part in radiation genetics. The type of mutations studied by Muller, and subsequently by many other workers, were recessive mutations which caused the organism to die before the completion of its development. These are called *recessive lethal mutations* and have been particularly useful because of their clear cut phenotypic expression. Recessive lethals on the sex chromosome offer a further advantage in that they are carried, without adverse effect, in the heterozygous condition in females, while in males their presence always results in death; the male *Drosophila* has only one X-chromosome.

One of the chief reasons for Muller's notable success in demon-strating the mutagenic properties of X-rays was his careful construction of a special experimental technique. The difficulty of establishing the origin of a mutant gene resides in the fact that the mutation will only be revealed when inherited under certain circumstances in a later generation. For example, an ordinary recessive mutation arising in a germ cell is transmitted to only one individual; subsequently, the mutation may pass to several of this individual's offspring which by mating with each other may produce offspring homozygous for the mutation. The mutation would be revealed in the latter homozygotes. The possible fates of a mutation arising in a single germ cell are illus-trated in Fig. 28. It can be seen that in the final brother-sister matings

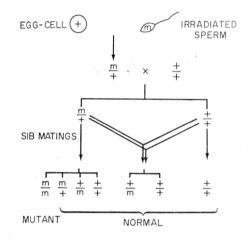

FIG. 28. POSSIBLE MODES OF INHERITANCE OF A RECESSIVE MUTATION *m* ARISING IN ONE SPERMATOZOAN

there is only a one-in-four chance that the mutation will be detectable and even in these instances non-mutant individuals will also be present among the offspring. The solution of these problems was to be able to distinguish the chromosome in the original sperm from any that were introduced in subsequent generations. Muller achieved this by using a dominant visible gene to mark any of the latter chromosomes. The marker was a gene on the X-chromosome called Bar (B) which greatly reduces the width of the eye. Having thus marked the X-chromosome it was then necessary to prevent recombination between it and any other chromosome: if recombination did occur it would render the marking virtually useless. The suppression of crossing-over was achieved by incorporating a large inversion into the marked chromosome. One final aspect of the special chromosome was that it carried a recessive lethal mutation. This combination of a cross-over suppressor, a lethal mutation, and the gene Bar is called the *ClB* chromosome. The use of the ClB chromosome for detecting sex-linked recessive lethal

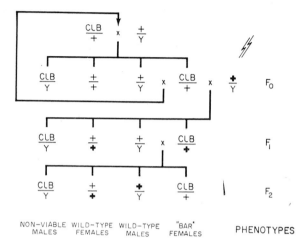

NON-VIABLE   WILD-TYPE   WILD-TYPE   "BAR"
MALES   FEMALES   MALES   FEMALES   PHENOTYPES

FIG. 29. THE *ClB* METHOD FOR DETECTING SEX-LINKED RECESSIVE LETHAL MUTATIONS. ABOVE, THE METHOD OF PERPETUATING THE *ClB* STOCK

The irradiated X-chromosome is shown in heavy type; if it contains a recessive lethal mutation the wild-type males in F_2 are non-viable

mutations is illustrated in Fig. 29 together with the method of perpetuating the ClB stock.

The manipulation of the ClB method for detecting radiation-induced mutation is as follows. Wild-type males are irradiated and then mated to heterozygous ClB females. The irradiated X-chromosome in the sperm of the treated male is inherited by the females of the F_1 generation. The females that also receive the ClB chromosome from the F_0 females are then mated to their wild-type brothers. These matings are done individually in small containers or vials such that irradiated chromosomes in the F_2 offspring of any one container all derive from one irradiated sperm cell in the F_0 male. If a recessive lethal mutation is induced in this spermatozoan it is carried normally in the F_1 females and passed on to half their sons in the F_2 generation; these males die. An induced lethal mutation cannot be lost from the treated X-chromosome in the F_1 females by crossing-over with the other chromosome as this is prevented by the large inversion. Since the ClB chromosome itself carries a recessive lethal the other half of the F_2 males also die such that in the presence of an induced mutation no males are observed at all in the F_2 generation. In the absence of an induced lethal, of course, half the F_2 males survive such that the frequency of mutation can be estimated as the proportion of vials in which no male offspring are found.

One defect of the ClB technique is that detected lethal mutations cannot be retained but are lost in the F_2 generation. To avoid this disadvantage, another method is now used for the detection of sex-linked recessive lethals. This method, again devised by Muller, is called the *Muller*-5 (M-5) technique. The operation of this method is identical in principle with that of the ClB, but the M-5 chromosome differs from the ClB principally in carrying a sex-linked recessive visible marker, the eye-colour mutation white apricot (w^a), instead of the lethal marker. Thus the treated males are mated to homozygous M-5 females and in the F_2, the irradiated chromosome is retained in the heterozygous M-5 female. Induced lethals can thus be kept as stocks for further study.

Similar methods are also available for detecting autosomal mutations in *Drosophila* but these involve an additional generation to produce flies homozygous for the treated chromosome. One method, for the second chromosome, uses a stock called Curly/Bristle Lobe (Cy/Bl.L.). Curly is a dominant mutation producing strong upcurling of the wings, it is associated with a large inversion which suppresses crossing-over, and is also lethal in the homozygous condition. The markers on the other chromosome are Bristle (Bl), shortening the bristles, and Lobe (L) reducing the size of the eye. Both are dominants and are again lethal in the homozygous form; crossing-over is not, however, suppressed by these markers. The method of use involves first an F_0 between irradiated wild-type males and Cy/BlL females. The backcrosses are put up as individual pair matings and the offspring therefore carry identical irradiated IInd chromosomes together with one or other of the marked chromosomes. In the final stage, matings between the Curly backcross offspring will themselves produce offspring including flies that are homozygous for the original irradiated chromosome. In the event of a lethal mutation being induced these presumptive normal flies do not appear. The reader might like to write out in detail the sequence of matings involved in this method.

The techniques have been described for detecting mutations arising in male flies. The M-5 and Cy/BlL methods may also be used for mutations induced in female germ cells.

RECESSIVE VISIBLE MUTATIONS

Recessive visible mutations, those that produce a change in the appearance of the fly, can also be scored with the techniques for lethal mutations. Instead of resulting in the absence of one type of fly, the visible mutation is observed as a change in the appearance of what otherwise would be normal wild-type flies.

An additional method for scoring sex-linked visibles makes use of the phenomenon of attached-X chromosomes (Chapter 2). The X-chromosome in the sperm of an irradiated male is passed on to his sons and the mutation is detectable, therefore, in the F_1.

An advantage of this method is that no laborious breeding tests are required. It does suffer from one disadvantage, however; flies carrying mutant genes are usually less viable than the wild-type; some of the flies carrying induced mutations will therefore die before they can be scored and this will result in spuriously low estimates of mutation frequencies.

Induced visible mutations can be identified fairly easily by allelism tests. Thus if a mutation is found which shortens the length of bristles

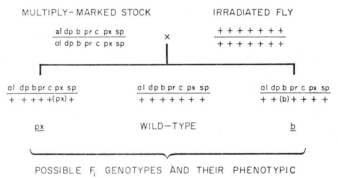

FIG. 30. THE SPECIFIC-LOCUS METHOD FOR DETECTING VISIBLE MUTATIONS
The stock is one that is in use and the mutant loci are:

al (aristales)	Absence of part of the antenna system
dp (dumpy)	Truncated wing
b (black)	Black body colour
pr (purple)	Purple eye colour
c (curved)	Curved wing
px (plexus)	Additional cross-veins in the wings
sp (speck)	Dark spot at the wing axil

it can be tested against previously discovered mutants of a similar appearance to determine with which, if any, it is allelic. In this way mutation rates at specific loci can be estimated. One further method which improves on this is the *specific-locus technique*. Irradiated males are mated to females which are homozygous for a number of recessive visible mutations. In the absence of mutation, offspring from these matings are normal in appearance since they carry the recessive genes in the heterozygous condition. If, however, the treatment induces a mutation at one of these loci the F_1 offspring which receives it will be homozygous for the mutant in question and will show the mutant phenotype (Fig. 30).

DETRIMENTAL MUTATIONS

Most visible mutations in *Drosophila* also have an adverse effect on viability. In some cases this is extreme such that as a class, visible mutations grade into full lethals. In addition, some mutations have no observable effect on the appearance of the organism but nevertheless render it less viable than the wild-type. These mutations are called *detrimentals* and in their effect may vary from almost undetectable to nearly fully lethal. They may be detected by the M-5 or Cy/BlL techniques as cultures in which the frequency of normal flies is lower than expectation. In practice, only the more extreme mutants are detectable with any precision, since the effects of the less severe mutants progressively overlap the results of random fluctuations in the frequency with which wild-type flies appear in non-mutant cultures.

The category of detrimental mutations is very important. It has seemed probable from the earliest work in radiation genetics that detrimental mutations are far more frequent than the more spectacular visibles or lethals; their effect in populations, as discussed in Chapter 8, may be considerable.

MUTATIONS IN THE MOUSE

In the early years of the study of radiation genetics, *Drosophila* played a major part because of the simple techniques available and because of the relative ease and cheapness of breeding. Studies with other organisms soon began, however, and have continued at an ever increasing pace. Of particular importance are those with mouse, the only mammal so far found generally amenable to genetic studies. With the potential for widespread use of atomic energy in industry and increasing use in research and in medicine, current trends in radiation genetics have largely centred around radiation hazards to Man. The principles of genetics in their fundamental aspects, apply to all living organisms. If, however, information derived from experimental animals is to be used in safeguarding the health of Man, this should be derived from, or confirmed by, experiments with organisms as closely related to Man as possible. In this respect the mouse has an advantage over all other organisms used in experimental work.

No special techniques such as the M-5 and Cy/BlL in *Drosophila* have yet been devised in the mouse. The specific-locus method is applicable, however, and a stock that is commonly used carries the mutant alleles non-agouti (a); brown (b); chinchilla (c^{ch}); blue-dilution (d); short ear (se); pink eye (p); and piebald spotting (s). Induced mutations have been observed at each of these loci and they include known alleles which are viable in the homozygous condition and also alleles which are non-viable in this condition. The latter are recessive lethals and may, perhaps, be comparable to deficiency coverage recessive lethal mutations in *Drosophila*.

The specific-locus method for observing recessive lethal mutations is naturally limited to mutation in only a very small part of the chromosome set of the mouse. A more comprehensive technique has been used by T. C. Carter. This involves a statistical analysis of litter size. Male mice are irradiated and mated to unirradiated females. The male off-spring (F_0) have each received one irradiated sperm. These are now mated to unirradiated females and the irradiated chromosomes appear in half the F_1 offspring. Female F_1 offspring are backcrossed to the original F_0 male and induced lethal mutations will therefore segregate in half of the litters. This mating scheme is shown in Fig. 31. If a

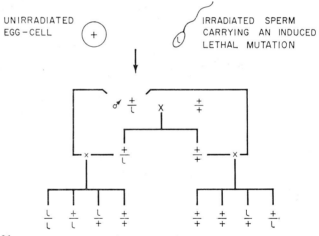

FIG. 31. LITTER-SIZE METHOD FOR ESTIMATING INDUCED LETHAL MUTATION FREQUENCIES IN THE MOUSE

recessive lethal mutation was induced in the original sperm, half of the final litters will be smaller than the average by one quarter. One drawback of this method is that the induction of a mutation can only be inferred; it is not possible to detect and confirm the presence of an individual mutation.

MUTATIONS IN PLANTS

The higher plants have not been used very much in the study of induced recessive mutations. This material has proved very valuable in studies on chromosome changes, however, but these will be described later. The lower plants, such as fungi and yeasts, have become very important in genetic studies and of these the fungus *Neurospora* has been the most widely used.

MUTATIONS IN NEUROSPORA

Neurospora is a simple fungus and grows in the form of branching filaments. These filaments or *hyphae* are made up of single cells joined end to end. Each cell contains many nuclei, each with a haploid set of chromosomes. The organism can be grown in a liquid medium, or one solidified with Agar, containing salts and a source of nitrogen, sugar, and an essential growth factor, biotin. Asexual reproduction occurs by hyphal fragmentation or by budding off uninucleate or multinucleate *conidia*. There are two different mating types or sexes in *Neurospora* but in other fungi there may be more than two. Sexual reproduction occurs by the penetration of a hyphal fragment or a conidium of one mating type into the female organ, the *protoperithecium*, of the other. The hyphal nucleus fuses with the egg nucleus and the diploid product immediately undergoes meiosis and one post-meiotic mitosis to produce eight *ascospores*. These are arranged linearly in an *ascus* and the arrangement reflects the process of meiosis. The distal and proximal four ascospores derive, respectively, from the products of the first meiotic division and, within each half of the ascus, the distal and proximal pairs of ascospores derive from the second meiotic divisions, respectively (Fig. 32).

Genetic analysis is fairly simple in *Neurospora*. The organism is haploid and clones can be grown from a uninucleate conidium or from an ascospore which has been removed from the ascus by micromanipulation. In view of the precise arrangement of ascospores, analysis of segregation can be very precise. Allelism tests are also quite simple. The cells of the organism are normally multinucleate. Apart from being of the same mating type, the nuclei may have different genotypes; this is brought about by fusion of hyphae of different colonies and the heterogeneous mixture of nuclei so produced is called a *heterocaryon*. The important property of the heterocaryon is that it permits allelic interaction. Consider, for example, a heterocaryon between two arginineless mutant strains. If the two strains carry mutant alleles at different argininess loci the heterocaryon is, in effect, a double heterozygote and grows normally on the basic medium: if both strains carry alleles

at the same arginineless locus, the heterocaryon behaves like a homozygote and still requires arginine for growth.

As already noted, the mutants most commonly studied in *Neurospora*
and other micro-organisms are of the biochemical deficiency type.

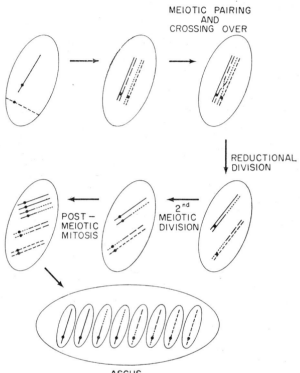

FIG. 32. DIAGRAM OF MEIOSIS AND ASCUS FORMATION IN *Neurospora*

These may be produced and isolated in the following way. One mating
type is irradiated and then mated to the other mating type. Individual
ascospores are collected and grown in a medium that is supplemented
with a large number of amino-acids and vitamins. The cultures are
then tested on minimal medium and if they fail to grow they can be
tested on all the separate constituents of the original supplemented
medium. Thus by trial and error the specific requirement of any mutant
culture can be determined.

Other, less laborious, methods are available. Uninucleate conidia or
ascospores may be irradiated and then grown in a liquid minimal

medium for a few hours. If the medium is filtered, using an appropriate grade of filter, the normal strongly growing cultures are filtered off, while the mutants, not having grown, pass through the filter. Alternatively, if the irradiated cells are plated on a solid medium, the normal cultures can be discerned after a short period of growth and separated from the mutants that grow very poorly. A more precise method has been described by E. L. Tatum and J. Lederberg. In this, ascospores are allowed to fall on the surface of a solid minimal medium; a short period of growth is permitted and the position of the growing colonies (non-mutant) is noted. A second thin layer of supplemented medium is then poured on top of the first and after a second period of growth any newly arisen cultures can be detected and removed for analysis. These, which were unable to grow on minimal medium but could grow on supplemented medium, comprise the mutant colonies.

Large numbers of irradiated nuclei can be handled in studies with micro-organisms and this has made possible a very specific technique, the detection of reverse mutation; that is, the change from a mutant back to a wild-type allele. A heavy suspension of uninucleate cells from a mutant strain is irradiated. Portions of this suspension are plated out on minimal medium and the number of growing colonies is noted. These may have arisen either through reverse mutation to wild-type, or through the appearance of another mutation suppressing the action of the original; these alternatives can be distinguished by segregation analysis. The number of cells which remain alive after treatment is determined by plating dilutions of the irradiated suspensions on supplemented medium. Thus very large numbers can be used to determine induced reverse mutation frequencies.

An important implication of the phenomenon of reverse mutation might be mentioned. If a mutation represents a gene that is no longer functioning it can clearly arise either as a slight modification of the chemical structure of the wild-type gene, or as a gross destruction of the gene. In the latter case there seems little likelihood that the original configuration could be restored. Thus the occurrence of reverse mutation may be taken as evidence that a particular mutant represents only a slight change from the wild-type allele and not gross destruction or loss. As a corollary of this it also follows that the reverse mutation process itself represents a highly specific modification of gene structure.

MUTATION IN MAN

The methods that have been described for studying the mutation process in experimental organisms obviously cannot be used in Man; neither would it be acceptable to expose human beings to experimental mutagenic treatments. Methods are available, however, for observing mutants and measuring the rate at which they arise spontaneously. These are described in detail in Chapter 8.

CHROMOSOME STRUCTURAL CHANGES

Another marked effect of radiation on the genetic material is the production of structural changes in chromosomes. The first evidence of this phenomenon came from studies on *Drosophila* but these findings were quickly extended to other organisms and, in particular, have been exceedingly abundant in plant material. Chromosome structural changes or aberrations do arise normally, in the absence of radiation treatment, and many of the various types and their genetic properties were known prior to the study of radiation genetics. The rate at which such effects appear spontaneously, however, is very low and the discovery that radiation greatly increased this rate supplied a tool for more rapid analysis of the genetic implications of such structural alterations. This research has proceeded in both genetic and cytological fields to supply a comprehensive theory on the process of structural change.

The primary event in structural change is thought to be the formation of a break in the chromosome thread. The consequences which follow breakage depend on the number and proximity of breaks, the degree of ploidy of the chromosome set and the condition of the chromosomes with respect to their replication in the division cycles.

GENETIC STUDIES OF CHROMOSOMAL REARRANGEMENT

If a single break is produced in a chromosome, the two ends can either rejoin in the original way or remain separated. The first possibility is called *restitution* and re-establishes the normal chromosome structure; it is thus not directly observable. The second possibility leads to rather deleterious effects which result in cell lethality; this is obviously not amenable to further genetic study and will be discussed more fully in the following section on cytological observations.

With the occurrence of two or more breaks in a chromosome set, rejoining can occur between breaks. If both breaks occur in the same chromosome then this mutual rejoining of the broken ends results in an inversion or a deletion. If the breaks are in separate chromosomes four pieces of chromosome exist, two with a centromere, two without. The centric pieces of chromosome may join together, and likewise the acentric pieces, to produce a chromosome with two centromeres (*dicentric*) and one without a centromere (*acentric*). This again leads to marked deleterious effects and will be discussed later. In the remaining possibility for rearrangement, the acentric piece of one chromosome may join to the centric piece of the other, and *vice versa*. This produces a mutual exchange of parts between chromosomes, called *mutual translocation*, and is viable since it reconstitutes a balanced chromosome set with no dicentric or acentric pieces. These possibilities for re-arrangement following two chromosome breaks in a haploid set are shown in Fig. 33.

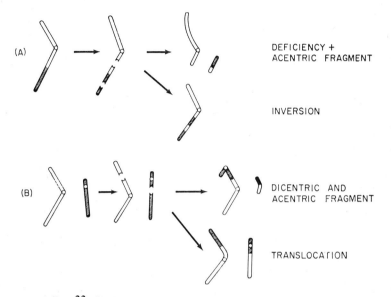

FIG. 33. CONSEQUENCES OF TWO CHROMOSOME BREAKS IN A
HAPLOID CHROMOSOME SET

Viable chromosome rearrangements, translocations, inversions and small deficiencies, can be detected by genetic means. Inversions greatly reduce the frequency of crossing-over; they can be detected by deter-mining the recombination frequencies between known marker genes on another chromosome when it is heterozygous with the suspected in-version. Deficiencies also reduce crossing-over but only in a small area of the chromosome. When they are in the heterozygous condition with a chromosome carrying one or more recessive genes situated within the area of the deficiency, the recessive genes take on a false appearance of dominance. This effect of deficiencies is called *coverage*; by it deficiencies may be detected, and also located fairly accurately.

The effect of translocations in producing spurious linkage between genes known to be on non-homologous chromosomes was described in the previous chapter. This property may be used to detect trans-locations by genetic means. These genetic methods for detecting chromosome structural change are illustrated in Fig. 34.

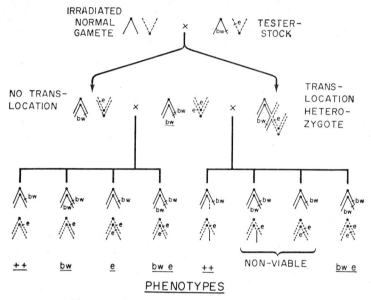

FIG. 34. DETECTION OF TRANSLOCATION BY GENETIC MEANS

The diagrams represent the second and third chromosomes of *Drosophila* and the markers are brown (*bw*) and ebony (*e*) respectively

CYTOLOGICAL STUDIES OF CHROMOSOMAL ABERRATIONS

Cytological methods offer direct ways of studying chromosomal structural aberrations. Tissues or organisms are irradiated and the effects may be observed by microscopical examination of the chromosomes after suitable preparation and staining. Several dyes are available which stain chromosomal material specifically to the exclusion of other cell constituents. If the material is small or thin, like pollen grains or bacteria, it may be stained for microscopical examination without further preparation. More commonly the material is too thick, or composed of many layers of cells, and must be treated in such a way as to produce thin, preferably unicellular, layers for examination. This can be done by cutting thin sections, by squashing the material, or by maceration.

Cytological techniques are particularly useful when used in conjunction with genetic analysis and for this salivary gland chromosomes of *Drosophila* have proved extremely valuable. Since these chromosomes are very much stretched out it is possible not only to confirm the genetic evidence of structural change but also to determine very precisely the positions at which rearrangements have occurred in the chromosome.

The initial discovery of X-ray induced chromosomal structural changes was again made in *Drosophila*. Similar observations, independent of these, were soon made in maize and barley; subsequently, plant material became pre-eminent in cytological studies. Much of the work with plants has been concerned with somatic tissues and, therefore, is not of direct genetic interest. It has, nevertheless, contributed greatly to an understanding of the effects of radiations on chromosomes. Genetic effects are almost always discernible only after a great number of cell divisions have occurred subsequent to the treatment. Cytological studies, on the other hand, can be made any time after the irradiation of the material.

Chromosomes are most suitable for cytological examination during metaphase and anaphase of division; they are, at this time, highly condensed and stain well. The effect of irradiation on chromosomes in mitotic stages is most easily studied in root tip material where the cells are dividing continuously. A plant which has been used extensively in this respect is the broad bean, *Vicia faba*, one advantage of which is its small chromosome number (see Plate IV).

During mitosis the chromosomes replicate and then divide such that the chromosome thread changes from a single to a double structure and then, on separation of daughter chromatids at metaphase, back to a single state. Irradiation can act, therefore, on either the single thread, to produce what is called a chromosome break, or on the double thread to produce chromatid breaks.

CHROMOSOME BREAKS

If a bean root is irradiated and then prepared for cytological examination about 20 to 24 hours later, the cells observed in metaphase or anaphase would have been in the early resting stage when irradiated. Any aberrations observed in the metaphase or anaphase must have arisen from breaks produced in a single thread (i.e. *chromosome breaks*). If a single break is produced in a chromosome and fails to restitute, it will be reproduced when the chromosome duplicates and will appear at metaphase as a break in each chromatid. Two or more breaks may rejoin to produce a dicentric chromosome and an acentric fragment. During anaphase the acentric fragment is lost since it has no means of attachment to the spindle fibre and fails to become transported to either daughter nucleus. The two centromeres in the dicentric fragment are attracted towards opposite poles of the metaphase plate and the chromosome threads are stretched out forming a bridge between the daughter nuclei. If the nuclear membranes are formed at this stage, the dicentric chromosomes may not be included in either nucleus; the resultant chromosomal deletion usually results in death of the cell. The dicentric chromosome may break, however, allowing the centric fragments to enter the nuclei. The new broken ends now present in each nucleus may then repeat the whole process. This phenomenon is called the *breakage-fusion-bridge cycle* (Fig. 35); it was first reported by B. McClintock as a spontaneous process occurring in maize. The cycle may go on for many generations of cell divisions. The point at which breakage occurs on the dicentric chromosome varies at each division; as cell division proceeds the descendant cells become more and more genetically unbalanced, until finally they die.

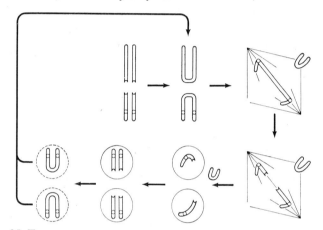

FIG. 35. THE BREAKAGE–FUSION–BRIDGE CYCLE FOLLOWING CHROMOSOME BREAKAGE AND RE-UNION

Similar effects occur in germinal tissue. In the pre-meiotic germ cell stages this results in cell death as in the somatic tissue above. Haploid gametes, however, are not dependent on their own genetic material but rely on nurse cells for their nutrition, etc.; they may therefore carry quite extensive chromosomal damage and yet remain viable and capable of forming zygotes on fertilisation. With the beginning of division in the zygote, however, the breakage-fusion-bridge cycle continues and the resultant chromosomal unbalance leads to the death of the embryo. This is always the case in animal tissue, the effect representing one type of *dominant lethal* mutation. These may be observed by cytological examination of *Drosophila* eggs which fail to hatch; such unhatched eggs frequently show gross aberrations in size and clumping of nuclei. Plants are much more able than animals to withstand the harmful effects of chromosomal unbalance, probably because they are frequently polyploid. In tissues such as the endosperm of maize, which is triploid, the effect of the breakage-fusion-bridge cycle may not be lethal. In endosperm which contains suitable genetic markers the effect of variation in the transmission of genetic material may be observed as a pattern of mosaicism.

CHROMATID BREAKS

If the irradiated bean root is examined 3 to 4 hours after irradiation, the aberrations observed at metaphase will have arisen from breaks produced in cells whose chromosomes had duplicated. These breaks usually affect only one thread (chromatid); they are called *chromatid breaks*.

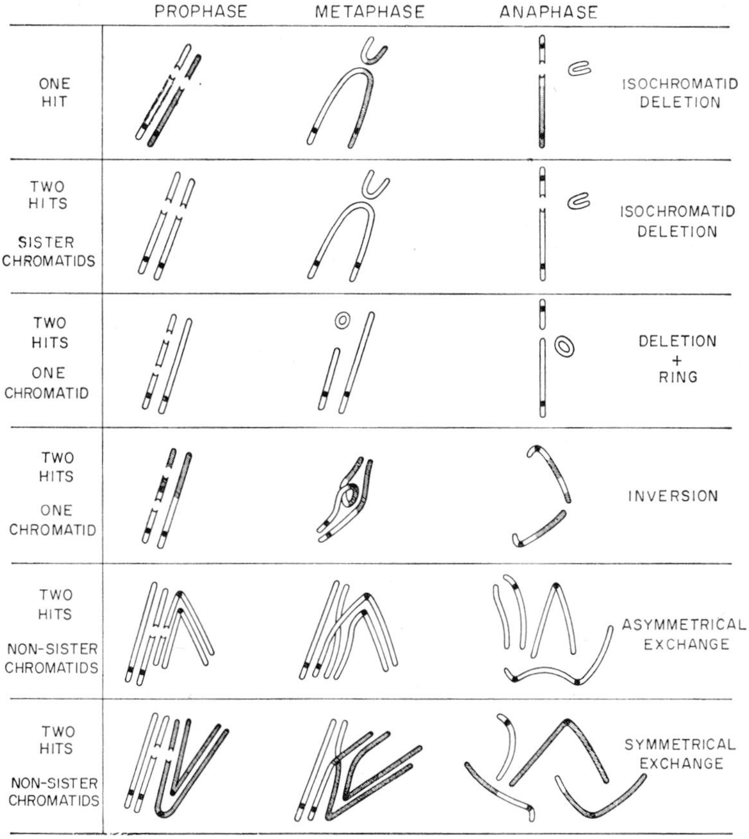

FIG. 36. THE CONSEQUENCES OF TWO CHROMATID BREAKS

If a single break occurs in one of the pair of chromatids it is seen at metaphase as a discontinuity in the thread and is called a chromatid deletion. Because of the intimate pairing of daughter chromatids, the two pieces produced by a single break at prophase remain in their original alignment and mostly restitute before metaphase. If the break does remain open the acentric piece is lost and the centric piece behaves in subsequent cell divisions as if it were a chromosome break.

It is sometimes found that both sister chromatids are broken at the same place; these are called *iso-chromatid* deletions. Unlike chromosome deletions, these usually show rejoining between sister threads (i.e. *sister union*) in the centric and acentric fragments. The dicentric and acentric chromosomes suffer the usual consequences, i.e. bridge formation and loss.

From evidence to be described in the next chapter iso-chromatid breaks appear to be derived from either a single event which affects both chromatids simultaneously or from two separate events. In the latter, two hit phenomena, the chromatids are usually broken in two different places. These again produce iso-chromatid deletions when the breaks are located one in each of a pair of sister chromatids. If the breaks are both in one chromatid this may lead to an inversion, or to a deletion accompanied by the formation of a ring chromosome; these are called *intrachanges*. If the breaks are in non-sister chromatids, deletions and/or translocations are possible and these are termed *interchanges*. Figure 36 shows, in a diagrammatic form, the consequences of chromatid breaks as observed at metaphase following irradiation of prophase stages.

QUANTITATIVE ASPECTS OF RADIATION MUTAGENESIS

In this chapter we will consider the magnitude of the genetic effect of radiation exposure in relation to different modes of irradiation. The first, and obvious problem concerns the effect of giving different doses of radiation; second, there is the question of the effect of doses given at various radiation intensities, and third, there is the nature of the effect of radiations of different energies. An analysis of these problems has been of great value in the construction of hypotheses on the mode of action of radiations in the production of mutations and chromosome aberrations. Such studies are also of value in supplying a basis for the prediction of the amount of genetic damage that might follow exposure to radiations: this is of particular importance to the estimation of genetic risks that Man may run in his use of radiations in medicine and industry.

Before describing the nature of the genetic effects following different modes of irradiation, one elementary point should be stressed. It is to be expected that higher doses of radiation will produce more genetic damage than low doses. This increased genetic damage, however, is not represented by bigger or more deleterious types of mutation. Higher radiation exposure produces the same types of mutations that are produced at low radiation doses. The effect of increasing dose is to produce higher frequencies of mutations.

"POINT MUTATION" FREQUENCY AND RADIATION DOSE

Point mutation is a term that has been applied to those mutations, commonly recessive, that are not associated with chromosomal structural change. The category of point mutations that has been studied most extensively, with respect to dose effects, is that of sex-linked recessive lethals in *Drosophila*. The earliest experiments were performed by C. P. Oliver in 1930. He irradiated flies with various doses of X-rays ranging from 300 r up to 5000 r, and determined mutation frequencies by the ClB method. The results showed that mutation frequency was simply proportional to the dose of radiation received by the germ cells. This important discovery was soon confirmed and, in recent studies, C. Stern and his collaborators have shown that the principle holds true down to doses as low as 25 r. The results of several investigations are summarised in Fig. 37.

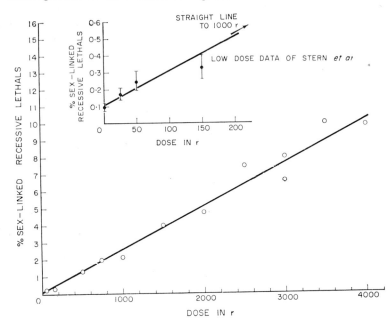

FIG. 37. THE RELATIONSHIP BETWEEN RADIATION DOSE AND THE FREQUENCY OF SEX-LINKED RECESSIVE LETHALS INDUCED IN *Drosophila* SPERMATOZOA

The data in Fig. 37 refer to the induction of mutations in mature spermatozoa in *Drosophila*. Identical findings have been reported for the induction of visible mutation in the spermatozoa of *Drosophila* and mouse, for visible mutants in some higher plants such as maize and antirrhinum, and for biochemical mutants in *Neurospora* and in other micro-organisms.

The results of numerous investigations, covering a range of different organisms, support the principle that the frequency of radiation-induced point mutation is simply proportional, or linearly related, to the total radiation dose received by the germ cells. It would also appear that this principle is valid even below the lowest doses that have been used experimentally. When the dose/mutation frequency relationship is plotted on graph paper, as in Fig. 37, the straight line may be extrapolated back to zero dose where it cuts the mutation frequency ordinate at a point corresponding to the control or spontaneous mutation frequency. There is no evidence, therefore, that a threshold situation exists in radiation mutagenesis; it appears that any amount of radiation, however small, will result in an increase in the frequency of mutation.*

RADIATION INTENSITY AND POINT MUTATION FREQUENCY

The dose of radiation given to any organism is the product of the radiation intensity and the duration of the exposure; different doses can be given by varying either of these. Both of these methods were used by investigators in the above studies on dose effect. In that the results of these experiments all agree in respect of the quantitative relationship between dose and mutation frequency, it would appear that variation in the duration or in the intensity of irradiation, is each without effect on the efficiency with which radiations produce mutations.

The first studies bearing directly on the effect of radiation intensity were made by J. T. Patterson in 1931; these were in the nature of fractionation experiments. Patterson found that in spermatozoa of *Drosophila* a given dose of X-rays produced the same frequency of mutations irrespective of whether it was given continuously, in one period, or in two or more fractions separated by intervals of up to several days. This work was confirmed by subsequent research in which the effect of low intensity irradiation, given over long periods of time, has been compared to that given in short periods at very high intensity. The total range of intensity studied extends at the present from 0·002 r/min to 2000 r/min. Over this range, differing by a factor of 1,000,000, no variation has been observed in the efficiency with which radiations induce mutations in *Drosophila* spermatozoa.

The physical effect of the passage of radiation particles through materials is the production of a track of ionisations. The track ends when the particle finally expends its energy in a short tail in which ionisations are densely clustered. The production of ionisations along the track, and also in the terminal clusters of the tail, is directly proportional to dose and is independent of the intensity of irradiation. The data on the effects of dose and intensity have been interpreted, therefore, as indicating that the production of a mutation is a single event, determined by one ionisation or one ionisation cluster and independent of the proximity, either spatial or temporal, of other

* Recent experimental results from radiation doses of 5 r are in agreement with the principle of a linear relationship between dose and mutation frequency.

ionisations or clusters. This hypothesis will be amended and discussed more fully in a later part of this chapter dealing with the effects of different types of radiations.

CHROMOSOME ABERRATIONS

Studies on the manner of production of chromosome aberrations have been made in both germinal and somatic cells in a wide variety of organisms. Quantitative studies in animal cells have been conducted chiefly by genetic analysis following irradiation of mature spermatozoa. The latter are highly specialised cells and therefore rather abnormal. More generalised conclusions have come from cytological studies on dividing cells in plants. These will be described first.

The frequency with which chromosome or chromatid deletions arise is linearly related to dose and independent of the intensity at which the irradiation is given. In this respect they behave in a similar way to point mutations. They are again "one hit" phenomena and are interpreted as arising from a single break in the chromosome thread,

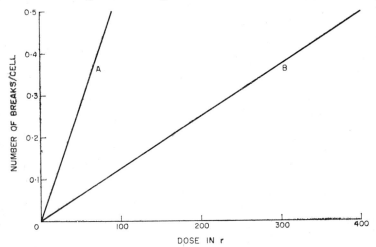

FIG. 38. RELATIONSHIP BETWEEN RADIATION DOSE AND PRODUCTION OF CHROMATID **A** AND CHROMOSOME **B** BREAKS IN POLLEN CELLS OF *Tradescantia*

induced by one ionisation or one ionisation cluster. The linear relationship between X-ray dose and the production of chromatid and chromosome breaks in mature pollen (microspores) of the spider-wort, *Tradescantia*, is illustrated in Fig. 38.

Exchanges between chromatids and chromosomes arise with a frequency which is proportional to a power of the dose higher than one following X- or γ-irradiation; with increasing dose an even more increasing frequency of aberrations is observed. The degree to which the curve differs from linearity is dependent, however, on the intensity of irradiation. At intensities greater than 160 r/min aberration frequency is proportional to the square of the dose. At lower intensities the yield of aberrations is proportional to a progressively lower power of dose (approximating to a power of about 3/2 at 2 r/min). If the exposure time is kept constant, and the radiation intensity varied, the aberration frequency is again dependent on the square of the dose. These relationships are described in Fig. 39.

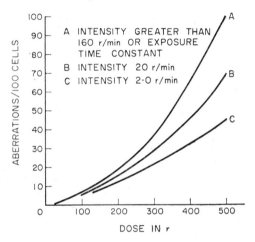

FIG. 39. RELATIONSHIP BETWEEN DOSE OF X-RAYS AND ABERRATION FREQUENCY IN *Tradescantia* MICROSPORES

From the square relationship for the high intensity irradiation it is concluded that two independent events are necessary for the production of an aberration. These events, probably breaks, are again produced in a manner proportional to dose. The dependence of the dose relationship on intensity can be explained by assuming that a break in a chromosome may restitute in a given period of time. If this restitution occurs before the formation of a second break, a rearrangement aberration is no longer possible; the frequency with which rearrangement occurs will be depressed, therefore, with increasing duration or decreasing intensity of irradiation. That this depression is related to a time factor in restitution is confirmed by the dose square relationship found with a constant exposure time.

Fractionation experiments provide a means of determining the period of time during which one break may remain open and available for recombination with another break. If the period between two fractions is sufficiently long to allow restitution or reunion of all breaks from the first fraction, the total yield of aberrations would simply be the sum of the yields that each fraction would have produced by itself. For example, if the fractions were equal and each produced 5 per cent aberrations, both together would produce 10 per cent. If on the other hand, no breaks rejoined during the interval, the aberration yield would be dependent on the squares of the total dose of irradiation. The second fraction in the above example produces a doubling of the dose and the aberration frequency would therefore be increased fourfold to 20 per cent.

Applying this approach and using different intervals between fractions, it has been shown that restitution and rejoining usually occur within 20 minutes in *Tradescantia* and within about 2 hours in the bean *Vicia*. Some breaks, however, appear to retain their rejoining potentialities for very much longer periods.

Iso-chromatid breaks are produced at a rate that is intermediate between that for simple breaks and that for exchanges. This may be explained by supposing that breaks in each of two sister chromatids may be produced either by two independent ionising tracks or by one track passing through both chromatids. Iso-chromatid deletions would thus comprise a mixture of "one"- and "two-event" effects; an "event" in this case being the passage of a single ionising ray. A similar interpretation can be applied to the action of neutrons and α-rays. Following the use of these radiations, all aberration types are produced in a manner linearly related to dose. It is probable that multiple breakage in a nucleus is again produced by the passage of a single ionising particle.

ABERRATIONS IN DROSOPHILA

One class of mutation that has not yet been mentioned is that of dominant lethals. These, as their name implies, are lethal in the heterozygous condition; normally they result in death in early embryonic life. In *Drosophila* they are scored as unhatched eggs, in the mouse they may be observed as "moles" on the wall of the uterus.

Dominant lethal mutations are produced in *Drosophila* at a frequency that is linearly related to dose up to about 4000 r. At higher doses the frequency increases less rapidly; this is demonstrated in Fig. 40.

Cytological examination of unhatched eggs show gross abnormalities in nuclear division. This is observed chiefly as extensive clumping or aggregation of nuclei (Plate VI). The dose relationship and the cytological appearance of dominant lethals both suggest that these mutations arise as single chromosome breaks followed by breakage-fusion-bridge cycles.   At the higher doses the mutation frequency falls off since progressively more of the breaks become involved in compli-cated rearrangements involving two or more breaks.   Thus where one break would have sufficed to produce dominant lethality two or more are actually involved.

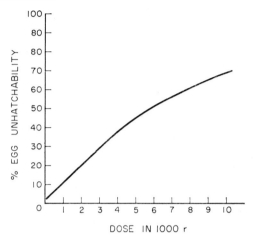

FIG. 40.   INDUCTION OF DOMINANT LETHALS (MEASURED AS EGG UNHATCH-ABILITY) IN MATURE SPERMATOZOA OF *Drosophila* AT VARIOUS X-RAY DOSES

Single breaks can lead to loss of a chromosome through bridge formation during division since, on the formation of nuclear mem-branes, the material forming the bridge may be excluded from the daughter nuclei.   Such a loss in the case of the long autosomes would be inviable.   If a female zygote (XX) loses an X-chromosome, however, it develops into a male fly with the genotype XO.   This fly is normal except that it is sterile. XO males are therefore produced in a manner similar to that for dominant lethals.   Such XO males are induced by irradiation in a manner proportional to dose and this offers corrobor-ative evidence of the single break nature of dominant lethals and of the dependence of the break on a single event.

One further observation on XO males is interesting.   Although pro-duced at a frequency linearly related to dose, the rate of accumulation is less than expected on the basis of estimates of the number of breaks induced on the X-chromosome.   This would agree with the expectation that all breaks need not lead to simple chromosome loss but that some should cause more general abnormalities in the process of division and lead to dominant lethality;   hence the consequent loss of the break as far as the scoring of XO males is concerned.

Viable chromosome aberrations, translocations, inversions and deficiencies, are produced in proportion to a 3/2 power of the dose. This is similar to the relationship found for "two hit" aberrations in plants produced by low intensity irradiations given over various time exposures. The similarity, however, is only superficial; completely different phenomena are involved in each case.

The important difference between the observations in animals and plants is that in the former only viable exchanges can be scored whereas in the latter even changes destined to become inviable remain observable by direct examination. The 3/2 power relationship for abberation in *Drosophila* sperm probably arises as a consequence of loss of breaks in non-viable rearrangements. With increasing numbers of breaks per chromosome set, the probability that one may remain open and lead to dominant lethality obviously increases. Similarly, with three as opposed to two breaks, more complex rearrangements are possible and this more frequently leads to inviability and cell deaths. Thus with an increasing probability of more than two breaks occurring. in a nucleus, as must arise with increasing dose, the number of breaks lost in inviable exchanges would increase, thereby depressing the dose-square relationship. From this hypothesis it can be predicted that the dose effect should approximate to a square relationship when the effect is measured at low dose levels. Preliminary results justify this prediction, but as yet, conclusive proof is lacking.

The explanation of the dose 3/2 relationship for two hit aberrations in plant material depended on the ability of breaks to restitute before the occurrence of a second break. In *Drosophila* spermatozoa, however, the dose relationship is independent of intensity and from this it has been concluded that breaks produced in spermatozoa are unable to rejoin until after the process of fertilisation. No matter how slowly the breaks are accumulated, therefore, all remain open to potential rearrangement when the chromosomes begin to move freely after entering the egg. Direct evidence that breaks remain open is available from the observation that induced breaks in spermatozoa may take part in rearrangements with spontaneously arisen breaks in the maternal chromosomes of the egg.

THE EFFECT OF VARIATION IN THE QUALITY OF RADIATION

In its passage through living tissue an ionising ray produces a track of secondary ionisations. The amount and distribution of ionisation along the track (linear energy transfer, LET) are dependent on the type and energy of the initial radiation. Radiation of the electromagnetic type such as X-rays and γ-rays produces a track along which ionisations are sparse except in the final tail where they are densely clustered. The degree of clustering in the tail being inversely related to the energy of the radiation. For particulate rays such as neutrons and α-rays the whole track is as densely ionised as the tail of an X-ray track.

In the early studies on lethal mutations in *Drosophila*, no difference was observed between the mutagenic efficiency of radiations ranging from X-rays of less than 10 keV up to over 80 keV and γ-rays of radium up to 600 keV. This was interpreted as supporting the concept, derived from data on dose and intensity effects, that mutation was caused by an ionisation independent of the proximity of other ionisations. This interpretation implied that variations in ion density produced by the use of radiations of different LET could be viewed as an extension of such variation produced by irradiation at different dose rates.

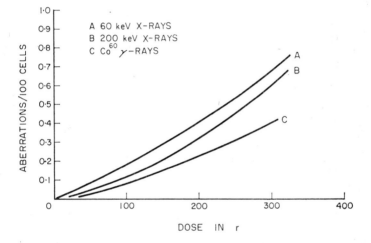

FIG. 41.   RELATIONSHIP BETWEEN CHROMOSOME BREAKAGE AND RADIATION QUALITY IN *Tradescantia* MICROSPORES

Early studies on chromosome breakage in *Tradescantia* microspores gave results similar to those for *Drosophila* lethals; but, in contrast, it was found that 3 keV X-rays were appreciably more effective than those over 10 keV. More recent studies on radiation effects in dry spores of *Tradescantia* have shown differences between the mutagenic efficiency of 60 keV X-rays, 200 keV X-rays and Co[60] γ-rays with a mean energy level of 1200 keV. The ratio of the efficiencies of these radiations (their *relative biological efficiency* or RBE) were of the order 2·0 : 1·5 : 1·0.   The data are illustrated in Fig. 41.

Still greater differences in mutagenic effects have been observed between X-rays and fast neutron irradiation. In *Tradescantia*, the latter have been shown to be several times more efficient than X-rays in the production of chromatid breaks. A slightly lower difference was found for exchanges but this was complicated by the marked difference in dose response for neutrons as compared with X-rays. No precise estimates are available for the measurement of the relative biological effectiveness of neutrons as compared to X-rays; neutron dosimetry is inaccurate and the radiation is always contaminated with a variable proportion of γ-rays. Nevertheless, it is clear that in *Tradescantia*, neutrons are very efficient producers of chromosome breakage (Fig. 42).

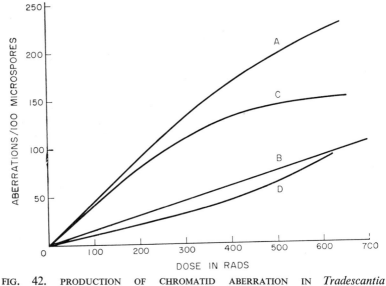

FIG. 42. PRODUCTION OF CHROMATID ABERRATION IN *Tradescantia*
MICROSPORES
A   simple breaks produced by fast neutrons
B   simple breaks produced by X-rays
C   exchanges produced by fast neutrons
D   exchanges produced by X-rays

Early studies on the effects of neutrons in *Drosophila* indicated that they were, if anything, less effective than X-rays. More recent studies however, have shown that for the induction of dominant lethal mutations, neutrons were more efficient than X-rays; the magnitude of the effect was similar to that found for chromatid breaks in *Tradescantia*. It seemed possible that the early results were affected by inaccurate neutron dosimetry, a subject that has advanced considerably in recent years. Recent studies on recessive lethal mutations have also shown quantitative differences between the effect of fast neutrons, X-rays and Co⁶⁰ γ-rays. (Fig. 43.) These results were also comparable with the

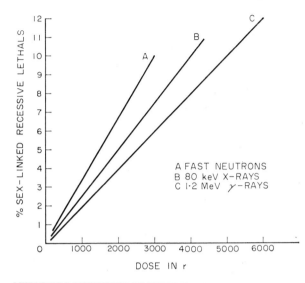

FIG. 43.   MUTAGENIC EFFICIENCY OF DIFFERENT RADIATIONS IN SPERMATOZOA
OF *Drosophila*

results in *Tradescantia*. Thus, in spite of the early results, it is now accepted that the more densely ionising radiations are more efficient in the production of mutation and chromosome breakage.

The dependence of chromosome breakage frequency on the degree of clustering of ionisations was interpreted by D. H. Lea as evidence that a single ionisation was insufficient to cause chromosome breakage. Mathematical analysis of the effects of neutrons and X-rays suggested that about 17 ionisations were necessary for chromosome breakage. Muller has advanced explanations of the dependence of chromatid breakage on the degree of ionisation which still accord with the view that breakage is produced by one ionisation. The basis of the argument rests on the logical assumption that a chromatid is less likely to restitute if it is broken in more than one place in a small locality. In *Tradescantia* microspores chromatid breaks are induced at a time when sister chromatids are closely paired. If only a single break occcurred in one chromatid, the separate pieces would be kept in their original position by the forces of mutual attraction from the unbroken sister chromatid. Thus restitution might be expected to occur easily. If, however, an ionisation cluster produced nearby breaks in each chromatid this would destroy the mechanical alignment of broken pieces and allow movement which would reduce the probability of restitution and hence increase the frequency of observed breaks. This principle will still hold if the chromatid is but a single thread. Multiple breaks may allow movement of interstitial pieces; this would impede restitution which must occur at all sites of breakage to restore the chromatid to an unbroken condition. Figure 44 illustrates diagrammatically the possible explan-

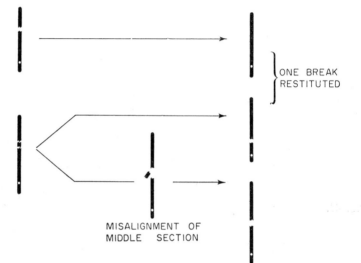

ONE BREAK
RESTITUTED

MISALIGNMENT OF
MIDDLE   SECTION

FIG. 44.   MULTIPLE BREAKAGE EXPLANATION OF THE HIGH RBE OF DENSELY
IONISING RADIATION

ation of the higher efficiency of the densely ionising radiations on the assumption that breakage is produced by one ionisation.

Theoretically, multiple breakage should lower the apparent efficiency of densely ionising radiations since several breaks would be scored as but a single event. If the multiple-breakage explanation of the high RBE of densely ionising rays is correct, it must follow that the probability that a break remains open is increased sufficiently to offset the theoretical loss of efficiency. This seems plausible where breakage is concerned, but with respect to point mutation the situation is more involved. If more than one mutation is induced in a chromosome due to a high local density of ionisations this can only be scored as a single mutation. A break may restitute but there is as yet no indication of a similar repair process in the induction of point mutations. If no recovery process exists, point mutation frequency should be inversely related to ionisation density and this is contrary to observation. The difficulties could be avoided, however, if mutation was a secondary consequence of chromosome breakage.

RELATIONSHIP BETWEEN MUTATION AND CHROMOSOME BREAKAGE

Ionising radiation and other mutagenic agents produce both point mutations and chromosome breaks, both of which also arise spontaneously. This parallelism raises the possibility that the two phenomena are produced by similar disturbances in the genetic material or, alternatively, that they are related in the sense that one is the consequence of the other; e.g. it has been suggested that re-joining may leave a point mutation "scar".

The best studied category of mutations in *Drosophila* is the recessive lethal. These mutations represent a very mixed assemblage of mutant types which may be divided roughly into three major groups according to their cytological appearance. The first group comprises those that are not accompanied by any detectable change in the pattern of the chromosome as observed in the salivary glands; the second consists of those that are detectable in polytene chromosomes as small deficiencies involving one to about a dozen bands; the third group is that associated with gross structural rearrangements such as inversions, translocations and deletions involving many bands. Mutations in the third group are clearly associated with breakage; they are found with increasing frequency, relative to the first two groups, after higher radiation doses.

It seems *a priori* possible that small deficiencies arise as a consequence of two breaks occurring near to each other, each break being produced by a separate ionisation within an ionisation cluster. Thus these two-break effects would be dependent on the non-random distribution of single ionisations. Their frequency would be expected to increase with dose because of the similar dose/relationship for ion clusters. Evidence against this hypothesis, however, comes from studies on certain chemical substances which are mutagenic. These produce recessive lethal mutations among which deficiencies occur in approximately the same proportions as among lethal mutations induced by ionising radiations. The molecules of the chemical mutagens are not clustered in a non-random manner; hence the two-break effects should be far fewer following the production of mutations by chemicals. Furthermore, chemicals are much less efficient than radiations in inducing chromosome breaks; compared with ionising radiations, chemicals produce far less chromosome rearrangement at doses producing equal frequencies of point mutations. Thus it would appear that deficiencies are not necessarily caused by chromosome breakage; possibly they are losses through gene destruction. If deficiencies need not be due to chromosome breakage there is even less reason to suppose that the cytologically undetectable mutations arise in this way.

Experimental evidence that point mutations do not arise as a consequence of breakage comes from comparative studies of induced mutation frequencies in ring and rod chromosomes in *Drosophila*. Ring chromosomes, which probably arose originally by rejoining of broken ends after two terminal deletions, are more frequently lost than rod chromosomes following irradiation. This is probably due to the restitution of breaks being hindered in a ring chromosome by the tendency of the ring to straighten. Thus fewer restituted breaks survive after the irradiation of ring chromosomes, and if mutation resulted from breakage and restitution there would also be fewer mutations. This is contrary to observation; recessive lethal and visible mutations are not less frequent after irradiation of ring chromosomes. Hence the majority of mutations cannot be by-products of chromosome breakage. The similarity between rod and ring chromosome mutation frequencies also extends to recessive lethals which are detectable as deficiencies, presenting further evidence that these also do not arise from the effects of chromosome breakage. Thus it would appear that chromosome breakage of the type that leads to chromosome structural change differs qualitatively from mutation or gene loss.

The observed high efficiency with which densely ionising radiations induce chromosome breaks was explained on the assumption that dense clustering produced multiple breaks which have a lower probability of restitution than single breaks. Since mutation is not a consequence of chromosome breakage this hypothesis cannot be applied to the observed fact that mutations are also produced more frequently by the more densely ionising rays. In fact, as explained earlier, the reverse should be true. One way of rationalising this paradox would be to assume that mutation is produced not only by direct ionisation within the gene or chromosome but also by effects of ionisation outside the chromosome. This involves the concept of an indirect effect in which induced chemical changes in the surrounding cellular environment secondarily affect the chromosomes.

One of the principle effects of ionising radiations in water is to produce the free radicals ^-OH and ^+H. These subsequently react with each other and with dissolved gases to produce peroxides HO_2 and H_2O_2. Peroxides are known to be strong mutagens and they, and other chemical mutagens, probably produce their effect through free radical formation. There is strong presumptive evidence, therefore, that some of the genetic effects of radiations arise in an indirect way through radiochemical processes.

The relevance of radiochemical events to the induction of mutations was originally thought to be negligible on the grounds of dose and intensity effects. Free radicals are highly reactive and if produced outside the chromosome would react preferentially with the non-genetic cellular constituents in their immediate neighbourhood. The degree to which free radicals would be absorbed in this way, and thus removed from potential genetic action, would depend on their concentration in the cell. Thus the frequency of mutation produced indirectly should depend on the intensity of irradiation. No such intensity effect was observed and it was concluded that ionisations produce their effects by direct hits on the chromosome.

Against this argument, however, it should be noted that ionisations following irradiation of living material are not randomly dispersed but are aggregated chiefly into small locally dense "pockets" representing the terminal sections of the particle tracks. The density of ionisations within one natural cluster is of far greater magnitude than that between clusters, even at the highest radiation intensities studied. Thus variation in intensity does not result in a marked change in proximity of single ionisations, but in the proximity of one cluster to another. The independence of mutation frequency on radiation intensity suggests only that individual clusters do not act in co-operative manner, not that individual ionisations within a cluster cannot act in this way. There is no evidence, therefore, against the hypothesis that some of the genetic action of ionising radiations arises indirectly through radiochemical effects which will be favoured by dense clustering of ionisations.

Consequently, it seems probable that for both chromosome breakage and mutation, the most effective part of the track of an ionising particle is the terminal cluster. This may produce genetic effects either directly when the ionisation occurs within the chromosome, or indirectly when they occur outside but close to the chromosome. The greater efficiency of the more densely ionising radiations can thus be interpreted as the consequence of two separate phenomena; multiple breakage on the one hand, increasing the frequency of observable breaks; indirect effects on the other hand, increasing both breakage and mutation. Thus breakage frequency may be increased in two ways, mutation frequency in one. This interpretation is consistent with the observations that breakage frequency is effected to a greater degree by variations in LET than is mutation frequency. Further evidence for indirect radiochemical events in radiation mutagenesis is presented in the following chapter in connection with oxygen effects.

7

RECESSIVE LETHAL EFFECTS OF CHROMOSOME STRUCTURAL CHANGE

Although the majority of lethal point mutations appear not to be connected in any way with the chromosome breakage, chromosome structural changes in *Drosophila* are frequently accompanied by recessive lethal effects. This is not surprising in the case of the larger deletions of two hit origin since a considerable amount of genetic material is lost. In the case of inversions and translocations, the majority of which act as recessive lethals, there is no deficiency. Since it has been shown that breakage *per se* does not lead to mutation, these lethal effects must be due, either to the induction of a mutation near to but independent of the rearrangement break, or, as suggested by Muller, to a genetic consequence of the altered position of the genes; in other words, a position effect as described in Chapter 3.

It is undeniable that the many ionisations present in a cluster at the end of a particle track may produce independent effects in the same chromosome; nevertheless, this cannot explain the majority of cases in which chromosome structural change is associated with recessive lethal effects, since a similar portion of restituted breaks should also be associated with mutation, contrary to previous conclusions. Thus

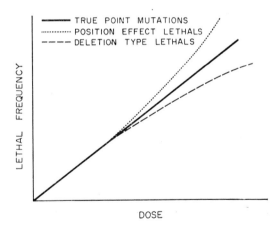

FIG. 45. HYPOTHETICAL DOSE/FREQUENCY CURVE FOR VARIOUS TYPES OF RECESSIVE LETHAL MUTATION

most of the recessive lethals which are accompanied by structural change must be of the position effect type.

In *Drosophila* sperm, chromosome aberrations arise at a frequency proportional to a 3/2 power of the radiation dose. Position effect lethals should arise in a similar way. Thus at high radiation doses, lethal mutations should consist of a higher proportion of position effect types than at lower doses, and this should lead to a more than linear increase in lethal mutation frequency (Fig. 45).

That the linear dose/mutation frequency relationship appears to exist even at high doses has been interpreted as evidence against the existence of position effect lethals and as support of the concept that breakage produces point mutation. This interpretation is erroneous, however, since an increasing proportion of breaks are lost at high doses due to inviable rearrangement and, on the hypothesis of mutation by breakage, the frequency of lethals should increase at a rate below linearity. Furthermore, when allowance is made for the coincidental induction of more than one lethal mutation on the same chromosome, which depresses the observed mutation frequency at higher doses, the data frequently show a trend towards a more than linear increase. Mutation frequency relationships are probably composite phenomena and more data are required on the various components before a convincing analysis can be made.

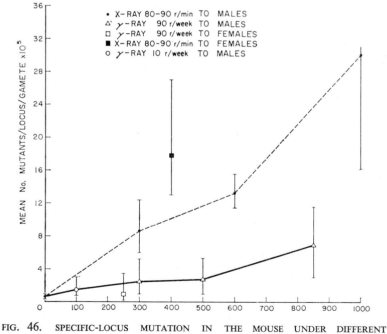

FIG. 46.   SPECIFIC-LOCUS   MUTATION   IN   THE   MOUSE   UNDER   DIFFERENT
MODES OF IRRADIATION

NEW EVIDENCE OF AN INTENSITY EFFECT IN RADIATION GENETICS

Recent work by W. L. Russell on radiation-induced mutations in the mouse has stimulated further interest in the possibility of an intensity effect in radiation genetics. Using the specific locus technique Russell and his collaborators demonstrated that in spermatogonia and oöcytes of the mouse, Cs^{137} γ-irradiation at 0.01 r/min was only a quarter as effective as ordinary X-radiation given at 80 r/min (Fig. 46). This difference was far too large to be attributable to the difference between X-rays and Cs^{137} γ-rays and must be due, therefore, to the different intensities at which irradiation was given.

Most of the quantitative studies on radiation mutagenesis in animals have been concerned with mutation in spermatozoa in *Drosophila*. No intensity effect has been observed in these cells and, likewise, no intensity effect was observed by Russell in mouse spermatozoa. The effect was restricted to the early germ cell stages for which little information was available in organisms other than mouse.

Subsequent research is filling this gap and it now seems likely that a comparable intensity effect is also operative in spermatogonia and oöcytes of *Drosophila*. No explanation of the intensity effect has yet been postulated; more information is urgently required on this problem since the genetic effects of low intensity radiation on gonial cells are of major importance with respect to human radiation hazards.

6

FACTORS WHICH MODIFY THE GENETIC EFFECTS OF RADIATIONS

The genetic effects of various types and doses of radiation were considered in the previous chapter. In comparing one treatment with another it was assumed that both were applied to similar biological entities under similar conditions such that variation observed in the genetic effects could be related solely to the difference between treatments. No mention was made of factors of a biological or environmental nature which could, in themselves, modify genetic effects of radiations. That such factors do exist, and may have very pronounced effects, has been known for a long time. They will be described in the present chapter.

BIOLOGICAL FACTORS WHICH INFLUENCE RADIATION EFFECTS

DIFFERENCES IN CHROMOSOME SENSITIVITY DURING DIVISION CYCLES

During division cycles, profound changes occur in the appearance and presumably also in the chemical structure of chromosomes. The genetic material is duplicated and, by complicated processes of contraction and alignment of chromosomes, divides into two equal halves. That these striking events should have some influence on radiation damage to chromosomes has been recognised since the beginning of radiation genetics. Numerous researches on this problem have, in fact, shown that marked differences of sensitivity do occur between stages of division. On the question of the relative sensitivity of stages, however, the results conflict in many ways. Earlier results probably owe their inconsistency to the technical difficulties of defining what stage was irradiated. More recent studies with improved methods have achieved a greater measure of agreement though apparent anomalies still exist. The underlying causes of radiation sensitivity differences between stages of division cannot yet be formulated; nevertheless, some generalisations are now possible.

Chromosome aberrations induced by radiations are usually scored at metaphase or anaphase of the division cycle. The reason for this is that the chromosomes at these stages are in a condensed and easily stainable condition, convenient for precise and accurate observation.

If the various stages of division are irradiated and then examined, for example, at metaphase, it follows that for each stage variable times elapse between treatment and observation. This introduces some difficulty in the interpretation of the results because of the following consequences of radiation damage to cells:

(a) Induced breaks may restitute, rejoin with other breaks, or remain open to produce fragmentation: these possibilities compete with one another and are dependent on time, which is variable.

(b) One of the effects of radiation is to delay division. Thus a cell examined at metaphase, t hours after irradiation, was not necessarily at a stage t hours prior to metaphase at the time of irradiation, relative to the timing of the normal division cycle.

(c) Cells with certain types of chromosome damage frequently die during division. If the treatment and scoring are separated by several cell divisions only the viable types of aberration remain to be scored.

In addition a fourth factor is apparent in that chromosome and chromatid types of aberration appear at different times in the division cycle merely because of the changes from single to double structure in the chromosome thread during division.

Meiosis in *Tradescantia* pollen grains is followed by two mitotic divisions. These are particularly amenable to cytological examination and have been used by several workers in studies on radiation sensitivity of chromosomes during mitosis. Buds are irradiated and at successive intervals after this, individual anthers are fixed for cytological examination. Aberrations are counted only in metaphase cells. In anthers fixed immediately after irradiation, metaphase cells must have been in, or very near, metaphase when irradiated. Subsequent samples of anthers contain metaphase cells which were in progressively earlier stages of division at the time of irradiation.

In 1941, K. Sax and C. P. Swanson showed that chromatid breaks appeared to be rare immediately after irradiation of *Tradescantia* pollen; i.e. following irradiation of metaphase cells. At this period, however, observation of chromosomes was hampered by certain physiological effects of irradiation. Cells examined 11 hours after irradiation, when the physiological effects had disappeared, also shared a low breakage frequency. In cells examined at longer periods after irradiation, breakage frequency rose sharply reaching a peak at 20 hours and subsequently dropping to a low level again at 50 hours after irradiation (Fig. 47). The peak was calculated to represent irradiation of early prophase but more recent studies of the timing of the division cycle now puts this peak at late interphase. These results have been confirmed in a number of plants in both pollen and root tip cells, and also in certain cells in the developing embryo of the grasshopper *Chortophaga*. In meiotic material in other animals, however, metaphase seemed to be the most sensitive stage. This was demonstrated by studies on lethal effects in parthenogenetically developing eggs

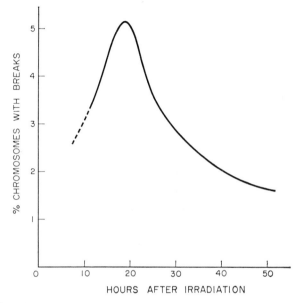

FIG. 47. INDUCTION OF CHROMATID BREAKS DURING MITOSIS IN THE MICROSPORES OF *Tradescantia*. DOSE: 150 R X-RAYS

of the wasp *Habrobracon* and also by studies of salivary gland chromosomes of individuals that developed from irradiated oöcytes of the Dipteran insect *Sciara*.

In these meiotic studies, many cell divisions elapsed between treatment and observation; as suggested above, this may have influenced the results. Direct studies of chromosome aberrations induced during meiosis have been made by A. H. Sparrow in the pollen grains of *Trillium*. In this plant the meiotic cycle is very long and proceeds synchronously in all the cells of one bud. This is a great advantage. A portion of bud can be examined to determine the stage of meiosis and the remainder of the bud can then be irradiated. Thus a very high degree of precision can be achieved in the irradiation of different meiotic stages.

Sparrow irradiated anthers containing known stages of meiosis and subsequently examined the chromosomes at metaphase I and also at the following microspore metaphase (1st post-meiotic mitosis). The results from examination at meiotic metaphase were similar in pattern to those derived from the earlier work on mitotic stages; chromosome fragmentation was greater after irradiation of pachytene of meiosis and least after irradiation at metaphase. However, a strikingly different picture emerged when the scoring was done at the following microspore metaphase. A pronounced peak was observed at diplotene and metaphase; the frequency of fragmentation being 60 times as great as that at the least sensitive stage, interphase. It followed, therefore, that many breaks were in existence during the meiotic metaphase but were unobservable. Sparrow has suggested that breaks induced at or near metaphase remain undetectable since the coiled and condensed nature of the chromosomes restricts the movement apart of the frag-

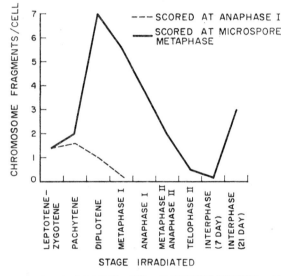

FIG. 48. SENSITIVITY PATTERN FOR RADIATION-INDUCED CHROMOSOME FRAGMENTATION DURING MEIOSIS IN *Trillium*. RADIATION DOSE: 50 R

ments. During the interphase before the first microspore mitosis the chromosomes uncoil; movement is permitted and on re-entering metaphase the consequences of the breaks become apparent. The sensitivity of the different stages of meiosis to radiation-induced chromosome breakage is illustrated diagrammatically in Fig. 48.

Confirmation of the high radiation sensitivity at late prophase and metaphase has come from recent studies of meiosis in *Lillium* and also from studies on the first pollen grain mitosis in *Tradescantia*. In the

PLATE I

Drosophila melanogaster MUTANTS (×25)
(a) Black body colour (b)
(b) Curly wings (Cy), lobed eye (L) and short bristles (Bl)

PLATE II

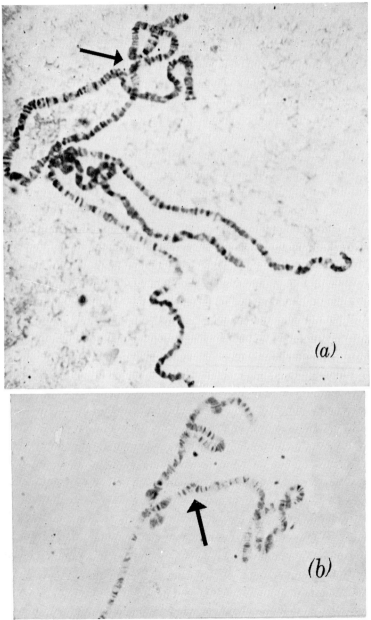

(a).

(b)

(*By courtesy of Dr. B. M. Slizyuski*)

SALIVARY GLAND CHROMOSOMES IN *Drosophila*
(a) Chromosome set showing an inversion in the X-chromosome (×75).
(b) Part of a chromosome showing a deficiency.   The position of each aberration is indicated by an arrow (×400).

PLATE III

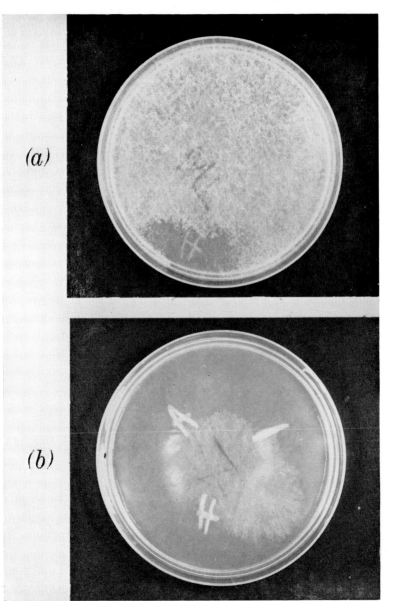

(a)

(b)

GROWTH REQUIREMENTS IN *Neurospora* (× ·75)

Each Petri dish was filled with minimal medium. Crystals of the amino-acids histidine, inositol and arginine were placed at points H, I and A, (seen clearly in (*b*)).

Dish (*a*) was plated with wild-type strain. Growth was uniform over the plate except in the region of histidine, which suppresses growth when in high concentrations.

Dish (*b*) was plated with a double mutant strain requiring both histidine and arginine. Growth occurred only where amino-acids were available.

PLATE IV

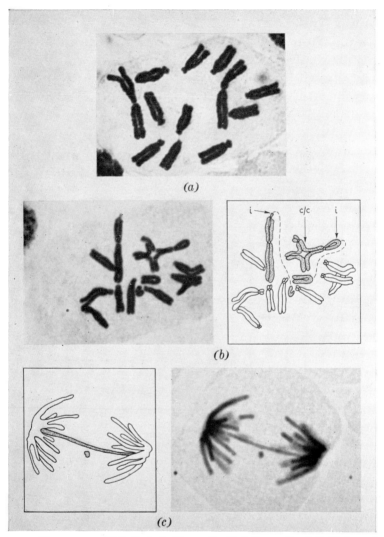

(a)

(b)

(c)

(By courtesy of Mr. T. R. L. Bigger, Dr. H. J. Evans, Dr. J. R. K. Savage)

CHROMATID ABERRATIONS IN *Vicia faba* ROOT-TIP CELLS (× 1200)
  (a) Normal chromosomes in metaphase.
  (b) Chromatid interchange (c/c) two isochromatid breaks (i) with sister union
  (c) Anaphase showing a bridge and fragment.

PLATE V

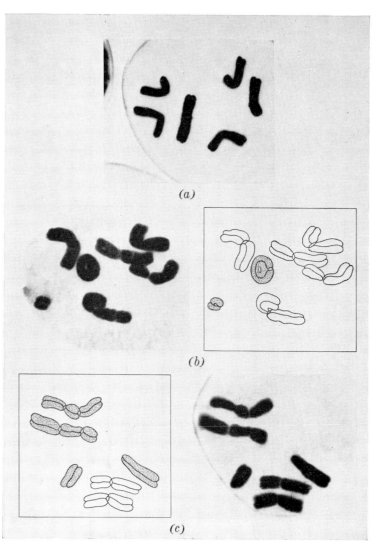

(a)

(b)

(c)

(By courtesy of Mr. T. R. L. Bigger, Dr. H. J. Evans, Dr. J. R. K. Savage)

CHROMOSOME ABERRATIONS IN *Tradescantia paludosa*
POLLEN CELLS (×13500)
  (a) Normal chromosome set (haploid)
  (b) Centric ring and fragment.
  (c) Two dicentric chromosomes and their fragments.

PLATE VI

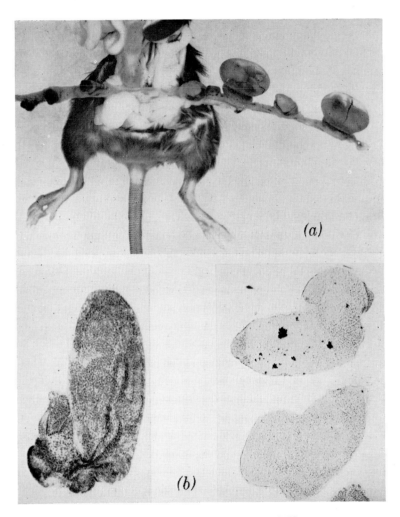

DOMINANT LETHAL MUTATIONS

(*a*) Moles in the uterus of the mouse. Two normal embryos can be seen in the right horn, four moles in the left horn (× ·85).

(*b*) Unhatched eggs in *Drosophila*. On the left is a normal late embryo; lower right an unfertilised egg; upper right, an egg showing marked clumping of nuclei (× 65).

thought to circumvent the corruptions of the clergy by passing over them almost entirely, by recourse directly to Christ, to Christ's blood. And with all this talk of blood I couldn't help remembering the sonnet I had written to my Medusa in Mauritania—Julius the Second—when I had fled from this very city thirty years before Vittoria, fearful of Julius' violence, sure that had I remained I would have been making my own tomb sooner than his.

> . . . e 'l sangue de Cristo si vend' a giumelle. . .
> . . . *and Christ's blood is sold by the quart* . . .

> . . . Ma non ci arrivi più 'n queste contrade
> chè n'andre 'l sangue suo 'insin alle stelle . . .
> . . . *But let Him beware of coming to this town*
> *lest His blood spout up to the stars.* . .

I signed that scribble *Your Michelangiolo in Turkey* but Pope Julius never got the joke. How could he? I made certain he never saw the sonnet. It was another of my private jokes with Julius. Like the acorns of the Sistine.

The blood of Christ was the theme. So there I sat in Vittoria's company while one learnèd divine after another expounded on Valdes' doctrine that salvation might be achieved by mediation of the blood of Christ alone and that this was indeed more to be valued than all the sacraments of Holy Church. I didn't realize then that this doctrine was not far removed from the pestiferous preachings of Brother Martin and that other heretic Jean Calvin in Geneva where one of our very company in the garden, the gaunt saintly Bernardino Occhino, with his white beard reaching to his navel, was soon to take refuge. Occhino, a Sienese, born in the very contrada of Santa Caterina, was General of the Cappuccini and the most famous preacher in Italy. I had heard him preach in S. Lorenzo in Damasso the Easter season after I had moved permanently to Roma; and his Christian fervor and purity and eloquence reminded me vividly of Fra Savonarola whom I had heard in my youth. Vittoria Colonna revered this saintly man. We none of us knew then how close to heresy our opinions ran, nor that within five years Occhino would have fled to Calvin's Geneva and converted to Protestantism. By the time the Council had made clear that all of us *Spirituali* were more heretic than spiritual, Vittoria was safely dead and though I am still here such disputations are like the buzzing of gnats to me now, a distant murmuration. I listen to a deeper music.

So, the early days of the Judgement passed: angels and saints flowing from my brush, a swirl of nudes about my central Christ-Centaur-Cavalieri. My figures were more fluid than the figures on the vault. I had dispensed not only with the painted architecture of their containment—the cornices, thrones, moldings,— but it seemed with the very architecture of their bodies, skeletons about which the flesh drapes, their inward structure of bones which serve as columns walls cornices and pulleys. Now I was painting bodies without skeletons, everything, even the flesh seemed to be dripping away like the flesh of candles. And all was a swirl around the central figure of my Christ, my ungentle Nazarene who seemed to be cursing them all—the saved as well as the damned—with his face of an Apollo and his body of a Hercules, and his arm raised in Judgement and his soundless voice thundering so that even his Mother shrinks in zigzag terror in the lee of her Son. All these boneless bodies swirled around him as the whirlpools that swirl under the arches of the Ponte Vecchio when the river runs high in the Spring floods. And all were damned, the saved as well as the damned, the figures rising to heaven for their pagan embracements that I could not seem to keep off the wall, and the figures being pulled down to Hell by demons who arose I know not out of what deeps of my soul. Some of them I realized later bore some resemblance to Maestro Luca Signorelli's demons at Orvieto which I had seen many times on my rides to and from Roma, but Signorelli's demons, dryly drawn and naive as a child's imagining, were harmless as the Blessed Angelico's paradisial attempts at demons. But mine were devils, they were not painted devils but the devils of my soul, the devils that ravaged me as I lay on the rack between Tommaso and Vittoria.

⁎

I had reached about a third of the way down my altar wall (I was painting my way down to Hell, you see, as on the vault above I had painted my way toward the Godhead) when I received an unexpected visit from my brother Gismondo. Gismondo has always been to me the most remote of my brothers. Sometimes I do not feel that he is related to me at all. He spends most of his time at our farm in Settignano, and did I not remind him of the noble ancestry of our House of Buonarroti he would spend his days following the oxen like any peasant. Well, now he had been shaken out of his furrow by the astonishing news of the assassination of the Duke and he wondered, cretino that he was, whether now I did not intend to drop my work for the Pope and return to Fiorenza to help my brothers prosper in their wool shop and involve myself in the various properties I had amassed in and around Fiorenza. Fortunately, Gismondo arrived accompanied by my niece Francesca's husband, Michele Guicciardini, a fine young man who moved in aristocratic circles and were it not for him the story would have come to us in gulps and gaps. For Gismondo is not much given to speech—or to anything else for that matter. He reminds me of nothing so much as a cabbage sitting in the fields waiting to be gathered up. His head is round, his hair reddish, his eyes the color of pumpkin seeds, his thick limbs seem to burst out of any doublet or long hose, his codpiece always reminds me of a bird's nest speckled in black. And he doesn't talk, he grunts, so that when first he blurted out that astonishing news, and I screamed "What?", he just nodded his heavy head

muttering: "Sì Sì Sì, Lorenzino has dispatched the Duke. It's because of this—"
And he made a lewd gesture, hunching up his codpiece in his palm.

Ser Michele laughed. He was smooth and urbane. He knew Lorenzino well, was
indeed distant kin to the Salviati family and apparently had been privy for a long
while to his cousin's secret intentions. So it was from Ser Michele that we first
learned the incredible details of the Duke's death, my brother merely nodding
bovine confirmation, as he munched his private cud. I in the midst of a Judgement
and that judgement up in Fiorenza. A cold day in February and the news of the
murder on everyone's lips so that whoever came from Fiorenza was sure to be
besieged by the exiles. Many of them that day had crowded into my home—my
banker Angiolini, Donato Giannotti, Luigi del Riccio, all gathered into my sorry
home—huge rooms, yes, but barren as a barn—on the Slaughter House of the
Crows to hear about the slaughter of the Duke Alessandro:

". . . of course many of us knew all along that Lorenzino's friendship for the
Duke was playacting and that he had meditated this deed for a long while. After
all, it is not for nothing that he is grandson to Lorenzo di Pier Francesco de' Medici
who was equally adapt at playacting during the revolution that ousted Piero the
Unfortunate. Wasn't his name suddenly metamorphosed from de' Medici to *dei
Popolani . . .*?"

And Michele smiled that typical small Florentine smile: that cynical radiance
of intelligence, that sardonic scimitar that I have seen all my life on the faces of my
fellow countrymen whenever they wish to demonstrate that they may be guilty of
all manner of human error, even the grossest sins, but never under any circumstances have they been taken in, never have they fallen into the slimy sentimental
pit of ingenuousness that might engulf naive Romans, overfed Bolognese, plu-
tocratic Venetians, fickle Neapolitans but Florentines never. After any event a
Florentine will always tell you that he had known it all the time, he had never been
taken in, he is subject to all human emotions except surprise.

Dei Popolani . . . When Michele uttered the word, it was as if he had stirred up a
mare's nest of memories. For the assassin's grandfather who had, following an anti-
Medici revolt, suddenly become "of the people" instead of "of the Medici" was the
very master of camouflage who had induced me to falsify the Cupid which was sold
at a great profit as a genuine Roman antique to the Cardinal Raffaello Riario. And
when that fake was discovered, I was summoned to Roma by the Cardinal, oh ages
ago, aeons ago, when I was the merest boy and had no beard. So that as Michele
Guicciardini recounted the doubledealing of Lorenzino, I could not help recalling
the doubledealing of his grandfather Lorenzo, nor was I entirely free of taint in
that enterprise.

". . . they are the same age, you see, they have the same inclinations. It was not
difficult for Lorenzino to become the closest friend and confidant of the Duke. But
Lorenzino's friendship was not sincere. Either he was envious that the grandeur of
the House of Medici had devolved upon a bastard, even if the Duke was, as many

claim, Pope Clement's, rather than Giuliano's son. Or else—as he let it be known discreetly amongst certain circles—because he wished to free his country of a tyrant, or perhaps because he wanted to be the tyrant himself. At any rate, no sooner had the Moor begun to reign, than Lorenzino was studying ways to dispatch him. And he soon learned that the most opportune road to achieve his end was by way of Alessandro's lechery—"

Gismondo again made that gesture with his codpiece as if to say: *Didn't I say as much without all these learnèd words?* He embarrasses me, my brother, he seems not to realize that we Buonarroti are not peasants, but of noble stock, of the Counts of Canossa. I saw Donato smile at Gismondo's gesture and I resolved that when I and my brother were alone . . .

". . . So instead of disssuading the Duke from such affairs he cunningly aroused him all the more, until the time came to set the plot in motion.

The Duke found him a most agreeable companion. Lorenzino is, as some of you know, well versed in letters, exceptionally witty. He has written some good tragedies and comedies in the style of Plautus in the Tuscan language, and had them presented; he writes sonnets and canzone, for the most part lascivious as was pleasing to the Duke, all to keep himself in his good graces and foment his passions. He went about dressed in the old style and neglectfully whence the Duke and the others of his house called him the Philosopher and made him the butt of their jokes.

Nor did he hesitate to have himself believed cowardly, refusing to carry arms as did all the other courtiers; rather he showed horror at seeing them and hearing talk about massacres and bloodshed. He affected solitude and retirement to the point of seeming rude and countrified like a peasant.

Furthermore it seemed that he cared little about his own decorum, nor was he distressed that he was considered—as he was truly,—the most faithful pimp of the Duke's loves nor that it was believed all over Fiorenza that he was the most shameless spy and vilest amongst the Duke's adulators. For which reason he had drawn upon himself the hatred of his friends, his relatives and even of his own mother.

Meanwhile his opponents who were many did not fail to keep their eyes on him, nor were there few who were aware of his perverse intentions. Piero Strozzi, greatest enemy of the greatness of the house of Medici, once informed the Duke by way of his confidant Lorenzo Pucci, that he marvelled greatly that he showed himself so ignorant as not to know that the cunning playacting of Lorenzino de' Medici was all calculated to take his life; that he Strozzi hated traitors to the greatest degree and therefore he was giving the Duke advice so that he be on guard. The Duke who was already disposed in favor of Lorenzino summoned him to the Palace: "Is it possible," he said "that you are plotting my death with such arts that my own enemies should have to give me warning?" Lorenzino immediately replied that he had indeed told many people that he wanted to kill the Duke; but that he had done this in order to draw from the mouths of the enemies of his Excellence whatever they were hatching and that this was the best way to serve him.

By means of such tricks and other ingenious modes he gained so much faith and benevolence in the soul of his Prince that Alesssandro used to say that if he had to leave Fiorenza for any length of time he would leave no other Lieutenant in the government of the city but Lorenzino.

However, in general, the Duke did not arrive at such neglect of himself as had Caesar who used to say that it was better to die once than always be on guard against the threats of traitors, and that his safety was of as much interest to the Republic as to himself. But Duke Alessandro, besides having disarmed the people, never rode abroad except in armor, and always accompanied by a guard of lancers.

After Lorenzino had therefore for some time brooded on his betrayal, finally came the favorable occasion to execute it. There was peradventure by chance in the neighborhood near the Duke's house, a gentlewoman of the house of Ginori, named Catherina, as extremely beautiful as she was virtuous; the Prince conceived a powerful passion for her; and since Lorenzino was related to her, Alessandro communicated his depraved desire to him, because he wanted him to help him seduce her as he had many others. Lorenzino said that he would do as he had done before and promised to succeed.

Well, last month, on the night of the sixth of January (which was the epiphany of our Lord) Lorenzino gave him to understand that he would be able to satisfy his desires; but that it couldn't take place in the palace in order not to arouse suspicion in the court. When the time came, the Duke wearing nothing but a green satin robe lined with sable, had himself secretly borne to Lorenzino's house where he had been told the meeting would take place. And arriving in the room in the company of the betrayer, he took off his sword and lay down on the bed, awaiting the arrival of the Dame; which sword Lorenzino cunningly took and twisting the belt at the hilt so that one could not easily unsheathe it, placed it at the bedside.

Then he leaves under the pretext of accompanying the Ginori girl, and summons his faithful servant, nicknamed Scoronconcolo, saying to him with a happy smile that the time has come when he might demonstrate his gratitude for all the favors Lorenzino has done for him, helping him to kill one of his enemies whom he held in his room. "Let's go," said Scoronconcolo; and Lorenzino: "Don't be upset if he turns out to be a friend of the Duke, and be sure to tie his hands." "I will do that," replies the other, "were it the Duke himself." "Well, that's precisely who it is, in person", says Lorenzino, "and this time he can't flee our hands."

Arriving in the room with his companion, "My Lord," he says, "are you sleeping?" And immediately strikes him a stab in the back with a short sword. The infuriated Duke thrusts himself back of the bed and exercising all his forces begins to flee toward the exit, shielding himself with a narrow chair—a sgabello—that fell under his hands; but Scoronconcolo plunges a knife into his face ripping his left cheek. Then the Duke drops the sgabello, grabs Lorenzino and twice calls him traitor, adding "I didn't expect this from you."

"No doubt," murmured messer Giannotti. It was startling, that murmured interjection. Thus far not a single one of our assembled Florentines had commented on Michele's story. We were familiar, all of us, with Alessandro's reputation (and I had indeed resolved never to return to Fiorenza once my shield against the Duke—Pope Clement—was dead). And we were familiar too with the long history of Florentine plot and counterplot. During Michele's bloody recital I scanned the faces of my friends—Luigi's ruddy amiability and smiling mouth not smiling now and Donato's long keen intelligent skull shaped I sometimes fancied like a thought honed to essence, and Angiolini whose nervous tic under the eye was out of control now—a circle of Florentine exiles, true heirs of that first great Florentine exile, Dante Alighieri, listening to a tale which might well have figured in his Inferno.

"—these were the only words he said in all that time. Then Lorenzino pushed him as hard as he could down against the bed and since he was holding his mouth closed with his left hand so that he could not cry out, the Duke seized his thumb in his teeth and bit so hard that he almost bit it off. Lorenzino fell atop the Duke in his pain and couldn't manipulate the sword and cried out to Scoronconcolo to help him. Running around the bed and not seeing how he could wound Alessandro without wounding his aggressor at the same time, he began to swing his weapon between Lorenzino's legs which achieved nothing but to make more holes in the sack. Then Lorenzino remembered that he had a knife in the pocket of his cape which was the only weapon he ever carried with him, sometimes showing it to the Duke, saying that was his sword and dagger; and the Duke used to laugh and told him that to become a true Diogenes all he lacked was a bowl and a wooden barrel. This innocuous knife then served Lorenzino to cut the Duke's throat and even when he was dead, continued to strike repeated blows at his corpse. Six wounds—"

"—The number 6, one could say, was fatal for Alessandro, since he was killed in 1536—"

"—1537," said my man Urbino.

"—1536, counting in our Florentine style," said my brother with surprising patriotic energy, "dating from the day of the Annunciation." He said this for all the world as if the Florentine style of starting the year from the 25th of March were the only true way to count anything and only farabuti and barbarians counted otherwise. Which is typical, I have observed, of our Fiorentini who are convinced of their own superiority in all things astronomical, diplomatical, and gastronomical, not to mention ecclesiastical. And I suppose I have inherited something of that too for it seems to me that our city has produced greater wits than all the rest of Italy combined. Perhaps it is the perfection of our air which is not too heavy as at Bolognia or too subtle as at Pisa. Certainly it is rare to find a stupid countryman of mine and even if one does encounter a stupid Florentine (my brother is not stupid so much as inanimate)—and I have encountered my share— he is likely to bear off the palm even in his stupidity, being as it were the champion of stupids, an excess of stupidity that is almost wit.

"—on the 6th of January at the 6th hour of the night with 6 wounds at the age of 26 years, the 6th year of his government and furthermore on Saturday, the 6th day of the week . . ."

"—And the situation in Fiorenza?" I asked Michele who had patiently endured my brother's numerological observation.

"What do you expect? Absolute disdain for the assassin. Nothing that Lorenzino had hoped for. No one speaks of Liberty as he had imagined, the spur that he thought would set off a new revolution. Nothing of the sort. Lorenzo's house has been sacked by the fury of the people and ruined in great part and the Signoria forbids that it be rebuilt and Lorenzino is under permanent ban with a price on his head and his likeness painted as a traitor on the walls of the fortress. So now he lurks in Venice under the protection of Strozzi and I warrant he needs that protection for there are surely hired sicuri of the new Duke only waiting their chance to do unto him what he did unto Alessandro."

The biblical echoes made my brother to cross himself in mock piety, or was it simply a reflex to the echoes? I don't really understand my brother. I couldn't wait for him to return to Fiorenza.

Well, the astonishing news of Alessandro's assassination was the chief talk of Roma for almost all that year. Even after the assassin's cousin, son of Giovanni delle Bande Nere, young Cosimo de' Medici, a mere boy of eighteen had been confirmed as the new Duke, the talk was only about the recent fatal event. Most of our exiles—many among my closest friends— looked upon Lorenzino as the new Brutus. He became in their eyes a tyrannicide, a hero, and even after he had fled to Bologna, and thence to Turkey, and thence to France and finally settled in Venice under the protection of Filippo Strozzi, all the talk was of him. He even published an Apologia for his deed written in the eloquent style of an ancient Roman, you would have thought it was the pen of Cassius and Brutus themselves speaking through this young man's pen. I read the *Apologia* (or had it translated since it was in Latin) and was more convinced by the literature than by the logic. I didn't quite trust Lorenzino, I wasn't convinced that his motivation had been love of country rather than love of power for himself. Yet several years later, I did yield to the importunities of my friend Giannotti who was acting in the name of the Cardinal Ridolfi, to carve a bust of Brutus in Lorenzino's honor. Of course I didn't even attempt, as some would have done,—say the Urbinate or even my good friend Sebastiano when he deigned to stir his lazy ecclesiatical fat (how he lolled in his sinecure as Keeper of the Seal!) into picking up the brush again,—I didn't attempt, as either of these might have done, to make a portrait of Lorenzino in the guise of Brutus. No, such playacting was not my art. Portraiture is too often the act of a courtier and I'm clumsy at that perfumed craft. I'm never interested anyway. I have tried, God forgive my presumptuousness, to delineate Man not a particular man. My David (still standing in front of the Palazzo Vecchio) is the Idea of a Hero, not a particular Hebrew King. My Moses is the Idea of the Judge, not a particular Judge of the Old Testament. So now I thought to make a Brutus who could exemplify the Idea of Tyrannicide, rather than the ancient Roman who bore that name, or Lorenzino who was being rebaptized with that name. I carved a Brutus—at least a Brutus as it seemed to me he might have been—with a neck like an olive tree (I made some use of young Cavaliere's magnificent neck here) and a firm powerful brow, rough hair (I merely blocked that in) and prominent cheek- bones. But the task bored me. I wanted to get back to my wall, and once the wall was done I wanted to supervise at any rate the abortion that was resulting of my long dream of Julius' tomb.

So I just blocked in enough of the Brutus to satisfy my friends and years later I gave the rest of it to a young sculptor named Tiberio Calcagni who has been coming often to my studio these days and is most gentle in his attentiveness, a kind and trustworthy young man, with no mean talent. He completed the toga and anyone with an eye can see at first glance that this chisel does not write the same language as mine. He is harsh and I am soft, my contour vibrates and his incises space. Somehow the older I have grown the more does my line, whether drawn or carved or painted, vibrate. Is it the vibrations of my soul approaching the dark Gate?

Just in the midst of all the agitation following Alessandro's slaying, letters arrived from my then two remaining brothers wondering whether I had any intention of coming "home" now and various tenders of affection from the new Duke who wanted me to enter his service. He could of course and did asserverate that I had left many works undone when I departed my homeland to enter Pope Paul's service. The tombs of the Medicis were not yet in place, the new library was still abuilding at St. Lorenzo's. All these works were being carried out now by Ammannati and a young Fleming named John of Boulogne and though they sought to follow my plans and communcated much with me by letters and messengers, yet my physical presence was wanted, said the Duke. Perhaps so. But I had no intention of returning now. My soul was entirely in Roma with Tommaso and the Marchesa, with my Judgement and my new appointment as architect of the Vatican, with my circle of Florentines in exile and the reforming cardinals around the Marchesa. Roma was always a foreign land but I cannot say in all truthfulness that I felt any longer that nostalgia for the cupolone (so typical of Fiorentini away from their homeland) although I may have expressed such longing once or twice in letters to the priest Fattucci or my brothers or my nephew

Lionardo. I was truly as happy in Roma as I would be likely to be anywhere . . . which is not to say terribly happy. I certainly knew that I would not return to Fiorenza in the near future, perhaps never; I was not much happier about serving Duke Cosimo than the terrible Alessandro. I had become in fact one of those exiles who enjoys— though he will not admit it to himself—the state of being exiled. The freedom of not belonging; the vision of seeing from the outside—truer to the mark surely than those whose sights are warped by violent partisanship. In the whirlpool of Pauline politics, I tried to float free. Twenty-five years before, in that same chapel, I had sought to immure myself from the wars of Julius II. Now it was Paul—less sword than serpent, but politics threatened as always incursions into my art; my Florentine friends thought, in view of my sympathy, to involve me in their plots and counter plots when all I wanted was to be untrammelled, free of idolatries and factiousness.

✳

Which brings to mind the Aretine. I had been two years at work on my Judgement when a letter arrived from Venice sent by messer Pietro of Arezzo who was living then like a sultan on the Grand Canal with a harem of whores and boys. Who in Europe did not know Aretino?—that tongue of his licking honey and spitting venom, fawn and viper at once. My friends Fra Sebastiano and Donato Giannotti had witnessed more than one revolting scene in the palace of this fat pasha who fancied himself—and what is more astonishing, earned his living—as a scourge of princes.

Now Pietro Aretino presumed to tell me how to paint my Judgement, assuming perhaps that I would be as amenable to his suggestions as was his dear friend Tiziano of Cador, a painter whose fleshy glowing color fails to bedazzle in my eyes his ignorance of the art of drawing. Well, now the Aretine lavished his usual pompous compliments on me: "the world has many kings but only one Michelangelo . . . and he who has seen you does not regret not to have seen Phidias Apelles, and Vitruvius . . ." etc., etc., The bombast of this man is astonishing. He foams multicolored bubbles of rhetoric which quickly turn to poison if one does not acquiesce to his blackmail. So I answered him with great caution: and trusted only that his enormous self-esteem would blind him to the irony of my letter:

Magnificent Messer Pietro: my Lord and brother: The receipt of your letter filled me with joy in that it came from you whose virtues are unique in the world: and much grief because having completed a great part of my fresco, I cannot make use of your conception, which is so perfect that if the day of Judgement had already come and you had witnessed it in person, your words could not have described it better. Now, as for answering my letter, I say that not only would I value a reply, but I beg you to write one seeing that kings and emperors esteem it the highest favor to be mentioned by your pen. Meanwhile, If I have anything that you would like, I offer it to you with all my heart. And finally, don't break your resolution not to come to Roma, just on account of seeing the picture I am making. That would be too much. And I recommend myself to you.

Michel' Angelo Buonarroti

Well, now I was a fool to write that letter. My letters are frequently to be read backward in a mirror. and I assumed that the Aretine was so unctuous with vanity that my barbs would slide off his hide like a greased pig at Carneval. I had lied of course when I said that a great part of my fresco was already done (I was scarcely a third down the wall), and I had no intention ever to satisfy his greed for one of my drawings for I knew from the first that this was the hook on which his wriggly wormy words were fleshed.

And later I was to regret that I had underestimated the Aretine's capacity to read mirror-writing. Oh, he caught my drift all right! And it was not long before I was to feel the lash of his poisonous tongue all the way from the lagoons.

❖

I try to put these memories in order. Now in this long night, alone with my skeletal Christ and his essential Mother, I look back at the last thirty years of my life and order eludes me. There are events which I seem to have forgotten entirely, and yet I know they have occurred; there are no interstices in Time. Now that I am face to face with the ultimate wall of Time, now that I am about to break through beyond that wall into timelessness, it seems to me that I have wrestled all my life (like Jacob with the angel, but not for a night, all my life,) with this riddle of Time. Il Tempo che consuma il Tutto.

I try, I say, to put these memories in order. But what is order? Is order the mechanical ticking of a clock? the clicking of a water-wheel? Or is it the dimension events finally assume in our memories? Of those years of the Judgement such a hodge-podge of incongruities remains in my head. Like the marble chips that spray from the chisel-blows—white jagged blood-bringing rain—during the making of a work. All that matters really is the work emerging from that jagged rain. That is what remains. As my Judgement remains still on the altar wall, and now in this Papacy of the fourth Pius, the Milanese, now in this rainy February of Anno Domini 1564, my Judgement still rings its prophecies and condemnations, its assignments to Heaven or Hell; its arrogation, Dantesque, to myself—myself!—of rewards and punishments; myself the Christ-Centaur at the eye of the whirlpool, setting all in motion with that denunciatory arm, that swathe, scythe, that cutting-down of the living and raising of the dead, that turbine of Last

Judgement setting all the world—all who ever lived and died—swirling from Heaven to Hell, from opened graves to wingless angels bearing the instruments of passion in the lunettes (painted over Perugino! palimpsest of my unorthodox faith over his pious atheism), a swirling as of leaves in the Mugello during wild tramontanas, a swirling of devils and saints, saved and damned (only all are damned), Adam (ancient now, no longer my Cavalieri-Adam) and Eve, withered-dugged mother of us all; Bartolommeo-Aretino and myself—myself!—in the flayed skin, and Minos-Biagio discomfited forever, and Sebastian without wounds, and Charon crossing the Arno-Styx on a cruel night, and Christian martyrs and Hebrew prophets, the sinking hopelessness of these descending and the joyless joy of those ascending; the unnameable embracements of those reunited in paradise; Herculean Pietro, quivering Madonna jagged as lightning in the thunder of her Son, merciless Christ, Judgement Judgement.

Myself. The audacity of it. Hybris. I judging them all. Save myself. I Christ, Mary, the saved and the damned. My ego center of that whirlpool.

May God have mercy on my soul!

✳

I was halfway down to Hell when I fell from the scaffold. Perhaps it was a fall from grace. Perhaps I had drunk too much that previous balmy evening at Priscianese's printshop, eaten too much, laughed too much, given too much of my love, as is my wont, to my friends. Tommaso's delightful account of his conversation with a contadino at Palestrina. "And you, Signor, may be privy with Popes but I know how to piss through my spigot as well as any Holy Father." Mathematic stars demonstrating that even such a lovely night in June, so fragrant with linden that one felt one had buried one's head in the perfumed thighs of a cortegiana honesta, was but a glaze of the senses over the orderly designs of God. Well, I had partaken of too much white wine of the Castelli, not clear and sober like our Trebbiano, and, as I say, given too much of myself so that when I returned to my barn I felt bereft of self, strangely in the pit of despond after all that laughter, dissatisfied that I had spent like a wastrel too many florins of my brief remaining time—a treasure which, at my venerable age, should be devoted to the contemplation of death. I know this has given me something of a reputation of being a recluse, a misanthrope, a hermit. On the contrary. I love my friends too much, I take too much joy in good company, in comradeship and conviviality. I am too vulnerable to love. It drains me.

So the next morning my head must still have been spinning, for suddenly I saw all Judgment flash upsidedown before my eyes and I landed ten feet below on the floor. In a flash Urbino had gathered me up in his arms, Dino the plasterer ran to cover me with a cape, and I was laid out on the Sistine floor for all the world like one of the corpses in Santo Spirito when I first saw an anatomy. It was a hard thump for any man, especially for a man of 65, but I must be made of marble, harder than my David, for his arm had been broken clear off by the stones dropped in defence of the Palazzo della Signoria (and it was still broken at that time!) but I seemingly had broken nothing, except pride in my sobriety. But everything inside me burned as if I were full of scalding water, and finally I persuaded Urbino (who was crying like a baby although I was the one with all the pain) and several other assistants to carry me home in a litter and put me to bed. I gave orders that the door be locked and I be left alone.

So there I was finally in the Slaughterhouse of the Crows waiting to die. I knew I hadn't broken any bones, but that didn't matter; my right foot was sprained and began to swell, and I knew from the inferno of my guts that my insides had been torn open in that fall, like the poor beasts who are thrown alive from the Testaccio hill by the Roman mobs during the hideous carnival celebrations of this city. I have seen that horror inadvertantly several times during the pagan Carnivals of this Urbs; inadvertantly because I never wanted to see those games again after the first time, but my home is near Testaccio, and so I cannot avoid the piercing scream of the pigs and the eerie wailing of the bulls as they are hurled off the cliff by Christians preparing to celebrate the passion of our Lord. I had seen them splatter with a sickening thump on the rocks below, and the mobs running with pans to take the hot foaming blood of the still screaming and writhing beasts; and that is how I felt now, and wondered what scoundrel was coming to take my blood. I resigned myself to death but because it didn't come soon enough I grew impatient and began to imprecate against death too for failure to perform his duty. I wanted a priest but no doctor, but my man Urbino—weeping all the time, a most ridiculous track of dirty tears streaming down his persimmon-blooming cheeks—disobeyed my orders and summoned a Physician of the Long Robe. This was a certain Maestro Baccio Rontini, a Florentine who, after the assassination of Duke Alessandro, had come to Roma where he immediately became part of the circle of anti-Medici exiles who were trying to concoct some medicament for the fatal maladies of our homeland. At the insistence of my friends, this good man ran to Macel de' Corvi and getting no response from his knocking at the gate, was let into a secret door by Urbino and ran through the house calling my name from room to room till he found me, my body shivering and sweating at once. The usual chills and fever of my spirit transmitted now to the flesh, and I waiting to die and not caring either, making ready my soul for a true Judgement instead of that absurd Judgement I was painting on a wall.

He was a good man, Maestro Baccio. I shall always remember him sitting by my bed day after day (for he refused to leave until he was certain there was no gangrene in the sprained leg), and with his sharp face and ready laughter bringing me back to the city of the Red Lily.

So while the worthy Maestro Baccio ministered to my leg and there came the

drove of visitors—from Cardinals to carters—I lay in a pool of sweat and memories. Rontini's worries about gangrene brought to mind my joy when 'gangrene'
appeared on my painting of the Flood and I thought to use this as an excuse to get
out of my unwanted commission to paint the vault of the Sistine.

And the daily presence of this physician with his anatomical talk brought back
to me also, with the peculiar vividness with which certain memories take flesh,
the image and the voice of Maestro Andrea the Jew, Physician of the Long Robe,
and friend of my youth, long gone now, gathered up with all the others in the
Omnium Gatherum.

How stiffnecked he was! failing to read his own Prophets aright, laughing with
those great glowing eyes (like Tomao's) at my analogical and anagogical interpretations of the Old Testament. The hours we spent together, at Fiorenza, at
Bologna, in such wrestling. But he was withal, a worthy combatant, more faithful
to his Doubt than many so-called Christians are to their Faith. After I removed to
Roma we never met again, never wrote. Another page turned. One of his sons,
too,—what was his name? Daniele? Davide? Elia? yes, Elia—studying medicine,
also a Master of the Long Robe dissecting cadavers in Bologna when last I saw
Maestro Andrea. All of them physicians. Now, since Pope Caraffa's decrees, one
scarcely sees them outside the wall, but I remember in my youth witnessing
dissections performed by Andrea's father, the Master Elijah of Crete, a Rabbi and a
Doctor of Physic, in the cenacolo of Santo Spirito, where I made a wooden
crucifix for the sacristan. In gratitude. A strange quid pro quo. O the stench of
those corpses! dogs licking up the guts slipping and sliding from the marble table
like live snakes. And Master Elijah's oriental cadences as he read from Master
Galen's book and pointed with a wand. All I could make out there was a pool of
guts but Master Elijah described exactly what was there according to the book of
Galen of Alexandria published in the 2nd century.

Well, that was my first experience with the miracle of the human body; since
then I have performed my own anatomies on occasion and assisted at Maestro
Realdo Colombo's: last on the body of a Moor, and Ascanio getting sick with the
stench of it, as we sat night after night, a candle set in the open thorax, and the
gulping shadows of the walls so that you would think the corpse was dancng. One
needs a strong stomach for this kind of work. I have always thought to prepare a
book of anatomical drawings but I lost interest once I realized that this was no
more than drawing from the model from within and I had given up all drawing
from the model after those two impossible Trasteverini who served me for the
Sistine—plump curlyheaded Rocco who ground my colors when he wasn't flinging his hip forward for my Delphic Sibyl and the blond languid boy—what was his
name?—from Palestrina, who modeled for many of my ignudi when he wasn't
pummeling Rocco on his full flanks. Well, after the Sistine all this deriving from
models ceased to mean anything to me. The language of the body is a language of

suggestion, and all my suggestions now come from within. I no longer need my eyes to draw and so I lost interest years ago in anatomy also for that was nothing but the same external vision peering from within the skin; while I wanted to depict the soul itself and that is not visible to any eye. I want to make visible the invisible. But Ascanio, despite his vomiting, is always goading me to make anatomies.

Maestro Andrea of the long Robe also used to speak to me of preparing a book on this subject. Andrea had the same doubts about Galen that Maestro Colombo later also expressed. Both felt the ancient Greek's descriptions were not true to nature. Andrea once asked me if I had ever seen a horned uterus and I told him they were all horned; and he laughed in his agreeable way and proposed that I attend his dissections, I to do the drawings and he the text. But Andrea, in his own way looked upon the body as a miracle though he denies the miracles of his own Scripture; and I with the advancing of the years have departed from this miracle. The forms I once adored now seem to me prisonhouses of the soul and I am tormented at the notion that I have spent my life depicting such jails.

One day Ascanio brought me a book of anatomy by the German Master Albrecht Durer of Nuremberg; but I did not admire it. Maestro Albrecht draws marionettes, stick figures; he fails to realize that the secret of the body resides in its movement. It's no use measuring out proportions— nose to chin, head to torso, and all the other proportions as he has done, if what results is lifeless as a puppet. The measurements of a true artist, anyway, reside not in rules; his compasses must be in his eyes.

My criticism of Maestro Albrecht made Ascanio excited as a child. He wanted me to write it all down. He looks upon every act of mine as a prodigy, that boy; he piously colors in the cartoons I have prepared for him, wrote down all my words more than ten years ago and published them to all the world as if I were one of my own Prophets of the Sistine Vault. And he were the Prophet of a Prophet. But of course I shall never prepare that book of anatomical drawings.

While I was recuperating from my fall, I talked a lot about it with Maestro Baccio. He urged me to do it (and that was before Ascanio). These physicians interest me, they search in their own way for the Mystery within the Body. But I have reached a stage when I confront true Nakedness, not nakedness clothed with flesh. I already inhabit another realm.

And that's why I shall not do it. Add that as another stone on the ever-mounting heap of the Undone. That is my true Purgatory, a hill of Purgatory that we never climb, alas.

I wonder if that crucifix I made for the sacristan is still in Santo Spirito? It was there when I ran off to Bologna to avoid the French. I must write to Lionardo or Francesca to visit the church and see how it is faring. My only work in wood. Probably all eaten with worms by now. Anatomies.

Soon I shall be a subject for a notomia myself. I will not make a very good corpse. No youth can study from the poor strings that remain as my muscles, these scraps of thin meat on my dry bones.

Fit for crows.

Slaughterhouse of the crows.

·❊·

So I went back to work, proceeding rapidly now to the grave. Below the toes of my angels the wall became dark and gloomy; I was entering the realm of Hell. And one day in bleak November, when I was consorting with skeletons and demons, came running Urbino and shouted up into the maze of the scaffolding (I like an ape there in my cage)—*the Pope is coming! the Pope is coming!*—And with Francesco's words still echoing in the vast spaces of the chapel, there did indeed enter, with that swish of velvet and lace and ceremonial that always accompanies a Pope, the Holy Father himself with a handful of Swiss guards, several Bishops and Cardinals, and other attendants, most prominent amongst them his Magister Caerimoniarum, Monsignor Biagio da Cesena, come to inspect my painting. Paul had been a most infrequent visitor to the chapel; in the four years that had now elapsed he had come to see my progress only three or four times; he was no exigent patron like Pope Julius. Some might say His Holiness had far too much on his mind—the preparation for the council, the need to unite Christendom against the grand Turk, the desire to reconcile Hapsburg and Valois, the Barbary pirates to the South, and to the North, spreading its contagion, the pestiferous Lutheran heresy—to concern himself with a mere painting on a wall.

But a quarter of a century earlier, when I was making the vault overhead, Pope Julius had had equally valid preoccupations to absent himself from mere picture-making. Europe was as ill then as now—when has there ever been peace?—and furthermore, the temperament of the della Rovere would have churned even the quietest pool. And yet that agitator of all repose, who had cast the keys of St. Peter into the Tiber to take up the sword of Paul, that Vicar of Mars, found time—oh too much time!—amidst his wars and preparations for wars, to climb the sixty-eight feet of my scaffolding many times, oh too many times, and whip and prod and fang me in the process of my art. He never understood, impatient Julius, that you cannot nag a peach tree into blossom.

So I was grateful that this Pope, once I agreed to enter his service, left me largely alone. He was an ideal patron, Paul; he attended to his business of saving souls. Mortar and pestle had no part in that. I was free to struggle with my own imaginings. I never had, with Paul, to attempt to squeeze ducats out of a Genovese stone. Farnese was a Roman and a gentleman.

Now he was looking up at my wall in his curious fox-like way: staring with sharp eyes out of a bone-brazed tight skull, hunched even when he stood, thin as some of my skeletons, whispery-husky-voiced, and pointing pointing with his rapier-finger at my angels (who were Carrara quarrymen wrestling with a marble column), at myself in Bartolommeo's skin (did he see it?), at my Christ and his timid Mother, at my colossal Saint Peter, and the paradisial embracements behind his back. Then he glanced quickly up at the Jonah and down again, but not so swiftly as to prevent me from seeing the bird-flicker of a tightening of the corners of his eyes, recalling my reluctance to substitute his arms of blazon for those of Pope Julius. He had not insisted.

Then his Holiness turned to the Magister and whispered: "Well, what do you think of it"

And Ser Biagio, replying like a Florentine, (though he was from Cesena) with no hair on his tongue: "In my judgement, your Holiness, the work is more fit for a public bath or for a house of ill-repute than for the chapel of the Pope . . ."

He was looking straight at Papa Paolo as he said this, but I felt his words were addressed to me, I felt the lash and burn of them.

". . . and it seems to me disgraceful that in so holy a place Maestro Michelangiolo should have seen fit to paint so many nudes, all of them blatantly displaying their shameful parts in the most vulgar fashion...". . .

With which this Magister does not hesitate to move closer to the desacrilized altar wall, and proceed to my embarrassment, to the fury of Urbino, and the scarcely concealed laughter of the other prelates—to specify with accusing gestures the various "vergogne" that offended him. His gestures flung his red robe into righteous flames. Like any Master of Ceremonies, Monsignor Biagio was a stickler for the surface of things; accident and not essence was his daily concern; so much did he fuss over the order of ceremonial that soul eluded him. And so he did not realize, this Magister who was thus insulting and humiliating me in the presence of the Vicar of Christ, that when God had come among us, He had taken upon himself the form of a man, and therefore the naked form of Man is Holiness itself and my love for male nudity is but my love for Christ. He did not understand that, this Magister, standing there near the yet unpainted lower section of the altar, and pointing upward with inquisitorial finger at the various pudenda that so offended him. And is the male stalk of Christ any less sacred than his nose? Is the mons veneris of Eve more indecent than the mind of a Master of Ceremonies? more pagan than the triangular meadow of Venus? Is there any subject more beautiful (and *therefore* more holy) in art than *un bel ignudo?*

I was furious. And waiting, with a sinking heart to hear Papa Paolo condemn my work, order the offending parts to be hacked out of the wall, or over-painted in some manner or other. But he said nothing. I could not tell whether he agreed or disagreed with the Magister's condemnation. He kept his council, as he always did, to himself; neither acquiesced nor rebutted; did not nod his head or indicate by the slightest sign what he thought. He reacted exactly as he did to the pleas of ambassadors Spaniard or French. He listened, looked some more at my wall (another five or ten minues), made some murmurous almost inaudible sounds (benediction or malediction?) in my direction and left.

But I was furious. As soon as those exalted visitors had gone, the fires stoked up in my soul burned more hotly and in a flash I knew exactly how I would take my revenge. In the lower right hand corner of my fresco I had planned a figure of Minos, hideous to behold, with ass's ears and a serpent coiled the number of times around his torso to indicate the circle of Hell to which the sinner was to be assigned. My description was a variant from Dante, Inferno V, lines 4-12:

> Stavvi Minos orribilmente, e ringhia;
> esamina le colpe nell' entrata,
> giudica e manda, secondo che avvinghia.
>
> Dico, che quando l' anima mal nata
> li vien dinanzi, tutta si confesa;
> e quel conoscitor delle peccata
>
> vede qual loco d' inferno è da essa;
> cignesi colla coda tante volte,
> quantunque gradi vuol che giù sia messa.

> There Minos sits horrific, and grins: examines
> the crimes upon the entrance; judges, and
> assigns according as he girds himself.
>
> I say, that when the ill-born spirit comes before
> him, it confesses all; and that sin-discerner
>
> sees what place in hell is for it, and with his
> tail makes as many circles round himself as
> the degrees he will have it to descend.

So it seemed to me that Magister horrifically grinning had presumed to judge the 'crimes' I had set upon the wall, every organ of our sex a sin as if I and not the Lord himself had shaped us thus, and there he was coiling his presumption around himself, assigning me to my proper place in Hell. "quel conoscitor delle peccata . . ." that "discerner of sin . . ."! Oh I knew exactly how to take my revenge.

So as soon as he had gone, his face fresh in my mind, in arctic fury, my brush

directed and sure as a dagger, I painted my hideous Minos . . . with the face of
Biagio da Cesena.
  Life-sized.
  Jackassed-eared and snake-coiled.

  I heard the repercussions soon enough. There was a fellow-countryman of my
man Urbino, a certain messer Annibale Caro, tutor to the children of a Florentine Luigi Gaddi and also—like so many of these literary fellows who buzz around
prelates for the honey of benefices—in the entourage of a Bishop, Monsignor
Guidiccioni. Caro was a most amusing fellow. His wit pricked me from the deepest
gloom. About a week or so after my contretemps with the Magister, into my studio
bounced long lean messer Annibale laughing laughing.
  "O Maestro! A delicious scene! You have twisted your Minos by the ears!"
  Urbino's donkey-guffaw from behind a marble block.
  "What are you saying?"
  "The story is making all the rounds of the Vatican!"
  "What story?"
  Urbino's face emerged, all ears. These Marchigiani.
  "Yesterday I was present at an audience which the Holy Father had granted my
Bishop . . .
  Caro had an odd way of referring to Monsignor Guiccioni as *his* Bishop.
  ". . . when in bursts the Magister, his face rage-red. He could hardly wait to
receive leave from the Pope to speak, and when he did, the words broke from his
mouth as from a broken dike:
  —Scandalo! your Holiness, scandalo! Maestro Michelangiolo has had the
audacity to portray me in his Judgement!—
  —In Paradise, no doubt, murmured Paul in that whispery voice of his.
  —No! In Hell! this salacious Florentine has presumed to depict me among the
damned in the guise of Minos with—with—
  He was choking.
  —with the ears of a jackass!—
  —Of a jackass? murmured the Pope.
  —Of a jackass! And fat coils of a serp—in Hell! in Hell! I beg your Holiness to
order this outrage effaced!—
  And as he choked to a halt, the Pope reflected silently for what seemed a long
while, then that scarcely-audible rumble began:
  —Had messer Michelangiolo assigned you to Purgatory I might have been able
to intervene. But having placed you in the Inferno *ubi nulla est redempti*—where
there is no redemption—I am afraid there is nothing I can do!
  "O Maestro, it was delicious. The Magister staring up at the Holy Father with
outraged incredulity; the corners of my Monsignor's lips twitching with suppressed
laughter, the cannonshot of coughing from the Chamberlain at the door and the

Holy Father calm as always, his little eyes glinting with irony, leaning forward as he uncoiled that marvelous witticism . . . *ubi non est redemptio* . . . Had I no other reason to love this Holy Father, that phrase alone would endear him to me forever."

Like most learnèd men, Caro's heart can always be conquered by a well-turned phrase, especially if it be in Latin. But even I, who am no Latinist, could not fail to appreciate Pope Paul's marvelous joke. His remark was, as it were, a Papal seal affixed to my outrageous vendetta.

I knew that the image would stand so long as Paul reigned. And my heart was flooded with love for his wisdom and I went back to complete my wall with renewed zeal.

·✳·

It took twenty-five years for the Magister to reap his revenge. But now as the rain drums on the roof and I wonder what to do with my disappearing Christ and looking back at my long life and forward to my longer death, I hear that Daniele will soon actually begin to paint over the nudities of my Last Judgement. And in my head, in the rain, there echoes the jibes of my friend Giannotti—O *Maestro mio, in the depiction of your Judgement, you have displayed no judgement at all.*

So it would seem. So it would seem.

Just a week ago, those learnèd divines at Trento who are setting all Christendom to order had nothing better to do than set my painting to order. And so they have commanded my assistant Daniele of Viterbo—poor soul!—to concoct fortuitous wisps and rags, draperies blowing in every whichway wind to cover those parts in which my saints and my Lord Himself display their common humanity.

A small matter.

"Tell the Pope—" not this present fourth Pius but his immediate predecessor the fourth Paul who, no sooner elected sent a message to me requesting that "At the very least, I make corrections" in my Judgement— "Tell the Pope," I replied to the terrified messenger, "that this is a small matter and can easily be rectified. Let him look to setting the world to rights; a picture can be adjusted very quickly."

I said *that* to the Caraffa! that fanatical old Neapolitan who never failed to attend the weekly meeting of his beloved Inquisition (although he might fail at times to attend other higher ecclesiastical functions) and who even threatened to whitewash over my entire altar wall.

Yet like so many of the Caraffa's threats, it was all Vesuvian rumble and little lava. He was himself expunged before my Judgement was.

That messenger's face. A boy. His feathers quaking.

But now at last the Council of Trent has issued the decree which has been threatening for twenty-three years (even by Paul III) and soon poor Daniele will become a britches-maker.

The world has darkened. The world has darkened. I can see it in my work in the Chapel. The vault floats luminous and contained for all the violence of the forms, within its illusionary architectural frame, as Dante's terza rima dams the spilling over of his imagery. But the lower down I get—down to the darkening lunettes, and the even darker and more grotesque putti below the thrones of my Prophets and Sibyls, and then down to the Judgement itself, to the very pit of Hell with its grinning devils—the lower down I get, the darker grow my images, the more distorted my forms.

As the world without grows grotesque and grim, so does my inner world.

But a quarter of a century ago when I depicted Biagio as Minos, everybody laughed.

·※·

Even the Lady Vittoria.

Not much given to outright laughter, yet she could not maintain her usual smiling tranquility. Smiling was not enough. She burst out laughing, a silvery trickle.

"And so he remains there on the wall? And every time he comes into the Chapel he must confront himself . . . with jackass ears?"

"Well, fortunately he doesn't come to the Chapel often. Since I began working on the altar wall it has been impossible to celebrate mass there."

"But didn't they celebrate mass when you were doing the vault?"

"Ah yes—But only when I was working on the first half beginning with Noah. When the second scaffolding went up above the altar, there were no masses either."

"So you not only assign Magisters to Hell, but you force Popes to suspend sacred functions in their own chapel. Oè Maestro!" (Odd to hear that popular Neapolitanism which the Lady Colonna had picked up at Ischia). "Isn't that being a bit bold?"

I shrugged my shoulders. It was a glorious Saturday afternoon in October. I never needed much urging when I received an invitation from the Marchesa. She had sent a servant to fetch me. My studio was near the Campidoglio only a few blocks away from Monte Cavallo where she lived.

San Silvestro on the Quirinale was Dominican and like all Dominican churches there was attached to it a convent and a cloister and a garden. I loved that garden; often strolling late afternoons with Tomao I found my steps urged in that direction. Perhaps it was the lodestone of the Marchesa who resided there, laic, more pious than the nuns; perhaps it was the cool rational space of that garden, the grave disposition of the greenery laid out like a verdant demonstration by Euclid. I loved the view of Roma from that height: the abundant gardens interspersed with ruins, the round brown Colosseum and the militant engraving of the Tower of the Militia. There in the blue-and-white distance a new Saint Peter's was being born within the shell of the old and next to it, in the Apostolic Palace, I was wrestling with my demons and my angels.

The talk turned from Minos-Magisters to the commentary which Fra Caterino—a Sienese who had taken that name because of his devotion to his countrywoman, Saint Catherine of Siena—had just made on his reading of the epistles of St. Paul. A pleasant slow-speaking gentleman whom I knew, the Sienese ambassador, Lattanzio Tolomei was expounding a theological thesis with angel-wing beating hands; and not looking at him at all, but staring at me as if he would devour me, was a fierce-moustachioed young man who was introduced as Francisco d'Olanda but turned out to be a Portuguese painter, enamored of Italy in general and of Michelangiolo Buonarroti in particular. What could I do? This young man was one of those who considered me 'divino', an epithet which always serves to make me all the more painfully aware of my quite undivine and sinning self. He had come to Roma, he said, to copy the ruins and meet me (an odd if not entirely inapt apposition, I thought.)

Well, this young man it appeared, had been brought to the Lady Victoria's this day especially to hear me discourse on the art of painting. Could I deny to this young man, burning incense in my face, that I was not a painter at all? Not a painter! When I had already painted the vault of the Sistine and was now half way through the Judgement? But we do not say to others what we say to ourselves; I knew I was not a painter but I did not hesitate to express myself at length on this ungrateful art, and the young man drank it all in, drank it with his eyes, with open mouth, with affirming gestures. He was called Francis of Holland but in truth was a preposterous Portuguese much inflated about his self-appointed role which was to search out those eminent in the arts of painting and sculpture, to suck fruit and knowledge from them which he (Francisco) would then put to the service of his King. He was filling sketchbook after sketchbook with studies of the Pantheon, its columns and proportions, the Colosseum, the thermae of Antoninus, the arches of Titus and Severus and all the other notable things in the city, making what so many were doing those days, a guide book to the Urbs, a Mirabilis Romae. All this he recited to me in his odd-inflected Italian-Portuguese, his eyes mad-bright since he was in the presence of divinity.

Me.

So to lead him on, the Marchesa laughing all the while (her laughter so hearty, so much at variance with the general piousness of her manner, the laughter of a true virago that was betrayed in the manly tone of her argumentation as well) I gave him a long roundabout monologue in which I demonstrated that there was no true painting except in Italy, and that if true painting did exist elsewhere it was called Italian. I even led him to believe that I considered painting the queen of the arts when in truth I am a stonecutter and nothing but a stonecutter, God knows this, even when I paint I am carving and I have carved the vault of the Sistine as anyone with eyes can see. I have never been anything but a stonecarver and feel that I am cutting into stone even when I wrestle with the treacherous non-substance of words.

As I expounded, I could read in the drinking-in expression of Francisco's eyes that he planned to return to his King and quote me as an incentive to fine commissions. I told him to draw and draw and draw—draughtsmanship is the mother of all the arts—and I never let a day go by without a line. It was a great treasure, draughtsmanship, more than color which so intrigues those Venetians.

So I discoursed on design which is the root of all the other arts be they sculpture or painting, architecture, or fortifications. All works of the human brain or hand are either design itself or a branch of that art.

The young man was very curious, too, about the pay we Italian artists received, and I gathered that in his country a painter or sculptor was considered little better than a barber. "A scandal!" Francisco said, "I shall quote your very words to my King,—with your permission, of course."

He could quote me as much as he liked. I would be dead soon anyway. And I did feel artists should be sufficiently rewarded in ducats as well as in honors. We serve not only lords but the Lord, for what is art—especially the depiction of the human form—but an imitation of the work of that First Artist, Immortal God, whose greatest work in his own image and likeness, is Man himself?

Vittoria's family—the Colonna,—owned many houses next to San Silvestro, but she chose not to dwell in her family possessions, always so full of people and tumults. The Colonna were Roman to the core, as I was Florentine, but Vittoria fled their machinations and turbulence, absented herself from intrigues (she even claimed innocence—or ignorance—of the treachery of her husband); she sought only oases of quiet.

So I would come willingly to these meetings in the garden and if there was not a preposterous Portuguese there was sure to be some learnèd prelate, perhaps even one so august as the English Cardinal Reginald Pole, noble to the very curl of his whiskers which were incredibly long and pointed and incredibly black and from which issued doctrines to which Vittoria was particularly attracted. Or there would be the famous Venetian humanist Gasparo Contarini who, though laic, had just been created Cardinal and whose praise was always being sung—in that gondoliering lilt—by my gossip Fra Sebastiano, also Venetian. Once there even came to Vittoria's garden the famous Cappuccino preacher Bernardino Ochino, brilliant and corrosive in his criticism of the Lutherans whose doctrines he was soon to embrace.

I never spoke very much at these gatherings. I was a good listener. They reminded me of those symposia of Lorenzo's neo-Platonic wits I had attended in my youth. I spoke even less then, especially in the presence of learnèd men who were effusing Latin and Greek from every pore: two languages of which I was entirely bereft. So I sat quietly as the polyglot Pico proved that other gods were

merely other names for Jesus Christ, the which he proved by Cabala and by
Zoroaster and by Mithras and the Magi and to look at his long golden hair and
boyish face it seemed impossible to believe all that learning flowing in Chaldean,
Hebrew (Andrea's father taught him), Greek or Persian from his bowed raspberry-
colored mouth. I just listened. I just listened to Pico. Or to Magister Marsilio
Ficino, house-physician to the Magnificent's family, who led one to believe that
Christ himself was really Plato (or was it the other way around?)

When these learnèd men unfurl their erudition at each other I just listen. And
enjoy the prismatic glistening. I have no peacock feathers to display although I
warrant I have planted some secret doctrines of my own here and there among my
works—in the Medici Tombs and in the Sistine—that will keep these wits
sufficiently occupied for several centuries to come.

So, now in Vittoria's circle where the central theme of conversation was less
Plato than Martin Luther, I was usually silent as I had been silent sixty years
before. I am not intimidated by the learnèd but there are erudite fools as there are
ignorant ones.

I find the erudite fools less tolerable.

But on the three or four occasions of Francisco d'Olanda's presence, I was
prompted by the Portuguese (as a bull is goaded) to speak out about those arts in
which I am not without competence.

One afternoon, that young man queried me about the relative merits of Flemish
and Italian art and I replied that the art of the Flemings generally pleased the
devout—especially old ladies and the very young—more than Italian, since it is
filled with charming details, green fields and shadows, streamlets and little
bridges, all jumbled together without proportion or symetry. And this art, I said—
to messer Francisco's discomfort (since he was a miniaturist)—brings abundant
tears to the eyes of the beholders (especially if they are devout) whereas Italian
painting will never bring forth a single tear.

On these occasions—whether I discoursed at too great length about my art or
sat in silent attentiveness while Vittoria and her ecclesiastical friends discoursed
on the doctrines of Juan Valdez—which she had attended in Naples—the justification by the blood of Christ alone, the equal role of faith in works, or the
political whirlpool these abstract arguments had set into motion, so that all of
Europe at the time I was painting my Judgement was a millrace of madness, a
turbine of Lutheran and Holy Church, heretic and holyman, Paul at the center of
it, old and astonishing, his arm raised in judgement as the Emperor Charles and
King Francis, Spaniard and German and Frenchman and Swiss swirled around and
around that virile form—on these occasions, I say, these afternoons at Vittoria
Colonna's, I took especial pleasure in observing the great art of the Marchesa of
Pescara. Not paint nor stone were the materials of her art, but people, her's was the
art of drawing people out, setting speaker against speaker, nudging confidences
out of the dour, and damming with tact and humor the tide of the loquacious. She

could make a stone talk and silence the wind. And all this she managed with such serenity that conversation at San Silvestro was harmonious as the sweet interplay of flutes and viols. I loved her for it. She was a consummate conversationalist and she led with smiles and touches the entrances and exits of the conversations of others as if she were playing the lute.

When I made my remark about all good painting being only Italian, the Lady Vittoria, to praise her young foreign guest, opined that Francisco possessed "the genius and knowledge not of an ultramontano but of an Italiano." When I expatiated on some singular painting in various cities of our Italia, the Lady Vittoria with the most gracious smile, interrupted:

"Do you not remark, messer Francisco, that Maestro" (she never called me anything but Maestro) "abstained from speaking of Roma, the mother of painting, so as not to talk of his own works? Now what he would not do, let us not fail to do for the purpose of ensnaring him the more, for when one deals with famous paintings, no other has such value as the fount from which they are derived . . ." and she went on to praise my work in the chapel, and I could not in all decency silence her.

Oh, she warmed my old heart and I responded even when I knew it was but adroit foolishness as when she embarrassed me in the presence of all by declaring that those who didn't know me esteemed me only for the works of my hands, but those who knew me esteemed me more than all my works themselves.

What could I say? that it was balsam and pumice and one very old man enjoyed the smoothing?

This great Lady who had received homage from Charles the Fifth paying homage to me!

·⁘·

At that time there was being celebrated in the ancient manner the feast of the twelve triumphal cars in the Piazza Navona, starting from the Capital with such magnificence and ancient pomp that it seemed as if one were back in the old times of the Emperors and the triumphs of the Romans. I witnessed it all with messer Tommaso and my man Urbino and it brought to my mind—thick with sediments of memory—the similar triumph I had witnessed many years before in that same piazza when Andrea the Jew and I had witnessed the triumph of Cesare Borgia. Now the occasion was the marriage of Ottavio, son of the Pope's son Pier Luigi, to Margherita, bastard daughter of the Emperor, and widow to the slain Alessandro de'Medici. Margherita was sixteen years old and beautiful, and widowhood ill became her. Ahi, the ways of the world! His Holiness, and His Majesty were delighted with the marriage which like all marriages above the commonality, was a linkage of lineages as well as loins, politics as well as petticoats. All Roma knew that the Emperor hoped to tie the Pope to his policies by this marriage; he took as little account of his daughter's wishes in this as when he had married her off at 14 years of age to Alessandro de'Medici. She would have preferred to marry young Cosimo the new Duke of Fiorenza, who had sought her hand. Toward Ottavio Farnese who was only 13 years of age and had inherited the French disease from his father, she felt only repugnance.

The child stubbornly refused to doff her widow's weeds for the wedding; as the widow of the slain Duke she married all in black, refused to say Yes at the wedding, did not conceal her disgust at her husband, and (so the gossip went) refused to perform her matrimonial duties with the young man.

Meanwhile, the sad nuptials of these children were being celebrated every night with serenades and banquets; all Roma was ablaze with lights and illuminations, especially the Castel Sant' Angelo; every day there were feasts and expenditures.

And I was painting San Bartolommeo extending to the Lord the sign of his martyrdom—his flayed skin—and at Monte Testaccio twenty bulls attached to twenty carts filled with piglets were flung alive over the cliff in honor of the bride and groom; buffaloes and horses raced along the entire Via di Nostra Signore Transportino to the Piazza of San Pietro; gilded triumphal cars ornamented with fine figures and noble devices; Romans of our time mimicked their ancient forefathers in togas of the ancients; one hundred sons of Roma on horseback, brave and bizarre and gallant, decked out in painted antiquity, phalanxes and ediles descending from the Capital; Giulio Cesarino with the standard of the city of Roma on a horse with trappings covered with a white coat of arms and black brocade. . .

I returned to my bridge, to San Bartolommeo and his skin, and somehow I know not how, the skin contained a writhing tormented face and the face was my own. How did it get there? I don't know. I had flayed myself. I hung like Marsyas' skin there in the Chapel of his Holiness. I was imprinted like the image of Christ himself on Veronica's veil.

And standing there in the darkening chapel gazing up at myself as Christ, his martyrdom my martyrdom, he flayed and whipped, uncomprehended, crucified as I—as I—

Should I? should I knock off that arm? I cannot. It is a Memory and now in this long night I pour forth Memory, memory issues forth from every pore of this old hide of mine. I cannot. Besides, the perfection of that arm belongs to the world of appearance. It *looks* like an arm. It *is* an arm except that it does not yield to the touch, it is cold and hard and its veins are marble. And so I leave it there because it reminds me of a shore departed from, a mode of art to which I no longer belong, a rendering of the senses which has long since ceased to interest me.

I wish to say more and more with less and less. I wish to say everything with nothing. So with every day that passes as I become less matter and more spirit, so does this Mother and Son. I am etherializing the material, carving pure Idea.

Indeed the Deposition with myself as Nicodemus, that group I intended for my own tomb, only to smash it in impatience at the obdurance of the marble and the nagging of Urbino, that Nicodemus is *here*, that Nicodemus is the brooding presence of this piece although the corporeal eye sees no Nicodemus at all. So I have succeeded in dematerializing myself entirely even before Death performs that necessary act: eliminating my body as I have eliminated Nicodemus's. O Death! O great eliminator. I no longer care about my tomb. At first I had thought to place this group upon my tomb to replace the shattered Nicodemus. But now I no longer care to have anything. I work on it simply because.

Simply because.

I have promised this to that silly boy of mine Antonio who pouted over the 200 ducats he received from messer Bandini for the shattered pieces of the Nicodemus.

What better Nicodemus than an invisible one? What better tomb than no tomb at all?

II

Messer Tommaso de' Cavalieri

Who can blame the old man of the Slaughterhouse of the Crows for calling Daniele a "britches-maker"? A mild enough epithet, and spoken too with a twinkle in his horncolored eyes, a sudden flicker—a minnow surfacing— in those dim inward-looking flat little eyes, always looking at death as he is staring now at the skull painted, out of his bizarre humor, right in the middle of the staircase.

"Well, it happened this morning," he said suddenly, out of nowhere. His voice was low, rumbling, a bit sepulchral. "The rumor, it seems, was not ill-founded."

I gazed at him perplexed, and he smiled, that trembling little smile he has these days, a trembling in his beard, a flickering of white hairs around his thin lips while the minnow-twinkle leaps in the rheumy eyes.

"Daniele is going to paint the britches after all. He's correcting my Jesus. What do you think of that? He's sanctifying my saints."

I didn't know what to say. The Maestro wasn't upset. We had been expecting it ever since news came from the Council which was meeting up at Trent that all works of art in the churches were being reviewed for the suitability of their images. And Daniele knew that he would be the instrument of this desecration in the name of consecration. He couldn't refuse. But how cruel to choose him! So loving of and so belovèd by the Maestro.

But the Maestro, I say, wasn't upset. He pronounced this bit of news calmly, and then went about his business, drafting in his careful round hand, which only trembles a bit now that he is approaching ninety, a letter to his nephew, Lionardo, up in Fiorenza.

I said nothing. I knew Michelangelo expected no saying from me. Our love, these thirty years, is cemented with silences. We say more with a glance, with a shrug, than all the saying of the letterati. I knew he expected nothing from me and so I stood outside in the garden, in the cool shade of the larches, and thought under this Roman sky of how many works of Michelangiolo Buonarroti have been maimed, lost, destroyed. His David up at Fiorenza, the left arm broken in three pieces by the stones the defenders of the Palace had dropped upon it, crippled for sixteen years until the Duke deigned to repair it. His cartoons for the bathers— that school of art for the world, as I have heard it described—ripped to bits by Baccio Bandinelli, according to the story told me by that talented ruffian Benvenuto Cellini. The great bronze Julius of Bologna, as huge seated as the David standing, melted down to make a cannon appropriately named La Giulia, the unfinished Prigioni for the Tomb, the unfinished figures in the new sacristy of the Medici which I saw seven years ago when I made my first trip to Fiorenza to deliver some messages to his family for the Maestro, the wooden crucifix he carved in his

54

youth for the sacristan of Santo Spirito and which is no longer there, a Hercules, a Cupid, a bronze David—oh the list is long and I know them all though almost of them suffered the calamities of Fortuna even before I met Michelangiolo Buonarroti:

How odd to think there was a time before I knew Michelangiolo Buonarroti! For it seems to me that I have known him forever, even now that I am a grandfather with a beard thicker and grayer than the little bifurcated goat-tuft that adorns his chin. I have known him forever, for what was I before he appeared in Roma in the days of ill-fated Pope Clement? Those pre-Michele days have been blotted out of my memory as the first three years of one's life no longer exist for a grown man. And yet there was such a time. There was a time before Michele the Angel.

What would I have been had his sun never risen on my horizon? Would I be now reshaping the Campidoglio according to his designs? Would I have known that the principles of good architecture are the same principles that govern draughtsmanship and sculpture? That the proportions of a noble edifice are the proportions of a man?

Would I have known any of these things had not the Maestro taught me? Although he disclaims being a teacher, scorns to keep a shop, talks back to Popes, growls at Cardinals, scolds his servants for their thievery, explodes at his nephew.

And loves me.

And so because I have been his dearest companion these three decades there are those venemous tongues who cannot accept our love for what it is, who cannot believe that he has ever been other than a father and a mentor to me. They point to those embracing men kissing on the lips in Michele's Judgement—and leer knowingly. They point to the acorn-genitalia of his vault. They find me in his Adam and in his Christ and in his Victory, knees on the neck of an old man. They point to the odd breasts of his Night and to the fact that the Maestro has never married (but I have) and the tongues wag and wag. Even Ascanio had to try to set these rumors at rest in his biography and you would think you were reading Socrates but still the tongues wag and wag. . . His art mistress enough?. . . ahah!. . . in Roma?!. . . Aretino poisoning the sweetest waters.

How furious the Meastro was when Aretino's letter came—furious to the point of illness, his head wracked with the familiar headache—suddenly unable to paint—what was he doing that day?—yes, the execution of Peter—and he almost falling off the scaffolding when I passed the letter up to him. ". . . and all those Tommaso's and Gerardo's . . ." And suddenly Michele almost falling like the drawing of the Phaeton he had made for me. The filth of that Aretino: he on the Grand Canal with his whores of both sexes piously offended by the nudities of Michele's Judgement.

From the very start of his Roman sojourn, Michele has been on the rack. I often think it is a rack of his own making. I suspect he takes pleasure in his sufferings and fears the loss of them would result in the drying-up of his art. Tears are to him what rain is to a farmer.

We had met at the home of the Cardinal Ridolfi, gathering place of the Florentine exiles in Roma. I didn't dare open my mouth.

Merely to be in the presence of this man—the Praxitiles of our time—greater than Praxitiles—was simply overwhelming. I must have gazed at him as if he had fallen from heaven. He was almost sixty years old then and I was twenty-three. I had seen him enter the salotta sure-footed and swift, swinging off his black cape with the gesture of a dancer. Messer Michelangiolo (he preferred being called that to Maestro) was simply dressed in a dun brown doublet and jerkin. He wore long cordovan boots and a sort of crumpled black velvet cap on his head which he did not remove even in the presence of the Cardinal (he sometimes forgot to remove it even in the presence of the Pope). Of medium height, broad-shouldered, he emanated strength, a brooding inwardness. His face had the look of boulders, of rock with a stubble of beard.

The Cardinal asked Michelangiolo's opinion regarding the fragment of an Apollo which he had recently acquired. Everyone gathered around as the artist began to examine it closely. I was struck by the prehensile sureness of his hands running over the piece: the spatulate powerful thumb rubbing here, the squarish fingers with short clipped nails pressing there. A physician's examination. Palpations of marble flesh.

When he spoke the accent was unmistakably Florentine:

"È una groria," he said, "—it's a glory—" transforming the "l" to an "r"— "a true work always reveals itself in the merest fragment. One can deduce the whole from the part . . ." and he went on to expand on the merits of the piece to the Cardinal.

I, on the periphery, listened. The voice was low, brooding, palpating as the fingers. Then suddenly—

"—What do you think, messer de' Cavalieri?" and he turned to me: that face of a ravaged fawn, the quivering tight lips in the grizzled bifurcated beard. And those eyes searching me—small flat horn-gray flickerings of old gold—a peculiar gaze that penetrated but did not permit you to penetrate. I stammered something. He turned those eyes on me several times during that evening. Each time I smiled nervously. I was tongue-tied. I babbled inane courtesies.

A few days later arrived that letter. I was astonished. No, embarrassed. I could not understand that letter. That he, Michelangiolo Buonarroti, the greatest of living artists, should address *me*, a mere boy, in such excessive terms was beyond my comprehension!

"Your Lordship," wrote the painter of the Sistine and the carver of the Moses and the Medici Tombs, "light of our century, unique in the world, cannot be satisfied with the work of anyone else, being without equal or peer . . ."

What work?! I had accomplished nothing (nor have I accomplished anything to this day). He, the Emperor of Art, prostrate before a novice! It was simply a madness. Or perhaps it was all irony. Against himself. The thrashings of a trapped man. I understood and did not understand. The Maestro was obviously infatuated. Thirty years ago I was a handsome youth as my mirror and the admiration of many friends attested. I do not hesitate to say so (now that I am in my middle fifties, a grandfather, and I have a beard longer and whiter than his). False modesty is as reprehensible as lying. I was a handsome young man, and I realized that the greatest artist in the world had fallen in love with me, and was uttering the foolishnesses that only the love-lorn are capable of. "Light of our century! . . ." My light had scarcely been lit.

I replied with circumspection. I said I was astonished (as indeed I was) to be so addressed, I who had only been born yesterday and was a mere babe and ignorant as could be. Still, since I did not wish to infer that he was a liar, the only explanation for the fervor of his letter was that messer Michelangiolo was constrained to love those who followed the arts with true devotion, and in this, I dared to say, I yielded to few.

Soon after, Michelangelo's man Pierantonio appeared with several drawings of the Maestro for me to "study"! They were rough sketches for a beautiful Ganymede being borne to Olympus on the back of an eagle and a Prometheus chained to the rock, while a vulture gnaws at his liver, and I was to decide which of them I wished him to develop as gifts to me. Or did I prefer some other subjects? Again I answered in delicate humility but since I longed for his friendship, and indeed felt honored by his proffers of it, I did not close the door but respectfully, with veneration, held him off while I led him on. O a curious game! More letters arrived in the intervals as he shuttled back and forth between Fiorenza and Roma in those early days of our friendship, and every demurer on my part only seemed to fan his flame the hotter. His Roman sojourns became longer and longer, and I knew—all his friends knew—that his passion for my person played its part in those protracted visits. On one occasion away from Roma he wrote that he could as soon forget me as the food on which he lived; nay, that "it were easier to forget the food, which only nourishes my body miserably, whilst your name nourishes both body and soul . . ." and other such incredibilities.

Well, all that was thirty years ago when the Maestro was still shuttling to and fro between his native Fiorenza and Roma. He had his obligations up there to complete the Medici Tombs and he was constantly under pressure from the Duke Alessandro de' Medici to plan a fortress into which the Duke could retire in the event of a popular anti-Medici insurrection (which, considering how much he was loathed by patricians and plebians, was not unlikely). And down here in Roma he had already begun to sketch out ideas for the Last Judgement which Pope Clement VII wished him to depict on the altar wall of the Sistine as a kind of gigantic ex-voto for the errors which the Holy Father felt he had committed and which had led to the terrible Sack of 1527. So whenever Michele would be called down to Roma to discuss this project with His Holiness he remained here as long as possible, mostly because of his infatuation for me, and also because he feared and distrusted the intention of Duke Alessandro in Fiorenza, and feared for his life because he had refused to serve that cruel sensual tyrant, giving his prior obligation to the Pope as his excuse. He knew that so long as Clement was alive, he would serve as a shield against the fearsome Duke (who was reputed to be the Pope's natural son by a Moorish slave). So it was Medici against Medici, father against son, competing for the services of Michelangiolo Buonarroti, who was anti-Medici in his political sentiments and who had served as Governor of Fortifications during the siege of Fiorenza against this very Medici Pope, Clement VII. All his life Michele has been on the rack between competing forces, all his life he has been forced to do that which he did not want to do.

And with every visit to Roma during those years as the flame of our friendship waxed, the vital forces of the Holy Father waned. The handsome cleanshaven assured Cardinal de' Medici was scarcely recognizable in this gaunt bearded Pope whose eyes bespoke an inexpressible sadness. He had never truly recovered his forces after those terrible years of Imperial invasion, his nine month imprisonment in the Castel Sant' Angelo, he the Vicar of Christ besieged by the forces (including many Lutheran landsknechts!) of the Most Catholic King of Spain, Hapsburg Emperor Charles V. And then in 1534, just thirty years ago, two days after Michele had arrived in Roma, the Pope died, the shield was gone and Michele knew that he could not return to Fiorenza to complete the tombs or for any other reason.

Nor has he ever returned. Thirty years.

And he is still a Florentine. He has never ceased to be a Florentine.

So that was the anvil. Those terrible last years of Pope Clement when our relationship was forged. Previous to his definite departure from his "ungrateful nest" (he often compared his exile to that of Dante), he found with every visit some excuse or other to remain in the Holy City. But the real reason was a quite unholy passion for my person. At first I was embarrassed by this sickly-sweet infatuation of Michelangiolo Buonarroti, the glory of his age, for a mere boy of twenty-three. Then I became immensely flattered by it. Soon I was cherishing his friendship as he cherished mine. He undertook to make my portrait in black chalks, much to the astonishment of all his friends (and perhaps to himself) for Michele abhors portraiture and has always avoided it as vehemently as Raffaello pursued it. Yet there he was, making my portrait, and could I set aside my regrettable vanity, a beautiful thing he made of it, too; if I *really* looked like that, (and I suppose I did in his eyes) one might be more compassionate with his infatuation. I gazed at myself in a mirror and then at Michele's drawing in which he had stressed my large wide mauve eyes, and straight nose and full curved lips and posed me as a Senator of ancient Rome with a certain haughty expression, bearing a medallion in my hand. I compared this portrait with my likeness in the mirror and saw at once that Michele had departed from the truth, upward, one might say, refining it, embellishing it, searching for the perfection only adumbrated in reality. For to Michelangelo always such perfection was divine, the beautiful was the divine. And so our love has never partaken of anything coarse, and some malpractices that I had known before knowing him, were quite burned away in the refining fires of that Socratic old man. But of course vulgar minds do not believe it and vulgar tongues prattled quite another tale of our relationship. Michele's attraction to young men has sometimes been spoken about as if it were related to the Greek practice which is so prevalent in our day and especially in the Holy City where there is a superabundance of supposed celibates. But I know the true nature of his love.

And now I look into the mirror and no longer see the raw material of that sketch Michele made of me, but the face of a venerable Roman, whitebearded and somewhat grave; and reflect upon my person—my belovèd wife, Lavinia della Valle, my two sons, my palace thronged from street level to third floor with a fine collection of antiquities—one of the finest in the Urbs. And I reflect—as a mirror reflects—upon my duties as a Conservator of this City of Rome, the obligations which I share with my friend Bacciagaluppa as Deputies to put the Campidoglio in order according to the Master's designs and my obligations as Prior of the Arch-Confraternity of the Most Holy Cross of Saint Marcello and my almost daily visits to old old Michelangiolo, still chipping away and growling in the vestibule of death.

This has been our friendship. This friendship has ennobled my life. And if fools wish to prattle sodomy, let them (and of course they will, let them or not) for Roma is Sodom itself and its inhabitants—many in clerical garb—cannot conceive of friendship that is love or any form of love which is other than the love of the flesh.

I have known love of the flesh too, and there are my two fine sons to attest to it. Yesterday, how exquisitely did my Emilio sing to his own accompaniment on the lute! What joy the Maestro took in it! nodding his head to the sprightly rhythm of fourteen-year-old Emilio's fingers dancing on the frets; the gold flecks in the Maestro's eyes, misted over with age, suddenly ashine to the boy's fine tenor voice.

We were sitting in the larch grove behind the house, dusk had powdered the air with golden pollen, the white thrust of Trajan's column projected above the umbrella pines. Michele was listening enraptured. He closed his eyes. I thought the old man had fallen asleep. But as soon as the song was done, Michele arose and kissed my son on the forehead. "Exquisite," he murmured. Then he turned to me:

"Have you heard, Tomao, that the Council decreed britches for music even before they decreed it for my Judgement?"

The Old One's irony grows thicker with his hurts. But this was perplexing.

"Ah, you don't understand? Well, neither do I. The Master of the Sistine Choir visited me the other day and when I made some wry remark about the Council's preoccupation with my nudities, he exclaimed—But Maestro! We musicians were breeched more than a year and a half ago! The canon on music approved by the Council declared a general ban against worldly and impure melodies.

—What are worldly and impure melodies?

—I suppose they mean tavern tunes employed in the Mass. I can understand that. Or even their objection to excessive polyphony. Too many interweaving lines of melody. Now the words must be clearly understood by all. Everything must be executed at the right speed . . . What is the right speed for a Mass, Maestro?

—I don't know, said I. I'm not a musician.

—Well, I am. But I don't know what is a right speed, said he.

The presumption of these priests! . . . Emilio, another song, I pray you."

The lad began the madrigal by Arcadelt—*Spargendo il senso*—which the Netherlander master had set to Michelangiolo's poem written in the early days of our friendship. O I wanted to kiss my son! What a subtle choice!

A plangent chord stirred him again from his revery. "My brother Giovansimone played the lute beautifully. Unusual among us Buonarrotis. He played the lute like one of Bellini's or Carpaccio's angels. But he was no angel, Giovansimone. A ne'er-do-well." These latter days almost anything will set the Maestro off on excursions into his family, all of whom are dead except for his nephew Lionardo. In all the thirty years I have known him, Michelangiolo has been bound to that family like an ox to a plow. He worried about his brothers, gave them money, set them up in business, although they understood nothing of his art and looked upon him only as a sort of bottomless purse. I met Giovansimone and Gismondo on several occasions when they came down to Roma; but one had to see the Buonarrotis in their natural setting, Fiorenza, planted in their native earth, to understand them to the roots.

My own family, though Roman for many generations, has its Tuscan roots too. I feel at home with Tuscans; perhaps that is why I—the only Roman who frequented regularly the circle of Florentine exiles to whom Michele had introduced me during the early years of our friendship,—was so well accepted by that circle: messer Donato, and the Cardinal Ridolfi and Priscinese the printer and all those. I like the cadence of their speech, the harsh cutting wit, I even like the swallowed "c's" and thickened "t's." I suppose it's my own Tuscan heritage. Indeed we still own property in Fiorenza on the hill of San Miniato near the San Giorgio gate. In the Spring of 1547, I rode up there to look into the management of the Cavalieri estates; and bore with me messages from the Maestro to his family in Fiorenza.

Thus I met for the first time the other remaining Buonarrotis, and from the first encounter I could not but marvel all the more that such a bloom as Michele had blossomed from such a tree. Only two of his brothers were still alive then, Giovansimone and Sigismondo called Gismondo, the two youngest of the five brothers. Giansimone, four years his junior, was taller than Michele and hand-somer (by unperceptive standards) with something of disdain permanently imprinted on his fine-cut lips. He fancied French color rather than Spanish gloom in his dress (and this at a time when the Spaniards had already consolidated their domination all over the peninsula), he wore feathers in his cap, a fine damascened dagger bounced on his hip. Although ostensibly a wool merchant in a shop set up near the Strozzi Palace on money provided him by his famous brother, I think he tinkled more than traded. He had shared this business with his elder brother Buonarotto who had died in the Maestro's arms during the plague that added its needless moiety of woe to Fiorenza during the siege of 1530. Now he shared it with Buonarotto's son, Lionardo.

Giovansimone bestirred himself to make some yawning inquiries about Michelangelo. Did I think he would resolve his disinclination to serve the Duke Cosimo? Was it probable that Michelangelo would ultimately return to his native city? Or—

And here he looked about before speaking in a lowered voice (we were in the very heart of the Piazza Signoria dominated by that forbidding Palace of the Priors in front of which stood Michele's David: the first time I had seen it, an astonishing work, so beautiful I scarcely heard the lowered voice)

—was his brother so enmeshed with those political exiles down in Roma—the enemies of Duke Cosimo centering around the cardinal Ridolfi, the ex-chancellor of the Republic, Donato Giannotti, partisans of Piero Strozzi and all that *band* (that was the word he used) that he would not return to his own *patria* and his responsibilities to his own family?

'Responsibilities' clearly meant money for I was not to meet a single member of the tribe of Buonarrotis (other than his niece Francesca) who appreciated him as anything other than a cornucopia.

The other brother was up at his farm in Settignano, and I rode there on a fine bay up a gentle mountain slope, past sleepy hamlets, peasants on the hillsides plowing with white oxen, slanting rows of dark green vines, and the capricious crooked dance of silvery olive trees. Below me, from certain turnings of the path, stretched all Fiorenza, and seeing that marvelous city surrounded by its walls and bristling with towers sweet-ensconced in its valley, the Arno sinuously gleaming in the haze, the four bridges like cobwebs from this distance spanning the stream, the huddle of plebian roofs and jagged thrust of patrician towers,—all dominated from the very navel of the city by Brunelleschi's great brickred Dome and the crenellated brown tower of the Signori, I could easily understand why Michelangiolo, notwithstanding his many years in Roma and his eminence as Pope of the arts seated alongside (as Julius III always insisted) the Pope of the Church; notwithstanding, I say, all these honors paid to him, yet like all the Florentines I have known in the Urbs, never do they cease to long for their native city, though in exile they may curse it, as Dante did, or Michele and his friends sometimes do.

But it is the curse of the spurned lover who still loves. I have yet to meet a

Florentine distant from his hearth who does not suffer from nostalgia for his Cupolone.

I remember the Maestro saying one day when we were discussing the great Dome he has planned for the new fabric of San Pietro— "I cannot better Brunelleschi's Dome. I can only raise it to the skies."

Gismondo turned out to be as cloddish as Giansimone was elegant. Although he managed the family farm, he looked in dress and comportment little different from from any of the peasants who tilled his land. He grunted his inquiries and grunted his replies although withal I sensed in him an unspoken pride in his brother's accomplishment, a greater awareness indeed than I had discerned in quicksilvery Giansimone.

I delivered the letter. Messer Gismondo read it slowly and nodded. "Tell my brother that I will follow his instructions. When I get the receipt for this bill of exchange for 500 gold scudi from the Capponi I'll have them send him the copy. I've been out to the Monte Spertoli farm and it doesn't look like a good investment. As for the other scudi he's sending via the Altoviti, tell him that—"

"Write it, Messer. Write it all down. And include the Capponi and Altoviti receipts. I will deliver the letter to the Maestro."

Gismondo grumbled something about the nuisance of writing. Observing that potato of a Buonarroti, his laborious responses, the earth-clogged manner of his speech, it was hard to believe that this was indeed the Maestro's brother. Only the square-fingered earthcrusted hands and the little flatgray eyes betrayed their relationship.

Gismondo accompanied me to the Santa Croce quarter where his nephew Lionardo was building a fine new house. I had formed of the Maestro's ejaculations and impatient snortings every time he received a letter from this nephew, a certain image of Lionardo; an image, one might say, sculpted of anticipations, deductions, and air. The young man I met turned out to be quite unlike the portrait I had shaped in my head. Instead of flighty, he seemed imperturbable; he received me with a quite Castilian gravity; and indeed with his astonishingly long black beard, and coal black eyes and doublet and broad collar all in black black in the Spanish style then regnant in Cosimo's Fiorenza, which rested on Spanish cannon and blunderbusses, Lionardo struck me rather more as a counselor (which indeed he was) of the State than the frivolous and illiterate nephew whose letters always sent the Maestro into an incandescent rage.

With the most solemn mien, he inquired about his uncle's health and affairs and I felt that his concern was real and not at all feigned. His luminous great eyes were solicitous. Yet when this nephew had ridden posthaste down to Roma when his uncle fell ill during the painting of the Pauline, Michelangiolo had exploded that Lionardo had come not out of concern for him but to protect his inheritance. I hadn't met Lionardo during that visit. Now I felt that Michelangelo's distrust was entirely unfounded.

But he is a distrustful man. He is given to extremes: he loves, he hates; he yields himself entirely or remains impregnable in the fortress of himself.

I dined with Lionardo in the one salotta that was complete in his fine new house abuilding on the Via Ghibellina. The house indeed seemed much too large for a single man, even with several servants.

Just before my departure for Fiorenza, the Old One had confided in me his preoccupations in finding a "proper" wife for his nephew. Lionardo was in his late twenties and showed no sign of getting married. The Buonarrotis were not a marrying kind; of all Michele's brothers, only Lionardo's father had married. And now the son seemed to be carrying on the family tradition of celibacy. "Prick the fool into taking a wife," were my instructions. "Otherwise the name of Buonarroti will die with him. He needs a proper wife." An embarrassingly odd commission. I was still unmarried myself and nine years older than Lionardo! But Michele took great pride in his family name—which he believed to be noble, derived from the Counts of Canossa whereby he had taken unto himself an escutcheon consisting of a dog (*cane*) and a bone (*ossa*). The dog appeared again just a few years ago on the verso of Leone Leoni's medal—a dog leading an old blind man (which is Michele's own notion of himself these latter death-haunted years) with the slogan DOCEBO INIQUOS VIAS TUAS ET IMPII AD TE CONVERTENTUR.

"Is that meant as an admonition to the Pope?" I asked, knowing he had sent a copy of the medal to the Holy Father.

Michele smiled. "It means what it means."

He is given to these subtle messages. Why indeed did he choose a Crucifixion of St. Peter (the first Pope) in a chapel where Popes are chosen, instead of the traditional Handing of the Keys which would have been the more suitable companion piece to his Conversion of St. Paul? Indeed even the Conversion harbors secrets, broods with them, emanates iconographic mysteries.

Of course I didn't discuss the matrimonial lottery with this solemn counselor Lionardo. First we talked of grain yield and grape harvests. Then Lionardo began probing me. He pulled impatiently at his long beard. When would uncle Michelangiolo return to Fiorenza? The Duke, he said, would shower him with all honors. This was his native hearth, he had been away from his family too many years.

"But you know," I said, "that the Maestro considers the completion of St. Peter's as a sacred task. He refuses to accept a scudo for his labors . . ."

"All the more reason for him to return to Fiorenza. The Duke will treat him like a prince. He certainly would pay him better than the Pope."

As he went on singing Cosimo's praises, I gathered the definite impression that Lionardo was indeed the Duke's agent, that he, together with Giorgio Vasari and one of the superintendents at the Fabbrica were all in a conspiracy together to lure Michelangiolo back to Fiorenza. They even asked the madcap Cellini to put in a word for the Duke's invitation. I felt my clear blue Roman sky clouding over: the mere thought of being deprived of Michelangiolo's daily presence . . . "Besides, he is too old," Lionardo was saying. "He is too old and becoming a bit senile, according to certain information I have received."

"His mind is clear as spring water," I replied testily. "All that talk is simply being spread by his enemies on the Fabbrica, Nani di Biagio Bigio especially, and the remnants of the San Gallo cabal. Your uncle is a stubborn man. Only Death— from which I pray he might be spared a while— will force him to yield command of the works at St. Peter's. Certainly not now."

"But he is not well. He laments of being unable to urinate."

"Would he urinate better here?"

Messer Lionardo brushed my frivolity aside. "His family is here. The Duke will heap honors and ducats upon him, he will do anything to enlist his services. His Lordship is prepared to overlook my uncle's unfortunate fraternization with Cosimo's enemies in Roma, the Strozzi bank people, Giannotti, that gang."

Ten years later, on another visit, I met Lionardo's wife, Donna Cassandra. I was married myself then—in fact, soon after my return from that first visit to Fiorenza: I had applied the Maestro's proddings to myself sooner than to his nephew.

Cassandra Ridolfi—plebian-plain though patrician-born—had finally been selected as Lionardo's wife after more than six years of the most comic series of letters between the artist in Roma and his nephew in Fiorenza. I saw many of these letters from Lionardo, being called upon to help decipher them, and I could deduce from them the sort of communications he had received from his uncle.

O that was indeed a comic interval in Michele's life—comic, that is for me, but irritating for him. The list of candidates for Lionardo's hand, the rejections and admonitions, the adjurations to Lionardo that he must propagate the name of Buonarroti which ran the risk of disappearing from the world; nor need he be too finicky about acquiring a beautiful bride since he was no great beauty himself; all he was to require in his wife were health, sobriety and *onestà*—thus old Michelangiolo free with his conjugal advice as a priest (though he was more celibate than many of them). A Strozzi girl was considered, appraised, rejected; then a daughter of the Ginori; she almost made it. Oh, one would think the two of them were purchasing a brood mare at a horse fair!—teeth were examined, flanks slapped, buttocks pinched, dowries and lineage appraised,—all this went on for years. And Michele all the while painting the Crucifixion of Peter in the Pope Paul's new chapel. At one point in this matrimonial stakes a prophetess offered her services as a go-between and Michele snorted scorn at her masses and incense. He hated people whose piety was for public consumption. Another time Michelangiolo must have had an avuncular pang of conscience: Don't take a wife at all, he cautioned Lionardo, if you fear that the engendering of heirs will ruin your health.

In the late afternoon light the towers seemed to lean inward: I was pressed to provincialism; I was walking through an atmosphere of sifted gold. This quarter of

Santa Croce lying eastward between Palazzo Vecchio and the Gate was the oldest section of the City. The house on Via Torta followed the circumference of the ancient Roman arena. Most of the great palaces were built in rustico style: rough-hewn limestone, sand-colored blocks, huge portals, barred iron windows, merlons like fortresses. Huddled around these palaces of the great families were small wooden houses with thatched roofs, some with red-orange tiles. The streets were paved, unlike much of Roma. Hammering and the swishing of saws, scrapings, filing, cries of artisans, hawling and thumping of barrels, boys carrying bales, laden mules clinking along lady-footed on paving stones, gurgle of running water, suck and sibilant of woolens which had been imported raw from Flanders and were here being dipped and drawn and dyed into the famous Florentine serge sold all over Europe and the source of much Florentine wealth.

Wool and banking, I thought—those were your Florentines, and there was wool and banking in Michelangiolo's head too—together with the Bacchus in messer Gallo's garden and Redemption by the blood of Christ alone.

This was the quarter where my Michelangiolo had grown up, after his infancy at the breast of a stonecutter's wife in Settignano. Here in Santa Croce he had been formed and his soul was still, I thought, quartiere and cosmos, provincial and universal. He quarrels with God and jokes with a stonecutter. Intimate with Popes and Kings he is reluctant to buy property outside his own quarter of Santa Croce. A Uomo Universale and a provincial much attached to his own campanile: the bells in other parts of Fiorenza did not ring as sweetly.

Then it was I truly understood the paradox of messer Michelangiolo Buonarroti. The man who had brusquely denied Pope Julius his request for gold retouches without which the Vicar felt the Sistine vault looked "poor" ("those who are depicted there were poor, Your Holiness"), the same man who dressed simply, lived on crusts of bread, refused any title other than Messer, yet when it came to his family in Fiorenza, behaved like any merchant, vaunting the antiquity and presumed nobility of the Buonarrotis, wanting Lionardo to live in a proper big house, ashamed of Gismondo trudging after the oxen like a peasant. And when Lionardo's wife had finally been decided upon, the old man wanted to send her a present "so that it might be known that she's my nephew's wife."

We spent more than a week making the rounds of all the jewelers in Roma. How much Michelangiolo haggled! Finally, he found what he wanted at a gloomy little shop inserted amidst the ruins of the Teatro Marcellus, and run by an old Jew whose beard was three times as long as Michelangiolo's, and who visibly trembled at the honor paid him, when he learned that this exacting client was the famous sculptor of the Moses. (Every time one visited St. Peter's in Chains in those days, one saw Jews there gazing in awe at the Father of their faith. Now, since Caraffa, no Jews are permitted entrance.)

At first Michele had sought for a beautiful string of valuable pearls but now instead he chose two rings, a diamond and a ruby.

"Do you think Mona Cassandra will be pleased? Do you think they are sufficiently *signorile?*"

When he sent the jewels, he begged Lionardo to have them appraised.

"I just want to know if I've been fooled, Tomao."

I laughed.

"Well, I'm no expert in these things," he grumbled.

Then that same petty huge man went back to set his visions on the wall of the Pauline.

O the joy he took when he learned that his gifts were beautiful and valuable and that Cassandra was delighted. That was when she sent him eight linen shirts as a return gift for which he was most pleased but regretted that he who was lacking nothing should have deprived his nephew of these shirts.

A strange old man. For over thirty years I have never been able to put these two Michelangiolos together: the Titan who dwells on mountaintops and the provincial Florentine who dwells in Santa Croce, and boasts about the nobility and antiquity of the Buonarroti Simoni and buys and sells real estate and stows away most of his ducats in the banks (I know but he does not know that I know that he also has at Macel de' Corvi a hidden chest full of gold and silver coins of the Papal mint) of Santa Maria Nuova and with the Strozzi and sets his brothers up in the wool business and counsels his nephew that "an honorable house in the city brings very much prestige because it is seen, more than one's possessions."

Yet the same Michelangiolo gives much charity, especially dowries to enable poor girls to marry, and never wants this known. Nor would he ever accept a scudo for his gigantic responsibility as architect of St. Peter's (which his enemy Bandinelli interpreted as the maneuver of a miser.)

What puzzled (and puzzles) me is not that these two Michelangiolos dwell side by side. They dwell within the same skin.

Sometimes, watching him paint or carve, or discourse on Dante, the other Michelangiolo—that wily cranky burgher—abruptly appears, and as abruptly disappears.

The shift is frightening. There is sorcery in it. It's as if the old man were alternately possessed.

·✻·

The most attractive member of the tribe of Buonarroti was Lionardo's younger sister, Francesca. Plump and jolly as her brother was grave, Francesca was a pretty girl about thirty and one could see at a glance that her marriage to Michele Guicciardini was more than just another alliance of the Buonarrotis with one of the great patrician families of Fiorenza. She'd already been married ten years and had three children and had lost one in infancy. Her husband, a fair handsome man, ran the farm at Pozzolatico which Michelangiolo had provided as Francesca's dowry. Michele is related to the Papal Governor General, Francesco Guicciardini (now deceased) whose *History of Italy,* published three years ago by Cosimo's printer, Torrentino, has already been put upon the Index of forbidden books.

While Michele inquired much about messer Michelangiolo's affairs, laying special stress upon the political implications of his friendships with the anti-Cosimo Florentine exile colony in Roma, Francesca plied me with questions about her uncle's health. What could she send him? Did he like the ravioli and marzolini cheeses she had recently included in a bundle dispatched by brother Lionardo? Did Zio Michelangiolo really dislike ravioli or was it because it got wet on the way and soft things should not be sent? Should she heed Zio Michelangiolo's repeated admonitions not to send anything because he had no need, or wasn't this (and here she blossomed into a smile warm and glowing as a peach) just Zio's irritable way of expressing his pride and reluctance to accept gifts from anyone. She adored her Zio; it was obvious in every word she spoke.

"I had light shirts especially made for him after he complained to Lionardo about the rough material of the first batch. These are of the finest linen, not muslin like the others. I hope he will be pleased . . ."

I assured her that her famous uncle appreciated the shirts. As for the other gifts—the mule loads of white Trebbiano wine, the barrels of pears—he frequently gave most of that away. Thoughtlessly he had— during the pontificacy of Paul III—been accustomed to make lavish gifts of wine to a Pope who was totally abstemious!

That sojourn in Fiorenza was also a pilgrimage to all those works of Michelangiolo which I had heard about in Roma but never seen. Whenever my affairs permitted, I hurried back to the Piazza Signoria to look upon that incredible David. The White Giant was the true Signore of Fiorenza. Circling round him, I caught odd glimpses of Donatello's bronze Judith in the Loggia and the Marzocco Lion. Both powerful works, they seemed to cringe. David commanded the piazza. His fiercely beautiful frown, the potential menace of his stance, the glorious nude body rippling and quivering in the sunlight and at dusk casting his full shadow on the rusticated stones of the Palazzo as if in admonition to the creatures of the Duke within. In those three weeks in Fiorenza, I got to know David as if he were Michelangiolo himself: the Michelangelo of almost half a century before I came!

And to think that his Maker is still alive, still making, not a Hero now, but a strange Pietà which I don't understand but don't dare ask him to explain to me. He seems to be creating it by destroying it. Every time I see the work, more of the Christ has disappeared. And yet even in that mysterious Pietà and in the Nicodemus which the Maestro smashed and young Calcagni has recently glued together and completed—even in those works of his great old age, I see the power of the David: they are all sons of the same father.

Even his Roman Moses is the Florentine's son, simply his David grown older.

The one is Youth, the other Middle-Age. The one is the Idea of the Hero, the other is the Idea of the Judge. The left hand which had been broken during the uprisings of 1527 was now repaired. One could see the joints at the wrist where the three broken pieces had been doweled and cemented together. I recalled Michelangiolo's bitter remarks when that news arrived. "It has taken the Signori sixteen years to repair something which I—or any good artisan—could have done in a week or two.

A bouquet of withered lilies lay on the spot where Fra Girolamo had been burned.

✻

I visited the new sacristy at San Lorenzo accompanied by the most whimsical lively monk I have ever encountered. Anton Francesco Doni was a Servite at Santissima Annunziata, and Michelangiolo had recommended me to him. "He's a fantastical fellow who wrote me letters on the occasion of the opening of the Medici Tombs that set me crying for laughter." He set me crying for laughter too, even in that lugubrious space wherein recline the most melancholy monuments of despair I have ever seen.

In front of the Aurora, Doni ceased to bounce (which is his normal gait) for at least two full minutes, gazing up at that figure from all angles (especially from the right) with a most unecclesiastical expression on his ruddy velvet smooth young face. Finally he spoke the avowels of a lover: "I love all these figures, but the Aurora especially is so beautiful and so divine that every time I see her—and I see her often— I want to embrace her and kiss her—and I find more suavity in her and more consolation than in any other woman—"

All this in a loud voice, with other people—both laic and religious—in the Chapel and Doni bouncing now from one foot to the other and sending his black robes flying with gesticulations of her fervor—

"—more than any other woman alive! And isn't she alive, really?— Isn't Night alive? Can't you see her awaken? can't you hear her speak?— A thousand times I've thought to rouse her, as if she were a goddess formed in Paradise, but she will only awaken for her creator—who is a God himself—begging permission of our faith—I mean the divine Michelangiolo—"

He was off now like a palio horse at Siena who has thrown his rider (which would be in this case a certain Christian monastic self-control) speaking only in jets—

"—because just as Domineddio" (this Florentinism enunciated with a thickening of the accents of the Val d'Arno) "—just as Domineddio created Adam of earth breathing into him the spirit of life, so messer Michelangiolo infused spirit into those soft and muscular figures—the intelligence of their poses—the mastery—so that seeing them we become marble frozen in admiration while they pulse—"

But he had long passed his marmoreal phase. He wasn't frozen for a second, and he certainly wasn't silent.

I returned again that same afternoon to appreciate in silence what must be viewed in silence. Doni's orgiastic orgasms especially in front of Aurora were propitious for laughter and not for a true understanding of what Michele expressed in those statues. And if ever any works of his are remote from laughter, those are the Medici tombs.

For here, even more intensely than the melancholy that seems to engauze all Michele's figures—even the heroic David and Moses and the Pietà of Saint Peter's and the floating athletes of his vault—here I felt washed by waves of despair. Once entered into that small space, the tortured despondent allegories of the hours, the brooding Lorenzo, the Captain Giuliano, the long inward-dwelling Madonna with the Bambino straddling her knee—it was all a monument to melancholy, I thought; even the strange forms of the architecture, the converging windows under the vault, the agitated paralysis of upsidedown balusters and crowded pediments, the blind doors—everything here bespoke total paralysis of the will. He had made this chapel in a dark time and you could see it. Night was twisted about like a Jesuitical argument, her right elbow on her left thigh, the other arm twisted behind her back, her strange breasts like the breasts of no maiden I have ever known. Certainly not like the warm breasts of my Lavinia. These are mounds of snow, frozen concepts of the female who is not female at all, nor male either: but one of those androgynous creatures Michelangiolo makes, malefemales or femalemales, projections of a superrace combining the qualities of both sexes: strength and grace.

Just before my departure Lionardo took me to the studio on Via Mozza— a huge barnlike place—where Michelangiolo had left four of the Prigioni he had intended for Pope Julius' tomb, and forced to abandon by the repeated changes of contracts for that great monument of the Unfinished. I had never seen these works, although I had seen the two highly finished ones which Michele, after his illness, had left with messer Luigi del Riccio to be sent as gifts to Roberto Strozzi, in his bank at Lyon. Stupendous gifts which, I always felt, should have been given to messer Luigi himself, who managed the Strozzi bank in Roma. After all, it had been messer Luigi who had insisted on taking Michele into his own quarters in the Strozzi Palace when the Maestro fell so deathly ill that we all feared for his life. He had nursed him and put up with his grumbling and complaints. Messer Luigi loved Michelangiolo as all his close friends loved him; we all saw the palpitating heart through the sour crust. Alas, now he too is dead, so unexpectedly at Lyon whither he had gone on business. No more banking or sonneteering, poor Luigi!

By comparison with the two highly finished Slaves I had seen before they went to France, these Prigioni in the studio puzzled me. They were altogether different not only in scale but in manner. At first glance I saw what I took to be only huge rough blocks of stone. Then as the figures emerged throbbing from the rock I thought of giant caryatids. There was certainly none of the languor and elegant fervor of the other two pieces. These seemed to be engaged in a death struggle against bondage; they were still embedded in the rock; one of them made me think of a giant in placenta.

I knew that Michelangiolo had done several tondos, two in stone, one painted, but though I made efforts to see these I did not succeed in gaining entrance to the palaces of the Doni, the Pitti and the Taddei where they were housed. The great families in Fiorenza are not altogether hospitable. Under Cosimo there is an atmosphere of suspicion against all outsiders, especially those who come from the Holy City. I felt it was time to depart. Luckily I recalled at the last moment the packet of drawings left in Lionardo's house on Via Ghibellina. Michelangiolo had been worried about leaving these stored in such a flood-vulnerable area.

·✳·

When I returned to Roma, full of Buonarroti images—Francesca's peach-cheeked smile and lugubrious Lionardo, Gismondo following his oxen and Gian-simone's ironic indifference—and those other silent brooding suffering Buonar-rotis: the Slaves in Via Mozza—the first thing I did was ask the Maestro what he proposed to do with them and whether he intended to leave them in that unfinished state—

"Well, they are Prisoners, are they not?" he replied with something of a frown. "E allora?"

"E allora, do they not suggest more successfully the notion of imprisonment insofar as they are only half liberated from the block?"

And before I could remonstrate (I meant particularly that figure without a head, the head still unborn, still in the block, a marmoreal foetus), he added murmurously:

"Are we not all prisoners? Prisoners in this flesh? Prisoners of the body from which we struggle to emerge as my Prigioni are struggling to free themselves of the encumbering rock?—"

"—but Maestro—"

"—O let it pass, Tomao! That tomb of Julius was my ultimate prison! I gave up thirty years of my life to it! Those Prisoners up in Fiorenza are all myself, don't you see, imprisoned in the Tomb of Julius! Which was finally finished, was it not?—" he added scornfully. "—Finished by other hands but what does that matter, finished to that abortion flanking the wall in St. Peter's in Chains! Michelangiolo in Chains! And only my Moses seated in the midst of that mediocrity, passing violent judgement on me, on dead Julius, on the Dukes of Urbino! Imprisonment! Imprisonment! What else is there? Finito! Non-finito! . . ."

He was becoming very agitated now and I rose and embraced him and left the packet of drawings.

✳

That first prolonged visit to Fiorenza, those encounters—brief though they were—with his family, served to illuminate for me much that had been obscure in Michelangiolo's character, intimate though we already were and friends then for ten years. He was always a Fiorentino, I realized more than ever before, always a provincial from the Santa Croce quarter, citizen of the universe and campanilista: ringer of his own bell-tower.

And from then on I understood more deeply his curious blend of alienation and attachment to his family—his explosions whenever he received one of Lionardo's ill-scrawled letters 'running along like an ill-trained vineyard!' He was convinced, too, that none of the Buonarrotis were 'beauties', but Giansimone with all his scoffing indolence was certainly an attractive man; and I certainly do not share Michele's self-deprecations of his own appearance. It was unjustified.

For if the Maestro lacks the beauty of an Alcibiades he possesses that of a Socrates: the beauty of his intelligence that irradiates his face of an ancient fawn, sets malicious lights foaming and sparkling in his seagreen eyes, and I find grace and wisdom which is the truest beauty in his countenance, in the flattish broken nose, the lips chiseled clean in the graybristling bifurcated little beard. There is not an ounce of fat in him, not in his speech or his demeanor. He remains, for all his many years here in Roma, more Florentine than ever. And though a son of the Arno may be lacking in one or another of the humors of earth or air or fire or water, you may be sure that he excels in the fifth element which is truly that of Florentines, intelligence.

Nor is he all Saturnian, the Old One. I have more than once seen the lightning flash out of that gloomy cloud. I have even been the victim of it. Not always the lightning of anger. Sometimes a flickering irony, Giovansimone. Sometimes a crude humor and then you see that he is Sigismondo's brother.

A difficult man. A difficult man.

And yet my Michelangiolo has never wanted for friends. Indeed, I have never known a man more inclined to love his friends, more loyal to them, more given to take joy in their company. And yet he has the reputation for being the great solitary, "lonely as a hangman" as Raffaello put it, incapable of human concourse according to Giovio and Aretino. But this only proves that these writers were not in the close circle of the Maestro's friends. If he guards his solitude it is as a fortress into which he withdraws to renew his forces, resharpen his artistic weapons and forge new ones. "Tomao mio," he said to me on more than one occasion, particularly after some annoying visit, "valiant artists avoid too much conversation, not out of pride but because there are few—very few—people whose talk is worthy of what the Lady Vittoria called 'the sweet colloquy with forms'." Michele's solitude is an ethical choice, a professional instrument, a training ground. He hates to waste his time in futile prattle with lazy people; he resents deflecting his mind from its proper realm: the upper reaches of the imagination.

One day he even avoided a summons to the Vatican where his good friend Pope Paul III wanted to talk with him. "His Holiness annoys me and wastes my time." And he invented some excuse for refusing the summons!

So it is no wonder that many people in Roma find him bizarre. O how often I have heard that word applied to the Maestro! O Yes, a great man, divine if you will, a genius . . . but he is somewhat *bizarre*, you will admit, messer Tomao, you who know him so well. He is not, should we say, a *normal* . . .

O via! I would expostulate. What is the great virtue in the *normal*? . . . Would a normal man paint the vault of the Sistine Chapel unaided, setting down almost four hundred greater than lifesized figures all by himself in four years? . . . so much for your normalcy . . .

O I will admit his humor has become somewhat bizarre. All those years heaped up on the acerb foundations of his native Fiorentinità. The ground has shifted a bit, I suppose. All that weight.

These last few years the Maestro has been furnishing copious sketches both for new fortifications and gates of Roma, much to the heart of the new Pope. One new gate is already under way, named the Porta Pia after the current Pontiff. Michele has a man named Pier Luigi Gaeta in charge of this operation and Pier Luigi who replaced the irreplaceable Urbino as Michelangiolo's chief assistant has certainly caused the Maestro a world of trouble.

Last year, near San Vitale, a treasure was unearthed in the vineyard of a certain Signor Oratio Muti when his gardener discovered a great quantity of ancient gold medals and valuable jewelry. The gardener fled and when Signor Orazio went to the vineyard, not finding the man, he began searching around for him, and came upon the pit strewn with bronze vases and some potshards. Digging in that spot several golden medals of ancient Roma were found. Well, Signor Muti immediately realized why his gardener had taken off; he advised all the banks and goldsmiths of Roma to hand over to the law anyone who might come in with golden Roman coins and jewelry.

Well, just about that time, Maestro Michelangiolo instructed his man Pier Luigi Gaeta to change some old coins which were no longer in use. The banker summoned the guard and poor Pier Luigi was arrested; and when under examination he said that he had obtained those coins from Michelangiolo, the judge ordered that the Maestro should also be put in prison! None of us could comprehend the ignorance of a judge who would dare to order the incarceration of a Michelangiolo! At any rate, Michele did appear in person at the examination; I accompanied the Old One and roared with laughter at the irony of his replies.

"What is your name?" asked the idiotic judge.

"I've been told that I used to be called Michel Angelo delli Buoni Arroti."

"What country are you from?"

"They tell me that I'm Fiorentino."

"Do you know the Muti?"

"How am I supposed to know the Mutes if I don't even know the Prattlers?"

Well, of course, certain cardinals who had heard about the affair immediately sent their agents to the judge, who had to let Michele go. But poor Pier Luigi remained in prison for several days.

During that inquiry I got a stitch in my side controlling my laughter. Laughter and at the same time a deep sadness. The Old One was speaking about himself in the *passato remoto*, as if he were already dead:

"*Mi fu detto che . . .* I've been told that I used to be called Michele of the Well-Roasted Ones (delli Buoni Arrosti). Was he referring to the Inferno? Surely a place in Paradise is already reserved for him. And yet he refers to himself as well-roasted in Hell. In the distant past. His humor is shot through with strangeness. One doesn't know whether to laugh or cry. His normally deep voice was deeper than ever: it seemed to rise to the living from the depths of posterity, a total idifference to the miseries of existence. They dared to consider him, the greatest maker of Prisoners, a prisoner of the court!

As we rode back to Macel de' Corvi, after that burlesque of a judicial hearing, Michelangiolo looked more than ever like a gaunt and terribly weary ancient fawn. He was cold, he said; he wanted to get back quickly and wrap himself up in a shawl and his woolen peasant cloak and sit by the fire.

And that's what he's been mainly doing this past rainy week. Sitting by the fire. Staring into the flames. He almost never speaks. The other day despite all of our objections he insisted on riding his mule a bit in the drizzle. Up to his eighty-sixth year he was still riding his horse every day. I used to marvel at his straight firm form in the saddle against the shattered ruins of the essedra of Trajan. He haunted those ruins: the horse spotted gray, Michele brown in his cloak, the ruins white, the sky Roman blue. Diminishing into that maze of antiquity. He has not ventured to Saint Peter's at all these recent years. Depends on detailed reports from Gaeta— when he is not in jail. Another trusted workman stabbed by a jealous cook who found his wife in bed with Michele's man.

The times are not good for art!

But the chief consolation of his old age are his friends. He has never wanted for friends notwithstanding Raffaello's jibe about him being 'lonely as a hangman'. Was there ever such a gregarious—if obstreperous— hangman?

Indeed, over three decades I have been coming to this house at Macel de' Corvi almost every day, and witnessed there a steady stream of visitors: Florentines in passage, that madcap Benvenuto Cellini, messer Lorenzo Ridolfi, Donato Giannotti, humble artisans, illustrious Romans, messer Claudio Tolomei, Berni the comic poet whom Michelangiolo so loved, Annibale Caro who served as patrician pumice to his kinsman (by marriage) Condivi's plebian memoire; Molza, poet and womanizer, Monsignor Giovio the historian; and amidst these cardinals and princes and humanists, a litany of artists from all the provinces of Italy: Daniele da Volterra, Sebastiano Luciano from Venice, who became the Keeper of the Pope's Seal, Giorgio Vasari, from Arezzo, that splendid courtier of Duke Cosimo who has never realized the bite and irony beneath the Maestro's courtesy whenever the question of Michelangiolo's return to Fiorenza arises, Taddeo Zucchero, Sansovino and il Rosso, the Redheaded one from Fiorenza, later to go to Fontainbleau in the service of the French King.

If there was anyone closer to Maestro Michelangiolo than I, it was his inseparable daily companion, his factotum and loyal servant, the stonecutter Francesco dell'Amadore, born at Castel Durante near Urbino and hence called Urbino. O the Maestro loved him like a son, gave him 2000 ducats on one occasion as a single payment for his assistance in completing that cursèd Tomb of Julius. And when at last Urbino got tired of tiptoeing about Roma on velvet feet (his odd phrase for visiting the courtesans) and took unto himself a wife, old Michelangiolo showered his wife Cornelia with gifts and served as godfather to his firstborn and obtained well-paying jobs for him and demanded his aid and counsel in all things and was greatly influenced by his advice. And I, watching that grand old man with his sculptured face, his sharp chiseled lips pursed and the lines of worry in his brow— seven like the circles of hell—and the little graygreen eyes quizzically attentive as Urbino discoursed on how the Maestro should deal with Holy Father or Most Christian King, I never ceased to be astonished. For Michelangiolo was a difficult man to advise. He listened to no one but the voice of his own conscience and he had threatened in the presence of Pope del Monte to resign from his task as architect of St. Peter's rather than share his plans with anyone. Yet here was the man who had told the committee of Cardinals that "My plans for the fabbrica are none of your business. Your business is to raise money—" here was the same Michelangiolo with his head bowed, listening gravely to the advice or admonitions or even nagging of his servant Urbino.

O but he truly loved that man and when, after twenty-six years of loyal service, Urbino died, we all feared the Maestro would not be able to sustain the loss.

As for the material drudgery of housework at Macel de' Corvi, Michelangiolo has always needed a fistful of domestics. It is a huge house, really, though sparsely furnished. So he needs servants, you see, he needs someone to shop and cook for him and tidy up the marble splinters and crusts of bread. Years ago he enlarged the main body of his dwelling with a small salotta and bedrooms and a little tower which gives access to a spiral staircase. So he needs servants but he has had no better luck with them than with all his studio assistants before Urbino. All the Maestro's friends have heard him give vent to the most picturesque appreciation of his *servitù*.

"Whores and pigs!" is a mild example. Yet he has always been kind to the most humble people of his quarter. Ten years ago he took into his house Vincenzina the daughter of Michele the grocer, and signed a contract to keep her for four years and to provide her with a dowry of fifty golden scudi that she might be enabled to marry. And she served him well and did marry and the Old One was pleased as if it were his own daughter.

And he has provided gratis all the designs to improve this neighborhood around the Trajan Forum and is indeed usually most kind with simple people, reserving his barbs for the mighty. He has always preserved the melodious cantilena of Fiorenza but when he becomes angry, he swallows his c's more than usual and his tongue thickens the t's into th's and he sounds for all the world like any artisan from Santa Croce. Although my family has long lost that lilt, I think we do preserve at the core a certain sense of our Fiorentino origin. Certainly it is curious that although we Cavalieri have been Romans as far back as we can remember, I found myself frequenting the considerable Florentine colony in the Holy City and my steps led most often to the region of the Banche across from the Castel where the great Tuscan merchants and bankers are concentrated.

Yet how typical of my Michelangiolo that he should choose to dwell so far apart from his countrymen. His house is right in the heart of the Trajan Forum almost directly opposite the great column with its spirals of reliefs. That column is the first thing he sees when he issues from his house and it is the last thing when he re-enters. I have heard him discourse on the nature of the carving and wherein the older Florentine masters, especially Donato (whom he so admires, and he admires few!) and Desiderio and Benedetto and the Rosselinis—all those sweet masters from those sweet hills of Fiesole and Settignano where Michele imbibed marble dust together with the milk of his wetnurse, a stonecutter's wife—how these masters have adopted the technique of very low relief, the *stiacciato* style, from the ancients. I have heard him compare della Robbia's singing choir with Roman reliefs like those on the column. But withal his admiration for the ancients, never did he himself derive any fundamental forms from them. He has always been too much his own man for that and he neither believes in copying ancient sculptures or even restoring them when the pieces are unearthed. After his curt refusal to restore the Laocoon during the time of the great Julius no Pope ever asked him again. His main concern was the making of Michelangiolos not the restoration of antiquities. Thus he didn't care even when other people copied him—even his worst enemy Bigio copied his early Pietà and it was sent to Fiorenza to be placed in the church of Santo Spirito. And the result was that slanderous anonymous letter Lionardo showed me. But I doubt that the writer of that letter would have responded less violently to the incomparably greater beauty of the original. What he was responding to was what he felt was a Lutheran image: a beautiful youthful Mother with her grown Son in her lap, not how well or poorly it was done.

But that is a sign of the times: no one looks at art any longer: one assays instead the degree of orthodoxy or heresy revealed in the image.

There is a garden in front which the servant is supposed to keep trim but it is sadly neglected most of the time in the usual Roman fashion. On the emplacement there is a sort of orchard planted with laurels and great trees which looks like a Tuscan farmyard, so noisy is it with domestic animals: chickens, the Maestro's favorite cat, and horses, for up until very recently he was in the habit of riding every evening. And I think it is this riding, together with the piece of sculpture he always has under his hand (for reasons of health he says) that has kept him so remarkably healthy up until a month ago. All last year at the age of eighty-eight, he rode every day and sometimes as far as the workings of the new Saint Peter, riding tall and straight in his brown cloak, clinging his knees well to the ribs. This daily exercise not only refreshes his mind but tempers and makes supple his muscles. But for the past six months he has been riding only the mule for that is gentler on his ancient bones. For he is very old, O he is very old, my Michelangiolo, and we are all prepared to see him depart without notice at any time.

In the house there are no luxurious furnishings or decoration, even few household utensils. There are always supplies of marzolino goat cheese and Trebbiano white Tuscan wine which his grandnephew Lionardo ships him every year. Michele gives much of this away: sometimes to His Holiness, sometimes to his neighbors: the sacristan at the Madonna of Loreto or the nuns of San Giovanni Battista or the grocer or Capitano Capisucco or the Frangipane.

To look upon his austere garb, the sparse furnishings of his house, one would think he was as poor as he proclaims himself to be. But he is rich. He is so full of contradictions, my Michelangiolo. A yes and no moves him. Ardor and ashes. He always wants what he does not want. His clothes may be simple but his *lucco* is of velvet and the cape of fine serge (after all he is a Florentine). Yet he frequently wears dogskin boots over bare legs; and when he was working hard on the Pauline, he often went to bed with his boots on, and ate no midday meal and when Urbino finally pulled the boots off, some of Michele's skin came off with them. And though for the three decades of our friendship he has lamented his health and more than once predicated his departure to a better world, yet he remains in this one, and until this last month stronger than many younger men, and his shoulders tight and I have seen the bare torso roll and ripple with the powerful muscles he has developed in all these years of stonecutting and wielding a hammer and his handshake is powerful enough to crack your more delicate fingers and I think all this is the result of his austere living habits, the daily exercise with mallet and chisel, the riding of his horse.

Up until last year, he had a habit of riding to sites of antiquity and he often went to look at the ancient columns at the well of the monastery of St. Peter's in Chains where his poor aborted Julius tomb is situated and I have seen him stand frozen in contemplation for what seemed like hours at a time (although of course it was not) so that one would think he had become one of those columns himself.

Well, after numerous such meditations before the ancient columns, Michelangiolo chose and obtained the capital of one of the eight great columns of

Vespasiano's Temple of Peace to sculpt his Nicodemus deposition. And I knew that he took pride and fire from that choice before he was aware the ancient marble was hard, full of faults which sparked under his irons. And for years I watched him cutting into that stone in search of the Form already in his head, journeying into the unknown like the Navigator of the Ocean Sea, Colombo the Genovese, knowing what he was searching for but not what he would find.

So Michele wrestled with that group for many years, thinking to have it set upon his own tomb and that is why he has carved himself into the Nicodemus enclosing the Christ and the Madonna and the Magdalen within his arms, encircling them all in a supreme Misericordia as if He, Michelangiolo-Nicodemus pitied the Christ and his sorrowing Mother.

One day I came to Macel de' Corvi. The Maestro was not at home. The servant, Antonio Franzese met me. His eyes were full of tears. "O messer Cavalieri! He has smashed it!"

"Smashed what?"

"The Pietà!"

Antonio, sobbing, led me through the great barnlike rooms to the studio where he showed me the wreckage of the group. The left arm and wrist of the Christ were utterly smashed. The right leg in pieces (the left leg had been removed earlier. The scarcely blocked-out Magdalen gouged. The Madonna without an elbow.

Over the wreckage Michele's self-portrait in the guise of Nicodemus still gazed in pity.

"He said it was an obdurate vein in the lower torso."

"Perhaps his own vein."

"I heard the blows and the shouts in the middle of the night. O Messer, a fearful sight! The Maestro quivering with rage, the hammer in his hand!"

Fortunately, young Calcagni has now put it to rights. But alas! old Michelangiolo can never be put again to rights.

Death has the hammer in his hand.

That was eight years ago.

And since then he has been chipping away at another Pietà. And now that there is no more to remove, he will remove himself.

So he will join his Urbino, and all the others high and low, who have loved him—and there were many, notwithstanding his reputation as a bristling obstreperous man. What legions of affection this bristling obstreperous man has aroused!—Paul III and Julius III and Luigi del Riccio and Sebastiano del Piombo and the Marchesa of Pescara . . .

That was the one friendship I must confess I found difficult to comprehend. Perhaps I was jealous. For those were the years—immediately after the accession of Farnese to the Fisherman's throne—when Michele was shuttling so to speak between Vittoria Colonna and myself: she a great Lady and I an ignorant boy; she learnèd and pious as a nun (without wimpel) and I, at that time, not much given to Christian renunciation. I knew Michele loved me for my beauty; why then, at the same time did he seem to worship—verily worship—that far-from-beautiful middle-aged lady surrounded by Cardinals and Bishops and laics of the Reformist persuasion?

I accompanied Michele sometimes to those summer evening gatherings in the cloisters of San Silvestro or in the adjacent convent opening onto the Colonna gardens. But I must confess that I not infrequently departed early on some pretext or other. I did not share Michele's admiration for this grand virago holding court as it were. I did not like to see my Michelangiolo as one of her courtiers. Even her poetry, which Michelangiolo read to me from the beautiful volume of one hundred and three of her sonnets which he had bound with his own hands, did not impress me as much as Michele's own verses which he disparaged but which all his friends, including the grand Vittoria, admired. Indeed, many of her verses had been written in response to his. Hers were thick sweetsick smelling of incense; his chisel-sparks.

She was a widow more than faded. In profile she looked a bit like a female Savonarola rather more than anybody's amorous inspiration. She would not have stung Petrarca into song. And so when I heard various foolish interpretations I had to laugh knowing the nature of their love was if anything more intellectual than ours.

Besides, Vittoria Colonna in her person and in her soul was as much man as woman. She was one of those virile women we call viragos, like Catherine of Siena or Caterina Sforza, who had armor specially shaped to fit her bosom as she accompanied her condottiere husband in his wars. Indeed, Michele once showed me a madrigal addressed to Vittoria which began:

> Through your mouth speaks
> a man in a woman, rather a god . . .

One of her friends said of her: "She has such force in reasoning that it is as if chains were issuing from her mouth with which she bound the senses of her listeners."

I must say the image struck me as somewhat less than elegant. Yet Vittoria Colonna aroused such things in one. She reminded me a bit of one of Michele's Sibyls in the vault; not the Cumaean of course, but, say, the Delphic. The only time Michele ever thought of kissing her was when she was laid out as a corpse. Afterward, he regretted that he had not bestowed his farewell kiss on her brow instead of on her hand. As it was, he had never even kissed that lofty forehead when it was warm. Indeed, that last kiss in the chapel was his first.

Well, that grand lady has now been dead for seventeen years and though Michele suffered from her loss almost as much as he suffered from the loss of his belovèd Urbino, he no longer speaks of her, he has not mentioned her name for many years. But of his faithful Urbino—his foibles and his devotions—he speaks almost every day.

So the Lady Vittoria is gone. And both Michele's brothers are gone. And Urbino is gone. And Fra Sebastiano with his lute and gondoliering jokes, has rowed off forever on the grandest of Grand Canals. And messer Luigi has rejoined his belovèd and too-publicly lamented Cecchino (what absurd commemoratory doggerel Michelangiolo wrote to please messer Luigi). And the two Popes who loved him best since mighty Julius, gone. All gone.

Of those who mattered in Michelangiolo's life during the past three decades, only a handful of us remain. His nephew Lionardo and his niece Mona Francesca Guicciardini in Fiorenza. Cornelia, Urbino's widow, back in the Marche and remarried (after asking the Maestro's permission!)

And here in the Holy City, myself and messer Donato and amusing Annibale Caro, uncle to Ascanio Condivi (who has also departed for his native town in the Marche) and young Tiberio Calcagni and Daniele da Volterra. Michele is fortunate no doubt that the 'rectifications' ordered by the Council (or by the Pope?) will be painted by Daniele. He loves his Master so much that the britches will be minimal, just enough to satisfy the clerics up at Trento.

So it has finally happened.

Ever since the unveiling of the Last Judgement thirteen years ago, attacks against it have never ceased. One would think his giant painting were somehow allied to the doctrines of the Lutheran heretics.

What excitement at the unveiling! What murmurings of wonder and horror!

Even the Cardinals Pole, Cervini and Contarini, generally so devoted to Michelangiolo, were disturbed.

"My young friend," Cervini said to me amidst all that bumble-bee buzz of prelates in red and black, "I have always shared your admiration for the Maestro. But in this work he has departed entirely from Christian tradition. In all the scenes of the Judgement we have known till now, the saints and martyrs are depicted as calm and contemplative, but here—" And he swung his arm like a pointer from Minos to the lunettes. "Look, messer Tomao, right up to the last file everyone is agitated, most agitated. They all seem stricken by some malady, woven together in a fabric of agitation, all, the Saved and the Damned, gazing toward the Judge."

"But is that not just?"

"Yes, but observe the Judge. That Christ with the face of an Apollo and the body of a Hercules, is he truly a Judge, separating the saved from the damned? No, he damns them all: his sentence is not a judgement; a judgement is a discrimination; But this is a condemnation, a universal condemnation. And that makes of this picture not a Universal Judgement but a *Dies Irae*, a Day of Wrath. I'm afraid our friend Michelangiolo shows his talent more in the sphere of the damned than in the saved. Those titans overflowing with too much flesh and blood—they offer rich alimentation to heretics."

"But your Reverence, don't you see echoes of Dante in all this? Those sinners pulled by demons to his Inferno. Those rising pulled by angels to his Purgatory. Those embracing—that group of the blessèd—are in Paradiso."

The Cardinal Cervini laughed.

"Blessèd! Those tormented writhing figures *blessèd?* Can you indicate to me a single expression of happiness in the entire work?"

"Those who are kissing there in the upper right."

"Look at them again, messer Tomao. Yes, they are embracing. But it is the embracement of tortured lovers. The embracements of Paolo and Francesca—in an ostensible Paradise that is really Hell."

"Well, I will grant you my Maestro Michelangiolo is at the opposite pole of the gentle Fra Angelico of Fiesole who hardly knew how to represent the damned, but only the saved."

The Cardinal gazed at me with a kind of lugubrious humor: solemn lips and twinkling eyes.

"Indeed! Indeed! Here even the Saved are damned. And what shall we say of that Savior, young, beautiful, immune to any grief . . . And do I imagine a certain resemblance to messer Tommaso de' Cavalieri?"

"The Maestro always avoids portraiture. You know that, your Reverence . . ."

"And the absolute nudities?"

"What you call absolute nudity simply conforms to Michelangiolo's notion of symbols of souls stripped of all that is terrestrial, summoned in all their nudity before the throne of God. Certainly those knotted anatomies and severe expressions arouse no one to sensuality. Michelangiolo is no Venetian."

"And Christ and his Saints are not ancient Gods and Titans."

But not all the debates I heard during that public unveiling were as good-humored as ours. Standing near his image Monsignor Biagio was lashing his serpent's tongue at the agent of the Cardinal Ercole Gonzaga, Nino Sernini who dared defend Michele's work.

"An outrage! An outrage! Nudes, nothing but nudes! In so holy a place, all showing their things!"

"But Monsignor, of those hundreds of figures, I see scarcely ten who 'show their things', as you so delicately put it."

"Ten is ten times too many! The entire fresco is rotten with heresy! Angels without wings! Saints without haloes! Saint Bartholomew beardless yet his beard is present in his flayed skin . . . which is not only heretical but illogical . . ."

"One hardly expects logic from artists."

". . . And worst of all, that Christ: beardless, too young, and utterly lacking in the majesty with which He must always be depicted."

"Do you discern," put in another member of the group (his back was to me) "anyone's portrait in that Christ?" Slow venom, just a pinch of maliciousness in the viola d'amore voice.

"The entire work is a portrait of heresy: of Michelangiolo the Lutheran. The entire fresco should be—"

"Do you not," pursued the urbane voice, "see in that Christ something of the lineaments of the Maestro's young friend messer Tommaso de' Cavalieri?"

"—plastered over! Hacked from the wall! There are a thousand heresies in it!"

And other voices, other quivering pointing fingers—

"There, there, don't you see where Maestro Michelangiolo has depicted himself?"

"Where?"

"There, in the flayed skin of San Bartolommeo."

"Ah, now I *do* see it! My God, what grief in that face! What suffering!"

"And what pride."

"Why pride?"

"Don't you see? The divine Michelangiolo feels himself skinned by the world, flayed by his enemies. And to such a degree does he dare to identify himself with the suffering Christ that he depicts his own portrait in the flayed skin as Christ's portrait was imprinted on Veronica's veil. Complacency in suffering always masks itself as pride. Surely the Maestro must know that. Does he not frequent the lessons of the Spirituali? Does he not realize that only one guilty of the greatest sin—which is the sin of pride—would dare identify himself with Christ on the Cross?"

And other voices:

"Now there, Monsignore, is a metamorphosis indeed. The mouth of Hell has taken the place of the altar-piece. So that henceforth the Holy Father will stare directly into the mouth of Hell as he celebrates Mass. Hardly propitious . . ."

The Holy Father was not present in the Chapel during the public opening. But he had rushed back from Bologna to celebrate Mass during the private opening on October 31st, the eve of All-Saints Day. What he felt then about celebrating Mass in the face of all those grinning skeletons and Charon's boat, nobody knew.

What hurt Michele most was the fact that some of his friends—the Cardinals belonging to the Reformist party—were among the most hostile critics. The English Cardinal Pole felt it was unsuitable for so many nude figures to be cavorting around in their painted Heaven (and Hell) in the house of God, or at least in the Chapel of the Pope.

And so did that gracious Venetian humanist, the Cardinal-before-priest Contarini, and Sadoleto and Cervini to whom I had spoken. In their condemnation of the Judgement the *Spirituali* found themselves aligned with the *Teatrini*: the fanatic Caraffa and other members of the Holy Office of the Inquisition!

I never learned what the Marchesa of Pescara thought of all this hullabaloo. I never even knew if she had visited the chapel.

Michele was in despair. He had painted himself a nest of enigmas, he was lying in a bed of thorns.

But Michele had his defenders too. The Cardinal Cornara openly declared that if Michelangiolo had painted for him just one of all those figures, he would pay him any price he demanded. And the Cardinal Alessandro Farnese, the Pope's own grandson, commissioned a large beautiful copy to be made by Marcello Venusti. And soon indeed there were so many copiers elbowing each other in the chapel that Michele said to me one day, with a bitter smile: "My most unforgivable sin is not the nudities but having provided occupation for so many mediocrities."

And then the buzz of theologians descended on that painted field. Oh how they probed and brewed honey for themselves and venom for their enemies! I was in the Chapel frequently and overheard the most astonishing dispute among these pedants. There were those who argued that Michelangiolo's Judgement supported the Catholic doctrine of the efficacy of Good Works ("For do you not see that the martyrs carry the *symbols* of their martyrdom—Saint Sebastian with his arrows, Saint Bartholomew with his flayed skin, Saint Catherine with her wheel— and they are *close* to the Savior in Paradise?"). To which others argued that Michele's fresco clearly (and heretically) supported the Lutheran doctrine of salvation by Faith alone ("But observe, Monsignore, those many nude souls in Paradise—look at that section in the upper right—whose hands are obviously *empty*! Yet they are also saved, close to the Divine Judge! The image is manifestly Lutheran!")

I duly reported all these interpretations to Michele who was already (against his will, of course) sketching out and preparing the Pauline frescoes for the adjacent chapel. "Oh let those learnèd divines put any meaning they wish upon my work. Those who understand art will understand it."

But the tumult over the nudities never ceased. In vain might Michele point out that there were nudities in the Orcagna Judgement he had seen as a child in Santa Croce or even in Fra Angelico's in San Marco or Barna's in the Collegiata of San Gimignano ("and obscene too, with devils poking spears up the culo's or vaginas of their sinners. There are no such lewdnesses in my Judgement! And what of Signorelli's panoplies of nudities in the Cathedral of Orvieto? Have you ever seen the Brixio Chapel, Tomao? No? . . . well you must see it. Signorelli populates the plain with naked men and women, resurrected souls or damned souls listening to the AntiChrist or riding astride winged demons, their lust expressed in the clutch of their thighs, the bulge of their bellies, their full buttocks (frequently *green*!) and breasts, the subtle smiles of enjoyed sin. Why, the walls of the Brixio Chapel simply pulsate with naked men and women and no one made—or makes—an outcry about that! Yet Signorelli's fresco was painted at least half a century before mine!!" He brooded a moment, then resumed less excitedly. "Perhaps that's the reason. The world has gloomed since the days of the Magnificent Lorenzo. The times are not good for art.")

Through all this tumult following the opening of the Last Judgement the Holy

Father preserved his calm diplomatic aloofness. He was a master of non-committal, Paul III, and if he could keep those mighty weights the Emperor Charles and King Francis always in balance, it was an easy matter for him to keep in balance the admirers and detractors of Michele's Judgement. Despite all the carping against him, the Holy Father did not hesitate to assign a new set of frescoes to Michelangiolo in the adjacent chapel named after himself; and grudgingly (as always) Michele began to prepare these works. Yet even through those seven years of the Pauline, violent attacks against the Last Judgement never ceased, and after a while we heard that even Pope Paul had been won over by the critics and was considering having the entire work destroyed, the very work which he himself had forced Michelangiolo to paint!

But Death destroyed him first.

And since Paul every Pope with the exception of Julius III, has at some time or other contemplated modifying or even destroying the Judgement. Even Cervini who was Michele's friend, when he became Marcello II associated himself with the censure but he died after only twenty-two days. And then came the terrible Neapolitan, Paul IV, who could not tolerate the work, and we expected it to be destroyed. No sooner elected he sent a messenger with a brusque order to put the Judgement "to rights" and received from Michele an agreement to do so together with an equally brusque admonition that the Holy Father focus his attention on setting the world "to rights."

And soon the Neapolitan was so concerned with the invasion of the Duke of Alba that he forgot about the Judgement.

And now at last it has come.

After thirteen years. After three years of pressure by the Council to induce the present Pius to take this step. Michele's indifference when he heard the news just two weeks ago.

"Soon, very soon, I'll be quite put to rights, Tomao mio," he said, smiling. "Without britches."

Westering. Yes. His sun is setting.

Yet he persists in chipping away at that sliver of a Christ.

Must write Lionardo.

III

Messer Donato Giannotti

Just this morning I received a letter from messer Tomao advising me that the old man is very ill and he is very likely reaching his end. And just as I was reading that news, a school of gondolas, black elegant dolphins, were leaping their jocular way across the lagoon from the Customs House to moor at the Palazzo of the Doges, all embroidery and dreamlike so one would never know it houses the most efficient and ruthless princedom in all Italy. I have been here in Venezia now for four years and I often think of old Michelangiolo down in Roma: the years we first met during the siege of Fiorenza, and later the years of our exile together in the Holy City. Though he was not really in exile. His ban was of his own making. Michelangiolo was the least political of us all, as I was perhaps the most. And yet there he was always at those gatherings in the lovely garden of the Cardinal Ridolfi, or in Luigi del Riccio's bank, or in Priscinese's printshop. There we were all of us Florentines: banned from the sweet nest of our native city: writing books, and sending sonnets to each other, and plotting how to overthrow the tyranny of the Duke Cosimo. And he part of our amiable circle and yet always in an orbit of his own.

So now when I learn that grand old Michelangiolo is soon to be gathered to his fathers, I am torn with a desire to rush to his bedside. I love Venezia but he did not, on the rare occasions he was here. I suppose the city is too frivolous for his taste:it is all moisty atmosphere and splendid palpitating sunsets and lacework of palaces and Murano glass and the dreamlike swish of gondolas along the Grand Canal and green mossy casements and staircases leading into water and even the cadence of these Venetians bobbing like tall masts at the Giudecca. No, this is not Michele's city, not even when the Grand Council made him the most attractive offers would he but stay. He needs the obdurance of stone and of mentality too. He has to hammer against his world as he hammers against the marble block. Then the sparks burst from his soul. He claims that he longs only for quiet and withdrawal. Michelangiolo, an eremite! He does not know his own polemical soul! He takes joy in conflict.

But now soon the conflict will end. For him. Not for us.

The Duke Cosimo remains, more in control than ever; and now after his cruel victory over Siena, his domain has grown, he has new ports upon the sea, and Florentine liberty, the liberty I fought for all my life seems more remote than ever. Ah those years when Michele was up at the hill of San Miniato building fortifications and hanging mattresses from the campanile and emplacing two columbines atop it. Fighting a war against the Medici while at the very moment he was supposed to be glorifying the Medici in their new sacristy he had been commissioned to build in San Lorenzo.

And soon that war was over. How could we fight when Spanish Imperials and Lutheran Landsknechts and Florentine traitors and Pope Clement VII himself had rung the noose tighter around us and Ferrucci killed in the Garfagnano and the Malatesta, ostensibly our condottiere, already treating with the enemy to betray us. When there were no more dogs and cats and rats to eat, we capitulated. What else was there to do?

After the fatigues of his body and the passions of his soul which messer Michelangiolo had suffered during that siege all of us old friends were very concerned about his health. In the fall of that year I met Giovan Battista Mini who had just come from the New Sacristy where he had seen the second female figure, that of Dawn, completed.

"And how does it compare with Night?" asked I.

"It supercedes it on all counts," he said. Have you ever opened your eyes at the moment of a woman's total surrender? . . . This is Michelangiolo's Dawn."

"And did you see the Maestro?"

"Yes. And he is gaunt, emaciated. I spoke to my son Antonio and to Buggiardini about him. And we all agreed that if the Maestro continues in this way, he will live but a short time. He works too much. He eats too little and bad food at that. He sleeps even less. For a month now he has been inflicted with headaches and dizziness. But everyone knows that these two ailments—one in his head and the other in his heart—can be cured because he is fundamentally healthy and knows the remedy for his troubles."

And the remedies were that he should cease to work winters in the cold wet atmosphere of the Sacristy where he was willfully killing himself. As for his heart, the Holy Father insisted that messer Michelangiolo come to an agreement with the Duke of Urbino with regard to that cursèd Tomb for his uncle. And finally the Pope simply ordered Michelangiolo under pain of excommunication that he wasn't to work on anything, whether sculpture or painting, except on the Medici tombs to which he had been assigned.

But of course the requests for other work never ceased. For example, the new governor of the city, Bartolommeo Valori, having been agent of Michelangiolo's reconciliation with the Holy Father after that siege (the governor of fortifications in a war against the Medici hiding out from the Medici Pope!), as I say, Valori, was now pressuring poor Michele for a statue and Michele didn't see how he could refuse.

When word of this came to Benvenuto della Volpaia at Roma he went to the Holy Father in order that Michelangiolo should be relieved of all these pressures. And Volpaia wrote to Michele:

His Holiness became very angry at your being pressed to take on other tasks and he said to me: 'Let him stick a paintbrush in his toes and make four dabs and say: here's your picture. As for that Apollo for Baccio Valori, just leave that to me.' And he told me that he had sent you a brief that you were not to work on anything other than the works for His Holiness. And he asked me whether this weren't enough to serve you as an excuse. And in truth he showed in every way, both in speech and act, that he is very sorry about your sorrows. And with regard to working in that chapel which will prove to be the death of you, he said: 'He musn't work there anymore.' He agrees with those of us who think you should have another studio either in a school or elsewhere. When I told him that you have need of a big room outside of the chapel, away from the chatter of the mob, he thought this made good sense and he asked whether the refectory of San Lorenzo would be satisfactory. I told him that in my opinion the best place would be Santa Caterina.

For his part, the Pope really did take to heart arranging the best possible settlement of the differences between Michelangiolo and the Duke of Urbino.

Ten years later I was requested by the Maestro to help adjudicate another dispute that had flared up during the final settlement of that Julius tomb. O poor Michele!—the tomb almost proved his own!

Well, after the siege, I was condemned to the frontier at least six miles outside of Florence but within twenty and forbidden to enter into any of the walled towns. Then I was confined to Bibbiena, and finally after the death of Duke Alessandro (praise be!) I returned to our patria. Michele was long gone to Roma when I returned to Fiorenza, and I too only remained a brief while, for realizing that Alamanno de' Pazzi was soon to be captured and taken to the Bargello, I left together with Benedetto Varchi for Bologna where all the Florentine exiles had converged under the leadership of Roberto Strozzi. So there we were in that city where the endless arcades are a maze of Bolognese casuistry and the towers lean more than at Pisa and in the echoing piazzas they talk and think only of the great sausages they eat and the heavy olive oil in which they bathe. There we were, a lean group of outraged Florentines, an austerity in all that fat.

Then after more than a year at Bologna, I came here to the Serenissima for the first time and fell in love with this admirable city whose history I have written and it has become a second homeland for me. Here I was honored with the friendship of the great letteratus Pietro Bembo now a Cardinal, and through Varchi at Padova where he was an instructor to the children of Filippo Strozzi, I met Iacopo Nardi, that sainted old man who deprived of all his possessions, continued to struggle against the disabilities of old age.

So we Florentines survive. We survive as exiles in the tradition of that supreme Exile, Dante Alighieri, and his bitterness echoes our own bitterness.

After the election of Paul III Farnese I gravitated as did so many other exiles down to Roma where I served as secretary of Cardinal Ridolfi. Roma still showed the signs of the Sack of 1527. The prosperous city of 50,000 had dwindled to

30,000; many palaces still showed the signs of fire and pillage; one of Michelangiolo's panels in the vault of the Sistine had been destroyed by a gunpowder explosion when the Imperial armies bivouacked in the Chapel and stabled their horses there. I met Michelangiolo often during those days: we would reminisce about the siege, the bullets flying past our ears from Giramonte, and the day the Florentines played calcio in the Piazza Santa Croce to show their contempt for the enemy camped on the heights two miles away, the cannon balls whizzing over their heads as they kicked the leathern ball.

When we met again in Roma, his love for messer Tomao and the Marchesa di Pescara had set him to floods of versifying. Michelangiolo has written poetry all his life, but the real outpouring of it began in his sixties, when he established himself permanently in the Holy City, swinging like an agitated compass needle between Cavalieri and Colonna, Athens and Jerusalem.

He also sent me a packet of madrigals addressed to some mysterious lady, 'fair and cruel'. He would not identify who this 'donna iniqua e bella' might be but had no hesitation showing me a sheaf of violent love poems addressed to her. Obviously his love for this mysterious lady was not in the same spiritual plane as his loves for messer Tomao and the Marchesa di Pescara. This was carnal love, yearning and unfulfilled, lashed with self-castigation, suffering from bondage to the flesh.

But his modesty about his literary accomplishments was excessive. He would send many of his poems to me (even those female-stung madrigals wherein he seemed to take a singular pleasure in his pain; even those passionate poems inspired by and addressed to Tomao) and I in turn would send them to his banker Luigi del Riccio for 'polishing' as he put it, although they needed no polishing. Indeed the occasional roughnesses were his personal mark, his stone cutter's mark, so to speak; these blocks of words were not infrequently as rough-hewn as his figures. He also sent his verses to the Marchesa and to his gossip Fra Sebastiano del Piombo, that amusing Venetian painter who had assumed ecclesiastical orders to entitle him to his Vatican post as Keeper of the Seal.

Oh, we were all writing poetry in those days: bankers like messer Luigi and politicians like myself; on occasion I would send one or two of mine to Luigi who passed it on to Michelangiolo. We were a sort of poetic turbine, a mill in the Chianti, and all of us (except Tomao) wrote poesie di occasione just to show our skilled hand.

When the Flemish capelmaestro Arcadelt set to music several of Michele's madrigals, he begged Luigi to compose the letter of thanks, containing a suitable gift; he felt he had little competence in these matters. And when Luigi's beloved nephew Ceccino Bracci died at the unjust age of sixteen, Michele and I and several of his friends sought to palliate Luigi's grief by writing commemoratory epigrams and epitaphs for the lad (really for the uncle, who was so addled by grief that he could not draw up proper letters of exchange for the Strozzi-Ulivieri bank and sent miscalculations to their Lyon branch). Michele soon tired of this game but continued to write doggerel in exchange for gifts of fish and sweetmeats, accompanying some of his memorial verses (supposedly of grief and condolence) with notes to messer Luigi: 'For the turtle-dove, Urbino will do one for the fish because he has gobbled it up . . . For the salted mushrooms . . . This stupid one, told a thousand times, for the *finocchio* . . . The trout say this, not I; so if you don't like the verses, don't marinate them again without pepper.' And so on. I was also expressing my condolences in suitable verses but without the culinary addenda.

That was the time Michelangiolo fell ill, dreadfully ill and we all feared for his life. He had fallen from the scaffolding of the Pauline (as he had earlier fallen from the scaffolding of the Judgement) and he would probably have died had not messer Luigi taken him into the Strozzi-Ulivieri palace and nursed him as a child. There was a great love between these two; as great a love as between the old man and messer Tomao, although I think that if Michele was a father to Tomao he was (despite the fact that he was much older than Luigi) a sort of son to the banker. He let him handle all his practical affairs, he leaned on him for all practical advice.

He even permitted messer Luigi to gather together for publication a packet of his verses which had been circulating for years among all of his friends. Michele never took his versifying seriously, writing poems on the backs of household accounts or on draft pages of letters to his brothers or nephew, or over beautiful drawings in brown ink or black or red chalk.

And so when messer Luigi proposed that the poems be published, Michele rather apologetically gave his nulla osta (which the Holy Office today probably would not have given).

Alas! the poems were never published. Perhaps to Michelangiolo's relief although I have no doubt about the sincerity of his grief although the two had had a falling-out over some matter or other and messer Luigi showed me, with tears in his eyes, the letter in which old Michelangiolo gave vent to one of his celebrated bursts of rage and signed himself

Michelangiolo Buonarroti

Not a painter or a sculptor or an architect,
but whatever you want; but not a drunkard
as I told you in your house.

Later I learned that the quarrel was occasioned by an engraved portrait which del Riccio had commissioned, and which Michelangiolo thought made him look like a drunkard.

"O that impossible old man! As if anybody in his right mind could—"

But Michele was given to these unpredictable turns of the compass even with his dearest friends; the winds of mistrust will suddenly shift quarter. Later it was the turn of Cavalieri who would give up his life for the Old One and who, for all his nobility and elegance and status in society and high position as a Conservatore of the City of Roma, is always so self-effacing and humble in the presence of Buonarroti—here is messer Tomao unjustly attacked for ingratitude because of some imagined offense he had given the old man. Well, that rent was fortunately mended, as was the rent with Luigi before he died. And this cheers those of us who love Michelangiolo because he needs our love, he suffers from the lack of love, and though he is not much given to tenderness (what Florentine is?) he has great need of tenderness from his friends, especially these last terrible years.

But in those earlier years in Roma he had been more open, one might say, more willing, even if reluctant, to share his innermost convictions with those of us who loved and admired him.

Fortunately, that quarrel with messer Luigi proved to be a momentary storm in a sunny sky. Soon Michele was again asking del Riccio's advice on all sorts of problems: the recent fire in the Pauline Chapel, and of course his financial problems. These financial problems existed only in the mind of Michelangiolo. When news came that Luigi had arrived in Lyon ill, Michele wrote that all his friends, especially he and I, were very grieved about his illness and hoped that with God's help it would prove to be but a small matter.

Michele showed me that letter and I was shocked (but kept the mask on) by the abruptness with which the Maestro went on, in the very next paragraph to lament that since he had lost the income of the ferry at Piacenza and since he couldn't remain in Roma without an income (!) he was thinking of spending as quickly as possible the little he had (!!) on hostelries, rather than "staying cooped up in Roma like a beggar. Therefore I'm inclined, if nothing else befalls, to make a pilgrimage to St. James of Galicia after Easter, and if you haven't returned yet, to start from wherever I hear you may be."

Of course all this gloomy talk about having no income and being poor and so on was discounted by the Maestro's old friends. He was not poor; indeed the value of his real estate holdings alone was considerable: the sprawling house on Macel de' Corvi, and up in Tuscany, the farms at Settignano and Pozzolatico, and the new house on Via Ghibellina which he was building for his nephew; not to mention whatever treasure in gold ducats and scudi he had stashed around the house in iron boxes. It is true he lived simply, ate austerely and dressed without ribands or furbelows. But his cloths were of the finest quality and his mode of life was not due to want of money but a desire to live franciscanly, so to speak.

Ahimè! he never got the chance to take that pilgrimage with messer Luigi! For del Riccio died in the Autumn among those French and surely he was sincerely mourned by his friends, without a slew of commissioned poetical effusions.

And five months later the Marchesa of Pescara also departed for a better life and four months after that the Ultimate Seal was stamped upon the brow of Fra Sebastiano del Piombo. So those years of the Pauline were terrible years for Michele, losing several of his most belovèd friends. For I had observed from the start of our relationship the uncommon joy he took in his friends, especially those of us who had a literary turn.

And the Roma of Paul III was as it were a flaring up of Leo's Roma. A gathering of Florentines, then pro- and now anti-Medici. We all lived in the shade of two ambitious cardinals, Salviati and Ridolfi, who in turn were financed by the King of France and Piero Strozzi; and all of us worshipped in old Michelangiolo a relic of the Republic we had loved and lost. We lived in a changed atmosphere of hopes that proved vain; insurrection against the brutal Medici was always on our minds. And into this circle occasionally would wander that venerable Florentine messer Michelangiolo in his brown cloak and doublet and black floppy velvet beret, and soft cordovan boots, a taciturn old man with a gray flecked beard wiry and sparse as a bush sprinkled with snow.

The only non-Florentine in this company was messer Tommaso. What most impressed me about this young (at that time) nobleman was the grace with which he warded off the Maestro's immoderate praise of his 'attainments'. For in truth—and Tomao knew this better than all of us—the young man's 'attainments' consisted primarily of his beauty and his courtesy and his devotion to the Old One.

Michelangiolo was then sending me his poems, with such notes as "I'd appreciate it if you'd see if you can polish a bit these badly-made things. . ." His "badly-made things" were frequently astonishing verses which he refused to take seriously and always seemed embarrassed by the praise of all his friends, especially del Riccio and myself.

Oddly enough, though many of the most beautiful of these verses were inspired by and addressed to messer Tomao, I never heard him praise those poems either to the Maestro or to any of us. Tomao's silence was ambiguous: I never knew whether it was embarrassment or modesty. Perhaps he didn't feel qualified to make literary judgements. Or perhaps he was too moved for words.

But I have observed that frequently those gifted with extraordinary beauty—whether men or women—take refuge in that beauty. When they are bidden to say something, they smile those ravishing smiles, or tilt their heads, and that is the end of it; they seem to emanate significances beyond words but perhaps they are merely taking refuge behind that fortress, Beauty.

And just as messer Tomao spoke not at all about Michele's poetry, neither—unlike the rest of us—did he write poetry, nor did he paint or sculpt or practice the art of architecture which he was vaguely considering at that time. I am told that some of his early sketches had been extravagantly praised by Michelangiolo but that merely proves that even giants may be blinded by love. To say his talents were modest would be a gross exaggeration. I certainly have never seen any design by Cavalieri that merited anyone's praise. He who possesses beauty of person and sweet speech and graceful manners is not spurred to create those qualities in some work of art. He is himself a work of art.

But Cavalieri ultimately did enjoy a solid reputation as a connoisseur. He has gathered in his Palace one of the finest collections of antiquities in Roma—but possesses very few works by Michelangiolo other than a few drawings and Tomao's portrait. He is also a Conservator of the Urbs and as such has been deputized with the carrying-out of Michele's old plans for the reorganization of the Campidoglio.

Most important to all of Michele's friends is Tomao's devotion to the Old One. That has never diminished; not even the years and his marriage and his two sons and his new dignities and his functions in the Confraternity—none of this has mitigated Tomao's devotion to Michelangiolo. Until I left Roma, he was at the Maestro's studio almost every day.

And surely now, though Michele's vision has blurred, he must see messer Tommaso de' Cavalieri exactly for what he is: a modest lover of the arts beloved by the greatest maker of the arts.

※

One beautiful Spring morning—it must have been twenty years ago during the latter years of the Pontificate of Paul III when Michele was still completing the new chapel bearing the Pope's name—I was with the Maestro up at the Camp-idoglio where we had been examining the site which the Holy Father had in mind to restore. And whatever artistic project came into the Vicar's mind—be it a new cornice and fenestrations for the Farnese Palace, or fortifications for the Borgo, or setting to order the ancient Campidoglio, Michelangiolo had to add that project to whatever other task he had then under way. So though he had not yet completed the Pauline, and the works at Saint Peter's were now entirely his responsibility, he was supposed to restore and revamp the ancient Capital Hill as well.

It certainly did need restoration.

The Pope had been ashamed of the wrecked and neglected state of the ruins at the time of the Emperor Charles V's visit during Eastertide of 1536; ironically it was this very Emperor who was responsible for adding new ruins to the old when his troops (including German Lutheran lance-knights) had sacked and plundered the Urbs only nine years before. At any rate, the Pope hastily cleaned up the areas adjacent to the route the Emperor would take. Wooden arches, painted to imitate marble, were prepared as the Holy Roman Emperor's entourage rode through the Forum of the ancient Roman Emperors. It was after that visit that Paul proposed to Michelangiolo the reorganization of the Campidoglio overlooking the Forum, so that Roma (which unlike our Fiorenza lacks a proper civic center) should have a secular center for its Senate and Conservators, as it has a religious center in the Vatican and St. Peter's.

It certainly did, as I say, need restoration (and even now, almost three decades later, the works have still not been carried out though messer Tomao I understand is pressing the Deputies to effectuate Michelangiolo's plans). The ground has not yet been leveled; the Pope wanted to make of this Campidoglio, center of ancient Roma, the Capital of Christian Roma. But then (as now) it is but a heap of wrecked antiquity; the ancient temple of Juno which Michele wishes to transform into the Roman Senate, is a total wreck through whose crumbling stones one might look down into the Forum where the cattle still graze. Across the Forum we could see the Palatine Hill wherefrom the Caesars once ruled the world. Now the hill is called Baa-latine. The shepherd's edict has supplanted the Caesar's, and a fellow who had leaned his rough barked crook against an olive tree, was urinating over Cicero's orations. The space to the left where Michele wants to erect a matching palazzo for the Palace of the Conservatori is still open and one can see clear up to the Church of the Aracoeli on the hill. A steep staircase leads to that church.

"Poor lad" the Maestro murmured, and I knew he was thinking of the Cecchini bust in the Church which he had designed at the importunities of messer Luigi. Only the equestrian statue of Marcus Aurelius stood in the middle of the Capitoline. Patrician in every curve of the great horse and its noble rider, glints of its gilding still flashing through scratches in the centuries-old patina. "A stupendous work", Michele said. "I opposed having it transported here from the Lateran Palace. The Holy Father overruled me. I am always being overruled by Holy Fathers. Now he wants to bring the colossal Dioscuri with their horses here, too, and I suppose I shall have to agree although I have different plans. At any rate, I have agreed to design a pedestal. And I shall make an oval pedestal which will echo the shape of the Piazza. For echoing is a basic rule in all the arts, even this art of architecture which is not my craft. But there are basic principles which apply to all the arts. And so, one extrapolates. Over here in front of the Senators Palace, I'm planning to set the ancient river gods Nile and Tigris (which we'll transform into a Tiber by changing his head and adding the Twins) now lying neglected over there. And a double staircase on the Senate facade facing this space . . ."

He wore that dreamlike look whenever he talks of projects a-building in his mind.

Just as we were descending from the Campidoglio (a precarious path which Michelangiolo intends to replace with a gentle ramp slightly stepped like those whereby one rides horseback into a castle), we were greeted by jovial cries of Salve! Salve! and there, arm-in-arm, were Luigi del Riccio and Antonio Petreo at the bottom of the hill.

It seems they had been strolling around Rome discussing how many days Dante had spent in Hell—an incongruous conversation for so sunny a day, but they seemed to have taken great joy in it.

"Ah welcome!" cried Michele, his creased leathery face breaking into a quick smile. Despite his frequent grumbling against the world, the old fellow takes great delight in company. "What good fortune brings you here?"

"Good fortune indeed," said Antonio, "since we've met you. Early this morning messer Luigi and I had to discuss some business relating to our most Reverend Cardinal Ridolfi. And since we've talked all this out, we thought to wander a bit along these solitary places toward St. John the Lateran. And if you're disposed to stroll with us it would be indeed a lucky morning for us."

Michelangiolo smiled. "If your felicity this morning depends on having us for company, you have found it. And I will walk with Antonio because I see that Donato has already set aside a special account (to speak like a merchant) with messer Luigi that he might enjoy him alone and not share his pleasure with the rest of us."

All this was simply a way of saying that I had drawn messer Luigi apart for a moment and whispered to him.

Our Michelangiolo is sometimes given to such elaborate turns of speech, always accompanied by an ironic flicker of a smile in his beard. I suppose the irony was directed against himself, usually so direct and even brutal in his discourse, sometimes wounding like a true Florentine with no hair on his tongue. But in the company of letterati, I have seen Michelangiolo adopt this elevated form of speech as if it were a kind of passport that entitled him, whom he considered unlettered, into that company. The fact is that he was not unlettered at all; and no sooner was the Florentine Academy established, he became, even in his absence, the Muse of all those learnèd men.

Now he was talking about the fatal divisions that constantly keep our Tuscany in a state of turmoil and ruin. But Luigi, sniffing the way the wind was blowing, said—"If we permit messer Michelangiolo to remain in these precincts, we'll talk of nothing else this morning but the complaints and quarrels of our time. Let's not get embroiled in Grand Councils and Senates and laws and customs and civil problems with which the Lord has provided us a-plenty. A prudent man should simply accommodate himself to His will. And so, strolling toward San Giovanni Laterano, let's return to our original conversation since we're run into so great a Danteist."

"You're quite right to call Michelangiolo a great Danteist," said I. "Certainly I don't know anyone who has the Poet so locked up in his memory."

"Oh no!" interjected the Maestro. "Everyone knows I am a sculptor and I suppose a painter and an architect but no one will believe I am a Danteist."

"Now you make me laugh," said Luigi. "Haven't you told me that when Orcagna, that ancient noble painter, painted the Inferno the second time in the chapel of Santa Maria Novella, he closely followed Dante's description? Obviously he must have been a student of the Divine Comedy. Why could you not have made the same sort of study?"

I was amused to observe how, in his great modesty, Michelangiolo skirmished like a lively fencer, protesting that literary commentary was not his profession.

By this time we were strolling through the Campo Vacina, our auditors a flock of goats grazing amongst the broken columns. We walked through the Arch of

Titus and ahead of us loomed the round brown Colosseum. Antonio was in the midst of a long disquisition on the necessity for artists of all sorts—sculptors, painters, architects,—to know not only Dante but all the sciences as well. Painting, he believed, had great similarities with poetry. To imitate human and divine actions, the painter like the poet must not only be aware of stories, true or fictitious, but also, in order to be able to well imitate the movements of natural living bodies, animals, and especially men, the painter should have made many dissections, taking into consideration not only all the parts of the human body that one sees but also those within, unseen, such as muscles veins nerves bones . . .

He was quite hot with this theme, flinging his arms against the ruins, those bones of empire. And Luigi turned to Michelangiolo and said— "Didn't you tell me that one day when you had the leisure you wanted to write about painting?"

And when old Michelangiolo nodded accord, Luigi went on—"Well then, how can you say that you don't have cognition of those sciences without whose help you couldn't compose any of your works? Every time we hear it said that someone is a good painter, we must assume that he not only knows how to paint well, but he must also have notions about the natural sciences and mathematics."

And while he was thus winging along on his argument Antonio interrupted midflight—excusing his interruption with the remark that if what messer Luigi said about any good painter were true, then it was all the more true of Michelangiolo who superseded anyone living or dead not only in painting, but also in sculpture or architecture.

At this, Michelangiolo, who always took praise reluctantly, put in— "I just want to say the truth. It seems to me that I'm being led to such a pass that if messer Donato doesn't come to my aid, I'll become like Aesop's raven: so much so that if the legitimate owners of these ornaments with which you have invested me should see through them to my nudity within, they'll have good reason to laugh!"

"Well, said I chuckling, "Don't expect any help from me since not only will I not see to it that your friends here cease to adorn you with those ornaments which you say are not yours; but I will add still another, affirming that you yourself are as great a Poet as anyone else in our time."

And when Luigi added his encomium to mine (we were approaching the Lateran now, a scud of cloud sitting directly over it), Michelangiolo became visibly embarrassed.

"You put me into great confusion this morning. When I consider the benevolence you all display toward me I can't imagine that you are merely mocking me. On the other hand, all these compliments make me suspicious."

"Do you deny what is known to all the world?" replied Luigi. "Isn't everyone in Roma these days reading your sonnets and your madrigals with delight and admiration?"

At which Luigi began to hum the setting which Archadelt had recently made of:

> Deh, dimmi, se l'alma di costei
> Fosse pietosa com' ha bell' il volto,
> S'alcun saria sì stolto . . .

He sang it, I must admit, more croakingly-crow than nightingale-mellifluous but the music was on his face if not in our ears.

"—and" (without permitting the stubborn old sculptor to interrupt) "the epigram which you just wrote about your figure of Night in the Medici Tombs; replying to that other one penned up in Fiorenza by I don't know who . . . Could it be better woven by anyone in the Florentine Academy? more sententious?"

> Caro m'è 'l sonno e più l'esser di sasso,
> Mentre che 'l danno e la vergogna dura;
> Non veder, non sentir m'è gran ventura;
> Però non mi destar, deh! parla basso.

Thus at last he was conquered by our affectionate insistence. And Luigi certainly helped to break down his resistance by reciting his poetry for although the Old One is always pooh-poohing his writings he never fails to take pleasure in hearing it recited by his friends. And so yielding to our entreaties, Michele entered the discussion. The nugget of the debate was this: whether Landino was correct in his asserveration that Dante must have consumed the night of Venerdi Santo and all Saturday to visit the Inferno and climb from the center of the earth to the surface of the other hemisphere, or whether, rather, Antonio Petreo was correct in claiming that the Poet must have spent in that journey three natural days from the evening of Holy Friday to the evening of Palm Sunday.

So, strolling now in a new foursome—I arm-in-arm with the Maestro, and Luigi with Antonio Petreo—Michelangiolo said:

"Dante says that night had taken two steps; and the third was already drooping its wings. That is, the third night was already almost completed. You understand this metaphor taken from the birds who when they are about to land, fly with wings held low. Thus Dante shows that the end of night was nigh and the sun rising at the horizon.

And so he spent seven natural days in this entire journey: two in Hell, one in climbing from the center to the surface of the earth in the other hemisphere, and four in climbing and encircling the entire mountain of Purgatory, and searching for the plain at its summit. So now you understand my opinions on this voyage, and as you see I have attempted more than I promised. Which I've done willingly, as much to entirely satisfy your desire as to discuss with you this Poet of whom I'm very fond. You know that you've made me enter upon material which is beyond my power, and each of you would have dealt with it better than I. However, to please you I've done that which doesn't apply to me. And I'm not so sorry seeing that I've done a pleasant thing and having conducted Dante to Heaven, I believe I've satisfied you. Now you follow him; as for me, it'll be sufficient to go there after death if God considers me worthy."

We all smiled at this rigmarole of a speech. He was given to that, at times: either impenetrable silence or terse flashing of a sword or this roundabout in which he seemed to take pleasure as if he were drawing with a pen, the very *ductus* of the discourse leading him on and on.

Luigi asked if Michelangiolo had observed how much time Dante spent in Heaven now that Michelangiolo had led him there.

Michele replied that there is no reference to time in Paradiso because while there is motion in heaven there is no distinction of days which are of the earth since the sun doesn't rise above and sink below the horizon.

All this while we had been walking past the gardens and vineyards from the Porta del Popolo going up Via Flaminia toward Ponte Molle. Michele mentioned a group of young people in Fiorenza who have founded the Accademia Fiorentina degli Umidi—

"—Umidi or Umili?" laughed Petreo. "Are they Humid or Humble?"

"It is indeed a strange title for an Academy," said Michele. "But there it is, according to my nephew. It's based apparently on the cult of writing and reading good vulgate Fiorentino and the major luminary of that cult—Dante Alighieri. When I have finished painting this Crucifixion of Peter, I shall have completed my seventieth year and that is too old for the art of fresco—"

"—but not too old for marble-carving?" messer Luigi interrupted.

Michele ignored the ironic admiration.

"—so I would hope the Holy Father might give me leave to return to my own native Fiorenza . . ."

"And the works at St. Peter's?"

He frowned. "Già. Già. I cannot leave those to be ruined by my enemies. But if I could return to Fiorenza it would be only to learn from these young people. They might know how much time Dante spent in Paradise."

"Well," said Antonio, "talking our way along, we've reached the Ponte Molle. Better to turn here without crossing the bridge because we would have to make too long a journey. And if there's time before entering Roma we can take several turns in one of those gardens along the way. The gardens of the Bishops Peruzzi or the Cardinal San Giorgio would permit us entrance."

So we wandered into those gardens, the delightful conversation continuing until we reached beyond San Giovanni and it was time for lunch. We agreed to resume our talk in the afternoon, meeting near Priscinese's house.

"Who is this Priscinese?"

"What? You don't know messer Priscinese?"

"I've heard of a certain messer Francesco Priscinese praised as a man who is widely informed and has set into our Tuscan tongue the rules for speaking Latin. I understand the work is highly praised by the erudite."

"The very man," said I. "And certainly anyone who wants to learn the art of speaking and reading and writing good Latin owes him great obligation, since he's reduced matters in such an easy way that one can learn by oneself without a teacher."

"Certainly he deserves to be praised very much for that. He almost makes me wish to study his book . . . "

Our Michele was always self-conscious about his lack of Latin, especially after the petition of notable Florentines was sent to Ravenna to bring back Dante's bones to his native city, and Michelangiolo found he was the only one who perforce signed his name in Italian.

"I've heard it said that Cato the Censor, the Roman citizen, learned to read Greek in his eightieth year. Would it therefore be such a big thing if Michelangiolo Buonarroti, Florentine citizen, learned Latin in his seventieth?"

"It really wouldn't be! And I strongly recommend you to set about this task. Especially because I know that you will be helped not only by his book but by Priscinese himself whenever you wish."

"Not now. We'll think another time whether at my age I should set myself to learn Latin as did Cato, many years older than I, with Greek. After lunch we'll meet at Priscinese's house, if you tell me where it is."

"There is no need for that", said Luigi. "Stay and eat with us. And then we can resume our conversation."

But Michelangiolo refused. He said that he wished to stay alone for a bit: he could not dine with us because he took too much pleasure in our company! And he didn't want to take so much pleasure because these were rather times to weep than to dance.

Petreo looked most perplexed at this unexpected remark. But I and Luigi were not so surprised. We had often observed these sudden swings of mood. He had that humor, old Michelangiolo. In the midst of joy he sought reasons to weep as if joy were either sinful or less meritorious or less worthy of a man than grief. He preferred, one might say, the night to the day and indeed I have heard him read stupendous sonnets on Night. He was, I suppose, a poet of darkness but it would be untrue to think that he was all gloom and solemnity. Not at all: no one took more joy in the company of his friends and his irony was a good Tuscan blade: his wit could be pungent as manure; and he laughed often and heartily: and you could see the wrinkles of a lifetime of laughing around his flat eyes. But in the very midst of such pleasure he would sometimes be stricken with a notion that it was illicit. He always felt that he wanted what he did not want.

And yet he wanted it.

A complicated man, our Michelangiolo. But not the Hangman some have depicted him. If he hung anybody it was himself.

And then before he went off alone he delivered himself of a little homily on the salutary effects of thinking about death. Only so can one discover and take pleasure in oneself. He spoke about death, or rather the awareness of death, as if it were a deeper joy, a truer joy, than mere merriness and good spirits, the company of friends, a fine meal, a lively mistress. The thought of death alone, says he, maintains us united without permitting us to be robbed by relatives (he was obviously thinking of those worthless brothers of his) or friends, great maestri (and I wondered what great maestri he might have been thinking of, though I knew I was having more than his share of troubles with the San Gallo clique at the Fabbrica), ambition, avarice, and all the other vices and sins that rob man of himself and dissipate his forces. O he exclaimed, warming to his theme, how marvelous is the effect of this thought of death which by its very nature destroys everything, yet conserves and maintains those who think about it and defends us from all human passions. And then he recited a little madrigal he had written in which only the thought of death defends him against his love for an iniquitous and beautiful woman.

> Non pur la morte, ma 'l timor di quella
> Da donna iniqua e bella
> Ch'ognor m'ancide, mi difende e scampa:
> E se talor m'avvampa
> Più che l'usato il foco in ch' io son corso,
> Non trovo altro soccorso
> Che l'immagin sua ferma in mezzo il core;
> Ché dove è morte non s'appressa amore.

> Not only death, but the mere fear of death
> defends me and sets me free
> from that lady lovely and iniquitous
> who tortures me unceasingly
> And if at times the fire into which I've fallen
> flares more than usual
> No other aid I find
> than that image fixed at my heart's core
> For where Death dwells Love cannot draw near

After he had gone, cloaked like Charon down the long avenue of pines, I asked Luigi:

"And who is that *donna iniqua e bella?*"

"I cannot imagine," said Luigi. "He has written a whole series of such verses to some mysterious lady beautiful and cruel. And he insists these be included in the collection we are planning to publish. But I have no idea who the lady might be . . ."

In the afternoon we met again at Priscinese's printshop. And I provoked the Maestro from the start. I suggested a new subject for the afternoon's discussion. "I don't know," I said, "whether messer Michelangiolo will agree because he is so fond of Dante that whatever he wrote seems to him to have been dictated by the Truth. It's true that Dante was so excellent in doctrine and had such knowledge of human action that one might assume that whatever he has written is either true or at least very close to the truth. But with all that, he was a man, and if he erred on something we should not be surprised."

My remarks were not intended solely for the Maestro. Too many of my countrymen look upon the Poet as Divine, the Fifth Gospel: Mathew Mark Luke John and Dante Alighieri. But Michelangiolo, who was himself considered Divino, immediately took fire at my aspersion.

"As you've seen I read this poet rather diligently, and I've yet to find anything in his work that I don't believe was said after consideration and on a good foundation. And if you can show me anything, of course, I'll admit to have been greatly mistaken."

"That would be very difficult," I said.

"Speak, please."

"Don't you think Dante erred in placing Brutus and Cassius in Lucifer's mouth?"

"Oh, that is an old quarrel, and has been confuted by others."

"It's been confuted by others, as you say, but if you can't confute it better I still won't change my opinion that Dante made a very great blunder in placing Brutus and Cassius in Hell for having slain Caesar."

"Just what are you trying to say?"

"I say that Dante erred most gravely in placing Brutus and Cassius in Lucifer's mouth, because thereby he showed that he was ignorant of history not to have known that Caesar was the tyrant of their country. Because, if he had known, he would not have assigned so grave a punishment upon those who slew Caesar. Secondly, he showed that he didn't understand the universal consensus of mankind, all of whom speaking with one mouth exalt those who kill tyrants to set their country free. Besides this, he showed that he didn't know that all the laws in the world confer the greatest and most honored rewards—and not the vilest punishments—upon those who extinguish tyrants. He showed that he didn't know how greatly the Roman people honored the first Brutus and Valerio Publicola for having expelled the Tarquins from Roma and restoring liberty to the city."

And I went on to cite all the tyrants in Roman history cast from the Tarpeian

Rock and the honorable list of those who had destroyed them. "And since we cannot attribute ignorance to the Supreme Poet, he knew what he was doing when he assigned those tyrannicides Brutus and Cassius to the bottommost pit of Hell while, to the contrary, they should have been honored for their deed. I don't intend," said I, "to make a diatribe against Dante—"

"—O but you have!" Michele interrupted hotly. "It won't be difficult to demonstrate the falsity of such a malevolent concept that you have fabricated of Dante. Now I see that when you said—yesterday or today, or whenever it was— that you didn't understand Dante you spoke the truth even though you didn't know it."

O he was in the lists now, sitting straight up on his charger, and bearing down on me with a long lance. And yet I was chuckling within. I could never bear this grand man any ill will, for all his tangled reasoning.

"I understand by this," I said, putting as much respectful sweetness into my reply as I could, "that he placed Brutus and Cassius in Lucifer's mouth and I would have placed them in the most honored part of Paradise."

Luigi and Petreo burst out laughing but Michele went right on:

"—that Brutus and Cassius deserve the praises which all the world has given them, I concur in altogether with you; nevertheless Dante doesn't deserve to have been spoken of by you in such a manner, blaming him as much as you have."

"You're saying two contradictory things! Since you want these two to be praised and honored and you don't want me to blame Dante who has vituperated them!"

"Deh, pazienza! Listen to me a while."

"Speak. I listen willingly."

We all dispersed ourselves comfortably around the shop as the Maestro, inflamed by my accusations against his belovèd Poet, sailed into me, banners flying, cannon booming. Dante, said he, was not unaware of the fact that Caesar was a tyrant and yet not contradictory in placing the slayers of that tyrant in the deepest pit of Hell. I exchanged glances with messer Luigi and Antonio. The old man was in a bind and we all wondered how he would get out of it. He hated tyrants and had he not made a Brutus (commissioned by my Cardinal Ridolfi at my instigation) in honor of the new Brutus, Lorenzino? He hated tyrants but he revered Dante and here was I accusing his noble Poet of ignorance.

His lips quivered in his beard. He quoted from the first Canto to demonstrate that Dante well understood the nature of tyrants by placing them in the first Girone of the Seventh Circle in boiling blood. And then he quoted from the Twelfth Canto:

Io vidi gente sotto insino al ciglio
E 'l gran Centauro disse: ei son tiranni . . .

And then he went on to cite all the tyrants mentioned by the Poet: Attila, Tarquinio, Dionisio, Siracusa and many others, and who was placed in Purgatory and who in Hell and the suitability of their punishments and purgations. And warming now to his theme and perambulating amongst the wooden presses, the stacks of typeface, the page proofs still smelling of ink, he pointed out that Dante would probably consider that whoever kills a tyrant does not even kill a man but a beast in human form and how Cato died for the liberty of Roma which proves that—

And I thought—O pathetic wonderful old man—supporting my thesis to the hilt by way of refuting it! He was orating at far greater length and with far more passion against tyrants than in defense of his Dante. And I knew and I could see by the flicking buds of laughter in Priscinese's and Luigi's cheeks that they realized as I did that at this stage of his peroration at any rate our messer Michelangiolo was talking really about the late Duke Alessandro rather than the Divine Comedy.

—that in Dante's judgement Caesar was a tyrant and hence justly assassinated and Brutus and Cassius deserve most honorable rewards and not most vituperous punishment.

And he stopped for a moment, his breast heaving. I said softly:

"Well then your conclusion finally is that Dante was not ignorant—"

"Of course not!"

"—and that he knew very well what he had written?—"

"Certo!"

"—that is, that is, that Brutus and Cassius were good valorous citizens? And nevertheless he placed them in Lucifer's mouth! . . . to reward them for their goodness and their valor? If so, Dante was not ignorant, but wicked, indeed criminal!"

O now the flat gray eyes glinted, the lips quivered, the deep voice took on a stridency, a cutting edge.

"You lack patience! Listen me out and perhaps you will quiet down. As you might have considered, Dante punishes the gravest sins in those circles which little by little are closest to the center so that in the last circle he punishes traitors who are separated into four categories—since these wickednesses are committed against four persons, that is—against relatives, against one's country, against one's friends, and against Imperial and Divine Majesty. This fourth species of betrayal, as more serious than the others, is punished in the last Sphere of the Ice, that is, in that circle surrounding the center that is called the Giudecca. And following Christian tradition (because he desired that by God's special providence, the dominion of the world should be the power of the Romans and then of the Emperors), it seemed to him that whoever betrays the majesty of the Roman Emperor must be punished in that same place and with the same punishment as he who betrays Divine Majesty. Therefore having to take example of those who had betrayed the Roman Emperor, he chose Brutus and Cassius who slew Caesar and in his person betrayed the said Roman Emperor."

"Couldn't he have chosen others?!" I expostulated. "So many Roman emperors have been slain that there weren't lacking persons to be placed in those mouths!"

"Well," said Michelangiolo (and I saw in his eyes the cunning of his father the Magistrate and the generations of Buonarroti magistrates) "he needed very famous examples and he didn't find anyone more famous—or equal—to Brutus and Cassius. And it didn't seem to him that he was slandering them since he wasn't setting them there as Brutus and Cassius but as those who betrayed the Imperial Majesty which he meant by Caesar, thereby exculpating him of the infamy of having reduced his country into servitude and having been a tyrant."

O now the Old Man was dancing on the head of a pin! More adroitly than all the schoolmen including Anselm and Aquinas! He was demonstrating (or thought he was) that Brutus and Cassius were not Brutus and Cassius at all! Or better, that they were and were not at the same time. And that Caesar was Caesar the tyrant (who deserved to be slain) and Caesar the Holy Emperor (who deserves only reverence)!

And I knew I could refute him but it was too easy and I forbore. He was an old man and divine in his art and I loved him. Should one not, out of love, read men's minds and not their mouths? Who can call messer Michelangiolo a foolish man even though he was now speaking the most foolish words, and contradicting himself, for all his disputatious subtlety, in a cobweb of Yes's and No's.

"Tell me," I said, keeping a tight bit on my irony. "When Dante says that he saw in Limbo among excellent men:

Cesare armato con gli occhi grifagni

Why did he place him in Limbo? Did he set him there as Ceasar or as the Imperial Majesty?

The old man flushed. You could see the darkening blood rush even behind the beard. I had hit him hard.

"Oh, you almost make me lose my temper!"

"Lose your temper as you please because if you can't bring up a better argument, Dante remains in my eyes as one who shows little judgement."

"You don't want to understand!"

"I understand very well what you say. And I believe that Dante, by Brutus and Cassius didn't signify Brutus and Cassius but those who betray Imperial Majesty, and by Caesar he doesn't mean Caesar but the Imperial Majesty as you have said. All this I believe—"

(but of course I didn't believe any of it but how could I wound that splendid old man, especially now that I saw how easy it was to wound him, how easy to box him in a corner. For one who lives by contradictions as he does, all one need do is seize one of the threads of contradiction by the edge and unfurl it to the end, and you will have your man in a net of his own making) "But that Caesar should be in Limbo, and Brutus and Cassius in Lucifer's mouth, displeases me too much . . ."

"I see that I've labored in vain, since you're so stubborn that it doesn't matter what I say. But still I'll tell you this also. How do you know whether Dante didn't think Cassius and Brutus had made a mistake in slaying Caesar? Only more troubles came into the world as a result of that assassination. Don't you see what a miserable succession of emperors followed? Wouldn't it have been better had he lived and carried out his ideas?"

Well, thought I, now you've shifted ground, Michelangiolo mio. But he glared at me, stubborn in his defense as he had been up at the bastions of San Miniato, the colombines flashing from his eyes, the line of earthworks and redoubts along his protruding cheekbones.

He was besieged.

"His idea! His idea!" I shouted. "His chief idea was to be crowned king."

"I grant that. But wouldn't that have been a lesser evil than that which followed? How do you know that he might not in time, satiated with ruling, have acted as Cornelius Sulla? That is, restored liberty to the people, reinstated the republic? Now, if living he had done this, then wouldn't have Brutus and Cassius committed a great evil in killing him?. . ."

O lovely old man, thought I, all these "if's" and "supposing that's!" You are indeed the supreme artist, but as a pleader of briefs. . . . Luigi and Antonio were smiling without smiling.

" . . . It's a great presumption to kill a prince of the public administration, no matter how just or unjust he might be. Since we never know what might be born of his death, perhaps we have more to hope for from his life . . . And it seems dangerous to me to think that good can only be introduced by beginning with evil, that is with murders . . ."

And on and on he went, citing changing times, alterations of resolve, the power of the unforeseen, and a plethora of suchlike banalities of which the supreme one was the fact that many times, quite unexpectedly, the good that we all desire suddenly appears without peril to anyone.

This was a side of Michelangiolo I had observed more than once. His caution, one might almost say, his pusillanimity in certain situations. The man who dared to say No to the Holy Father was subservient to his flesh-and -blood father, a worthless and exploitative old man.

Now he was going on how, in ancient times, many Romans, ardent for liberty, probably had hoped for the assassination of Cornelius Sulla. And how joyful they must have been when Sulla voluntarily resigned from the dictatorship. What joy they must have known to see the republic peacefully restored. If therefore Caesar had lived, and if he had acted as Sulla . . . And suppose Dante had perhaps had a similar opinion that Brutus and Cassius . . .

"—Orsù!" I cried. "Have you done with this preachment? Surely it's been beautiful and deserves to be written in letters of gold. Undoubtedly I shall some day set our discussion down in a little book. But now let's go home because we are at the door and it is already evening. Because I don't want to reply to all this gabble about praising Brutus and Cassius as tyrannicides and praising Dante for treating them as traitors. It's too much for my small head. And besides, I see these two are laughing at us."

"O we enjoy seeing you so heated," said Antonio.

"I'm well aware of it," said I "and therefore I don't want to offend a dear friend . . ."

A man after all is not a block of marble. Not every piece strikes off the same. The great artist and Florentine patriot we all admired coexisted in the same skin as this cautious counsellor mumbling in the sunset streaming through the window.

"And I will accompany messer Michelangiolo to his house; he is after all an old fellow and needs such offices, and even if he were annoyed at me, I will go with him and make peace."

And I took Maestro Michelangiolo by the arm, surprised as I always am by the powerful biceps I touched, but messer Luigi signed for us to wait. "We have reasoned all day about Dante," he said, "let our last words also be about him. Therefore, messer Michelangiolo, recite to us that sonnet which a few days ago you made in his honor."

Well, the old one protested that his poetising was not worthy to be listened to by such refined ears as ours. But he recited it nonetheless:

> Dal ciel discese, e col mortal suo, poi
> Che visto ebbe l'inferno giusto e 'l pio,
> Ritornò vivo a contemplar Dio,
> Per dar di tutto il vero lume a noi:
> Lucente stella, che co' raggi suoi
> Fe' chiaro, a torto, el nido ove nacqu' io;
> Nè sare' 'l premio tutto 'l mondo rio:
> Tu sol, che la creasti, esser quel puoi.
> Di Dante dico, che mal conosciute
> Fur l'opre suo da quel popolo ingrato,
> Che solo a' iusti manca di salute.
> Fuss'io pur lui! c'a tal fortuna nato,
> Per l'aspro esilio suo, con la virtute,
> Dare' del mondo il più felice stato.

> From Heaven he descended after, in his flesh,
> the Hell of justice and the purgatory of pity
> he had seen; thence alive returned

to contemplate God and that true light
to shed upon us all. O lucent star!
Who by his rays mistakenly illumines
the nest where I was born. For him the entire
wicked world would not suffice as prize,
Only Thou alone who hast created him.
Of Dante I speak, whose worth and work
were faintly honored by that ungrateful people
who fail to grant their favors only to the just.
Were I but him! to such fortune born,
with such virtue to confront his bitter exile,
the world's most happy state would I exchange.

Surely he speaks more sense in those burning verses than in the stubborn (but pitiful) casuistry whereby all afternoon he had attempted to defend every jot and tittle of Dante Alighieri.

✲

Nevertheless, despite his bold identification with a long dead exile in that sonnet, Buonarroti was most cautious about being identified with the living political exiles who were his friends. A feather from our ungrateful nest floated down from Fiorenza one windy day. When Michelangiolo, together with all of us political exiles, were placed on the ban—all our property and possessions impounded—he wrote a letter to his nephew Lionardo (who showed it to my spy in Cosimo's regime, who revealed it to me) stating among other things:

Lionardo, I'm grateful that you advised me of the ban; because if until recently I've been careful about speaking and fraternizing with the exiles, I'll be even more careful in the future. As far as my being taken into the Strozzi Palace when I was ill, I don't consider that I was in the house but rather in the apartment of messer Luigi del Riccio, who was my very close friend. And then when Bartolommeo Angelini died I found no one who could take care of my business affairs better nor more faithfully than he. And since messer Luigi's death I have never more had anything to do with that house of Strozzi, to which all Roma can testify; because I'm always alone, I seldom go out and I don't speak to anyone, especially to Florentines. And if I am greeted in the street, I can't do otherwise than respond courteously in kind, and go my way. And if I knew who the political exiles were, I would not respond in any manner whatsoever, and as I've said from now on I will be much on my guard, particularly since I have so many other preoccupations that living is very wearisome.

A pusillanimous letter surely but also politically calculated. Obviously the Maestro's intention was that his nephew should see to it that the sentiments of this letter be made known to the Duke and his advisors.

One could hardly say it was a noble and courageous act, but all his friends— even those most fiercely dedicated to the liberation of Fiorenza—understood the Old One's caution, and his fear of losing the property he was conserving for his family, and perhaps even an idea, never entirely absent from his mind, of returning—once he felt secure about the operations of the Fabbrica—to his homeland to die amongst his own. He was a Florentine after all, and to the core, and Duke Cosimo set no conditions to his promises. Michele would have returned there as a God, and it is indeed strange that to the last he refused the Duke's blandishments, always accompanied by that incongruous chorus of Vasari, Cellini, and Lionardo Buonarroti.

·✳·

Recently I had the great good fortune to witness Titian of Cadore working in his vast studio at Biri Grande on a Deposition. A strange work— all shadow and glow, the figures immersed in a golden haze as if they were under sea, there isn't a sharp contour in the entire work. And it was surprising to see that old man, who is as old or perhaps even older than Michelangiolo, painting not only with the accepted tools of his trade, that is brushes and knives, but with his fingers, and oil-soaked dirty cloths, smearing the colors into the exact degree of blurryness he is searching for. One might say Titian seeks for exactitudes of vagueness, his canvases throb like flesh—whether the solemn faces of his doges or the smiling bellies and breasts of his naked Venuses—wherever he paints flesh, it pulses with real blood and real life.

And watching the venerable Master at work, I seemed to see his erstwhile friend Aretino in the studio with several of the choicest females of his harem. I say 'erstwhile' because Aretino has been blessedly (for us) dead for twenty years and yet I cannot see the Master Titian without thinking of his long incongruous friendship with that master of blackmail, Pietro Aretino.

When I first came to Venice he was as much part of the scene as the Doge's Palace: a robust figure (richly swathed in velvets and brocades with the Imperial Cross suspended by a great gold chain around his neck) and with the longest blackest beard I have ever seen, and eyes that were glowing coals of roguery; and listening to the astonishing flow of his talk—still Tuscan-Aretine for all his years in Venice—as chromatic and erotic as anything that flows from Titian's brush, it was hard to believe that this elegant vulgarian could by a stroke of his talented pen make and unmake the reputations of great ones in the world, and by this art of blackmail had risen from a poverty-stricken youth with an unknown father and a prostitute mother—cortigiana della candela—to this flashy Signore who dwelt in a palace on the Canal Grande where he kept a mixed harem of boys and girls. His chatter was endless as a millrace but didn't seem to trouble Titian at all who went on imperturbably with his work, occasionally smiling at a particularly lewd jest of the Aretine. In fact, Aretino, self-styled Flail of Princes, died shortly after. He was in a house of ill-fame run by two of his sisters, and some filthy joke set him laughing so violently that he died of an apoplexy. Michelangiolo laughed almost as violently at the epitaph that soon made the rounds:

> Qui giace l'Aretin poeta tosco
> Che disse mal d'ognun fuorchè di Cristo
> Scusandosi col dir: non lo conosco.

> Here lies Aretino whose Tuscan poem
> spoke ill of everyone except Christ
> Pleading this excuse: I do not know him.

Our Michele had good reason for vengeful laughter. For just when he was so gravely ill in del Riccio's apartment, a letter had arrived from Pietro Aretino. The Master's hand trembled as he showed it to me. It was a violent attack against the "indecencies" of the Last Judgement which Michele had completed four years earlier. Messer Pietro had finally seen an engraving of the entire work and now that all his hopes and dunning for a gift of a Michelangiolo drawing were clearly never to be satisfied, all his disappointment boiled over into vituperousness beyond belief. Propped up in bed, fluttered over by Luigi and Urbino and Tommaso, pale as his pillow, Michelangiolo watched me for a moment through half-closed lids and then shut his weary eyes as I read:

> Sir, when I inspected the complete sketch of the whole of your Last Judgement, I arrived at recognising the eminent graciousness of Raffaello in its agreeable beauty of invention.
> Meanwhile, as a baptized Christian, I blush before the license, so forbidden to man's intellect, which you have used in expressing ideas connected with the highest aims and final ends to which our faith aspires. So, then, that Michelangiolo stupendous in his fame, that Michelangiolo whom all admire, has chosen to display to the whole world an impiety of irreligion only equalled by the perfection of his painting! Is it possible that you, who, since you are divine, do not condescend to consort with human beings, have done this in the greatest temple built to God, upon the highest altar raised to Christ, in the most sacred chapel upon earth, where the mighty hinges of the Church, the venerable priests of our religion, the Vicar of Christ, with solemn ceremonies and holy prayers, confess, contemplate, and adore his body, his blood, and his flesh?

If it were not infamous to introduce the comparison, I would plume myself upon my virtue when I wrote *La Nanna*. I would demonstrate the superiority of my reserve to your indiscretion, seeing that I, while handling themes lascivious and immodest, use language comely and decorous, speak in terms beyond reproach and inoffensive to chaste ears. You, on the contrary, presenting so awful a subject, exhibit saints and angels, these without earthly decency, and those without celestial honors.

The pagans, when they modelled a Diana, gave her clothes; when they made a naked Venus, hid the parts which are not shown with the hand of modesty. And here there comes a Christian, who, because he rates art higher than the faith, deems it a royal spectacle to portray martyrs and virgins in improper attitudes, to show men dragged down by their shame, before which things houses of ill-fame would shut the eyes in order not to see them. Your art would be at home in some voluptuous bagnio, certainly not in the highest chapel in the world. Less criminal were it if you were an infidel, than, being a believer, thus to sap the faith of others. Up to the present time the splendor of such audacious marvels hath not gone un-punished; for their very superexcellence is the death of your good name. Restore them to repute by turning the indecent parts of the damned to flames, and those of the blessed to sunbeams; or imitate the modesty of Florence, who hides your David's shame beneath some gilded leaves. And yet that statue is exposed upon a public square, not in a consecrated chapel.

As I wish that God may pardon you, I do not write this out of any resentment for the things I begged of you. In truth, if you had sent me what you promised, you would only have been doing what you ought to have desired most eagerly to do in your own interest; for this act of courtesy would silence the envious tongues which say that only certain Gerards and Thomases dispose of them.

Well, if the treasure bequeathed you by Pope Julius, in order that you might deposit his ashes in an urn of your own carving, was not enough to make you keep your plighted word, what can I expect from you? It is not your ingratitude, your avarice, great painter, but the grace and merit of the Supreme Shepherd, which decide his fame. God wills that Julius should live renowned forever in a simple tomb, inurned in his own merits, and not in some proud monument dependent on your genius. Meantime, your failure to discharge your obligations is reckoned to you as an act of thieving.

Our souls need the tranquil emotions of piety more than the lively impressions of plastic art. May God, then, inspire his Holiness Paul with the same thoughts as he instilled into Gregory of blessèd memory, who rather chose to despoil Rome of the proud statues of the Pagan deities than to let their magnificence deprive the humbler images of the saints of the devotion of the people.

Lastly, when you set about composing your picture of the universe and hell and heaven, if you had steeped your heart with those suggestions of glory, of honor, and of terror proper to the theme which I sketched out and offered to you in the letter I wrote you and the whole world reads, I venture to asset that not only would nature and all kind influences cease to regret the illustrious talents they endowed you with, and which today render you, by virtue of your art, an image of the marvellous: but Providence who sees all things, would herself continue to watch over such a masterpiece, so long as order lasts in her government of the hemisphere.

Your servant,
The Aretine

Now that I have blown off some of the rage I feel against you for the cruelty you used to my devotion, and have taught you to see that, while you may be divine, I am not made of water, I bid you tear up this letter, for I have done the like, and do not forget that I am one to whose epistles kings and emperors reply.

To the great MICHELANGIOLO BUONARROTI in Roma

Lashings of a viper. Forked tongue. Venom and holy water. This pseudo-pious Aretino who believes that it's all right to handle 'lascivious themes' if you do so with 'comely language'! The author of pornographic verses—accompanying Giulio Romano's etchings of the Modi of various sexual positions—indignant at the pure nudities of Michele's Judgement! The malignant allusion to Raffaello and to the Maestro's friendship with Tomao and other young men!

The Aretine's bosom friend Titian arrived in Roma shortly after the receipt of the insinuating letter. So it's not surprising that the two giants of Italian art did not meet on that occasion. Everyone knew of Titian's coziness with the Aretine. It was a bad time for Michelangiolo anyway: his second illness, his anxiety over the loss of his income from the Po ferry, his fury on learning that his nephew Lionardo had unexpectedly arrived in Roma, since the rumor had spread that his uncle was dead. "He would not have come so quickly had I been starving. He's just anxious not to lose his inheritance!" And so the not-dead uncle refused to see him and after a conference with del Riccio about a farm for sale next to Lionardo's house, the nephew returned to Fiorenza. Oh it was a bad time for Michele! He saw nobody those days except the handful of his old and trusted friends amongst whom I was proud to be numbered. Titian's journey to Roma in the Autumn of 1545 had been a triumph, with an escort of seven riders provided by the Duke of Urbino who had taken him under his protection. The Duke himself personally escorted the old master as far as Pesaro. In Roma he received a cordial welcome from his compatriot Bembo, and Paul the Third treated him as a royal guest. He was given rooms in the Belvedere Palace where he had easy access to the Pope and his family whose new portraits he was now to paint. The Cardinal Farnese had appointed Giorgio Vasari (who had just returned from Naples to paint an enormous fresco in the Cancelleria) to serve as his guide to the artistic treasures of the city and of course Vasari first took him to the gallery of antiques in the Vatican and then showed him Raffaello's tapestries and the paintings in the Farnesina.

But Titian's compatriot Sebastiano del Piombo was also acting as a cicerone to the old man. Although an ardent partisan of Michelangiolo, Sebastian always felt a strong sense of gratitude toward Titian who, notorious for his cupidity, had revealed an unsuspected sense of honor with regard to Fra Sebastiano three years earlier. At that time, Titian had completed in Venice an earlier version of portraits of the Holy Father and his son and nephew (he was now redoing them on a single canvas in Roma) and the only remuneration offered the Master of Cadore was the post of Keeper of the Papal Seal. But Titian refused to deprive a fellow Venetian of the remunerative post. It would have meant depriving Giovanni di Udine as well of his share of the income from the office, since Sebastiano paid 80 ducats a year of his income to Giovanni who had helped him secure the post. At any rate, Titian's honorable behavior in this matter (he had never been paid anything for the earlier portrait) as well as the fact that they were both Venetians served to mitigate in this case Sebastiano's fierce partisanship of Michelangiolo and the Michelangiolo style, especially the priority of drawing over color.

I am always intrigued by this fierce quarrelsomeness among artists. And inasmuch as I am no artist myself I can view these sallies and singing arrows from a safe position off the battleground. Even old Michelangiolo was not entirely immune from these battles. He certainly was never given to excessive praise of other people's art.

During the first months of Titian's stay, both Vasari and Sebastiano made regular reports to the ailing Florentine, now back at Macel de' Corvi.

"When I took him to the Stanze, he asked who was the barbarian who had dared to retouch Raffaello's frescoes. I had to confess," Sebastiano clucked, "I was the culprit."

"Yes", said Vasari in his booming fashion, "he seems most interested in Rafaello. When I took him to see the Tapestries he did some sketches right on the spot."

"Did he do any sketches of my work in the Sistine?" asked Michele of Sebastiano.

"No. He just stared, transfixed, from vault to altar wall then back to the vault and again to the altar wall. Then he murmured: "What a pity that time shall also destroy this.""

"Il tempo che consuma il tutto" said Michelangiolo as if to himself. "We are the same age. He understands the teeth of time."

"Then when he had ecovered a bit from his amazement, he told me that he had received a letter from Aretino—"

Tommaso hushed and Michele frowned.

"—warning him not to lose himself in contemplation of the Last Judgement lest he be kept all winter from the company of Sansovino and himself. So apparently the same Aretino who wrote so vituperously to you about your work, praises it to the skies when he writes to his friend Titian."

"Forked tongue."

"It seems the scoundrel wants regular reports from Titian regarding his art education. Viz: what does he think of the antiques and how far they surpass the work of Michelangiolo."

"Indeed?"

"And how far Buonarroti approaches or surpasses Raffaello as a painter. . ."

"Indeed?"

By the Spring, Michelangiolo had regained his usual strength, and Sebastiano brought Titian to Macel de' Corvi for a courtesy visit.

One can imagine Michele's surprise when the Master of Cadore remarked in that inimitable singsong of the lagoons: "I have seen your Judgement on the urgent recommendation of messer Aretino, and I must say that it is magnificent beyond all the praise he had sung of it."

Three heads—mine and Tomao's and Fra Sebastiano's swiveled in chorus to observe Michelangiolo's response to this astonishing intelligence. All of us were privy to the Aretine's scandalous letter. And now he was trumpeting his praises of the Judgement against which he had made worse accusations than those of the Magister Caerimoniarum Biagio!

Michele simply bowed his grizzled head in acknowledgement. Not even his friends could discern the slightest change of expression. Titian was going on quietly and gravely, in his pleasant deep voice, about the glories of the mighty fresco and of the vault above it, and all the other works of Michelangiolo which he had already witnessed in Roma.

"Your Moses surpasses any work of the ancients, Messer."

Michele nodded his head.

Watching those two old men—Titian taller, more richly garbed, more richly bearded, himself a Doge, diplomatic and acute—I thought of two potentates sounding out each other's hidden forces beneath the necessary courtesies.

Shortly afterward Giorgio Vasari accompanied Michelangiolo on a return visit to Titian's quarters in the Belvedere. Vasari recounted the story to Sebastiano and myself at Macel de' Corvi. Michele had gone out for his evening ride with

Tommaso. "We found the Venetian master, fresh from his triumph at the Campidoglio where he had been granted the honors of Roman citizenship in the usual
style of laurel wreaths and boring Latin orations by his friend Bembo among
others". (an honor which Michele had received ten year earlier). "He was putting
some finishing touches on the Danae. I saw a tiny flash of lightning in messer
Michelangiolo's eyes. Danae is lying on a couch nude except for a transparent veil
covering her spread-open thighs: an open chalice as it were into which Jupiter in
the form of a golden rain is pouring. And her head thrown back with an expression
of supreme gratification. And to think it as painted by a man in his sixty-ninth
year!"

"And to think also" I said, "that just at the very time Titian is setting down his
masterpiece of simony—Pope Paul with his grandsons—he is painting the supreme symbol of nepotism, Danae receiving the golden rain."

Sebastiano laughed. "Not nepotism. Eroticism. An old man's dream! I think I
discern Titian himself in the old servant witnessing the miracle."

"At any rate", Giorgio went on, "Michelangiolo walked up close to the canvas
and squinting his eyes, examined it closely. Then he praised it highly to Titian's
obvious gratification. But after we left, he told me that it was a pity that the
Venetians did not learn to draw well from the start. For if Titian (said he) had
developed the art of drawing, together with his native gifts, especially for living
portraiture and the natural tones of life, no one could do better."

I was thinking of these matters as I watched old Titian at work, speculating on
his political serenity, one might say, by contrast with Michelangiolo's tangled
state of soul. For the difference between them is surely not simply between the
preeminence of drawing in the one and color in the other, between Florentine
intellect and Venetian voluptuousness, between the solid and rocky Tuscan earth
out of which the one makes sculptures (and paintings and drawings and even
poetry that are sculptures) and the prismatic watery atmosphere of the lagoon, the
suspended bubbles out of which Titian brews the flesh of his Madonnas and his
Magdalens and his Venuses. He is the great poet of serenity. He maintains his
sobriety even as his brush metamosphoses buttocks breasts dogs brocades landscapes Crucifixions into a luminosity no master in Italia can match. He wore the
gold chain of a Knight of the Empire: rumor had it that while sitting for his portrait
the Emperor Charles, master of the world, had stooped to pick up this master's
brush.

An odd city, Venezia, I was thinking: watery streets and the most stable
government in all Italia. And like all his fellow Signori of the Serenissima, Titian
maintaining the utmost sobriety as he paints his voluptuous Venuses and provoking Magdalens who are closer to their departed sinfulness than to their approaching saintliness. I must admit that I admire these Venetians. I am, I imagine, one of
the very few Fiorentini who feels at home with these rich and somewhat pompous

Veneziani, much concerned with maintaining their wealth and good government against all those leagued against them, which is usually all the other principalities of Italy, plus the Papal state, and according to circumstances, the Hapsburg Empire and the Realm of France. Not to mention the Turk who threatens to deprive them always of their suzerainty in Rhodes and the Pelopennesus and Constantinople which they have already wrested from them.

So these Signori of the Serenissima are quite another breed than our Tuscans. They govern well if severely and could provide useful lessons in statecraft to us Fiorentini who are the most unstable people in the world, and who have known only intervals of freedom during the almost unbroken domination of the Medici.

But of course if all these political matters are at the center of my concern, they are but peripheral to Michelangiolo. He is at heart a Republican, he has consistently refused the enticements of Duke Cosimo, he had at my instigation carved a Brutus for the Cardinal Ridolfi as an oblique act of homage to Lorenzino the tyrannicide (although I doubt that Michelangiolo himself admired, or even trusted, Lorenzino). In all these things Michelangiolo was a good Florentine citizen, if you will, loyal always to the idea of a free republic, but like most artists, politics were in truth only at the periphery of his mind, outside the walls. He was cautious too; he had to be, working for Popes, and with a family in hostage, so to speak, up in Fiorenza. So he took great care not to be too closely identified with the more political-minded exiles, and if he wrote certain letters to his nephew dissociating himself from us, I could understand and forgive that. We all knew where his deepest loyalties lay.

And indeed, with all his cautiousness, he has never hesitated to take risks out of love for the freedom of his patria. During those two terrible illnesses he suffered while working on the Pauline when all of us in Roma feared he was soon to die, and when messer Luigi had him brought into his own apartment in the Strozzi Palace that he might better nurse him, and where every day it was a sight indeed to see the old man propped up in a huge canopied signorile bed, all carved and gilt, and himself gaunt and gray as *pietra serena*, visited in that condition by the principal signori and prelates of Roma, and even the Pope himself, Paul III, and others of the great house of the Farnese dispatching messengers every day to learn how the distinguished patient was doing. During that time Roberto di Filippo Strozzi who was attending to the business of his bank at Lyon wrote to messer del Riccio asking news of the great invalid, and Luigi replied that although Michelangiolo was still very weak he was beginning to walk about the house and hoped soon to be entirely cured. As long as I have known the Old One (even when he was a young one) he has lamented about his ailments and spoke of Death as his closest friend, yet that illness of the Pauline was almost twenty years ago, and Michele is still in this world although I fear from Tomao's letter that this time he is truly on the verge of departure.

Luigi also wrote Strozzi to remind the King of France what Michelangiolo had already said via Scipione and then through Deo the courier that "if the King restores liberty to Fiorenza, he Michelangiolo wants to make a bronze equestrian statue of Francis I to be set up in the Piazza de' Signori at his own expense."

And all this while he is warding off Duke Cosimo's proffers with diplomatic wile worthy of my predecessor as Secretary of the Ten, messer Niccolò Machiavelli. Never does he give Cosimo reason to believe that his persistent absence from Fiorenza is motivated by political enmity. O no, it's never that he wants to topple the House of Medici. It's rather that he must, for the good and welfare of his soul, erect the new House of God.

Of course, both are true.

Yet those latter years, as Cosimo's hold seems permanent as any government in Fiorenza can be permanent, Michele's nostalgia for his own belltower and cupolone grows stronger and he is not the only exile who in his old age is ready to make his peace with the tyrant and return to die in his native land.

·✳·

Although Duke Cosimo may think he has banned me permanently from Fiorenza, I have never failed to remain well informed of events in my turbulent patria. My spies—call them gossips—are amongst the most intimate courtiers of the Duke, and he can no more prevent leakages from Palazzo dei Signori than floods of the Arno.

Ever since the unveiling of the Last Judgement, criticism of Michele's nudes has become more and more violent. Anonymous letters were sent to the Farnese Pontiff and finally rumor had it that he who had insisted on the creation of the work was contemplating its destruction.

Shortly before Pope Paul III died, I received a letter from my gossip at the Medici court relating to an anonymous complaint against Michelangiolo which had just been received by the Duke. A copy of the anonymous complaint was enclosed; and I hastened to Macel de' Corvi to show it to the old man.

It was coming toward the twenty-third hour, the Trajan column raised a pink shaft against an amber-scudding sky. Michelangiolo had just returned from the Pauline Chapel; Urbino was leading the horse off to the stable. Michele's hands were still stained with color, the colors of Peter's Crucifixion; but despite his long hard day of work and the infamies he was reading, the hand that held the letter did not quiver, his graygold eyes simply grew colder and colder:

19th of March 1549
In the Cathedral of Santa Maria del Fiore there have been unveiled filthy and swinish marble figures of Adam and Eve by Baccio—

Adumbration of a smile.

"Read on," I said. Read on, Maestro."

—Bandinello, which were roundly condemned by everyone in the city, and someone close to the Duke complained that such a thing should be allowed in a Duomo—

"Ma, questa non mi tocca! But this has nothing to do with me!"
"Read on! Read on!"

—in a Duomo in front of the Altar where is celebrated the Most Holy Sacrament of the blood and body of the most Blessed Jesus Christ, which would give rise to agitations among the faithful, nonetheless those figures were installed there as if people were supposed to believe it was done by God's will.

"Boh! I'm sure I would also object to the figures, not because they are nude but because they are ugly. Which is not surprising since they are by messer Baccio who—"
"Read on, Maestro!" I said, waving an admonitory finger.

In the same month—

"Now!"

—there was uncovered in Santo Spirito a Pietà which a Florentine had sent to the said church, and it is bruited about that it is a copy of an original which came from the inventor of all such filthynesses, Michelangiolo Buonarrotto—

Michele sat down on the sgabello which the returning Urbino had just drawn up behind him, tapping him on the shoulder. He was no longer smiling.

—who among all modern painters and sculptors, excels in imitating suchlike Lutheran caprices so that today in our holy churches nothing is painted or carved but figures to undermine faith and piety, but I hope that some day God will send his saints to smash to the ground such idolatries as these.

"Well?"
"Well. This is the atmosphere we breathe, my dear Donato. I'm neither surprised nor angered."
But he *was* angered. Messer Tomao had just come in. He stared perplexedly at the Master's stony expression. Michele gave him the letter.
"O the man's illiterate!" Tomao said. "His sentences run on like froth from his mouth."

"That's the least of it," the Old One said. "I take small comfort that my enemies are also targets of this vitriolic attack. Bandinelli of course has fancied himself my rival for many years and he's ingratiated himself into the good graces of the Duke. Could it be that he—?"

He shook his old head. "No, I can't believe that. He looked up at me with clouded eyes. His anger had reached such a point of distress that it seemed merely a wearisomeness, a passivity in the face of the world's incomprehension. Baccio had been responsible, so rumor had it, for the destruction of his Cartoon of the Bathers. But that was a lifetime away! When Machiavelli, my predecessor as Secretary of the Ten, had been put to the rack, his republic destroyed. 1512, I reckoned, thirty-seven years ago! O Michele's hatreds run as long as his friend-ships!

"Baccio shapes ugly works," I said soothingly, "but not sentences like these. Besides his attacks against you are not anonymous, and certainly not motivated by piety."

"The irony," Michele murmured, after a long silence, "the irony—" and the lost smile faintly reappeared from behind the clouds "—to think that the copier of my Pietà which so outrages this pious citizen is none other than Nanni di Baccio Bigio, my worst enemy at the Fabbrica! Two Baccios damned!"

He even managed a single donkey-bray of laughter.

But with the expiring light, he became ever more glum and silent. Messer Tomao and I could not induce him to take our customary sunset stroll around the Mercato Traiano.

When we left, the white column pointed heavenward, a star-dial. Con-stellations and stars ticked over the holy city, Roma. Man stirred his petty froth, ambition sullied, pride preened, envy flickered its forked tongue.

Amongst the neighboring ruins, deathpale with the starlight, cats were howling their love.

IV

Maestro Michelangiolo Buonarroti

It was the Holy Year of 1550 and we still had no Holy Father. The great Farnese Paul had died the previous November—the only Pope at whose death I ever wept—and here it was February, three months gone, and no successor to Peter's Chair had yet been chosen. In St. Peter's Piazza throngs watched daily for the white smoke to appear and nothing but black issued from the chimneys, hanging like storm clouds over the Vatican. And this was especially troublesome in a year of Jubilee when pilgrims came to the capital of Christendom from all over the world, a capital with no one sitting on the Fisherman's throne and nothing but the buzz of political bickerings emerging from spies at the long conclave.

It was 1550 and I was completing the martyrdom of St. Peter and I was completing my seventy-fifth year toward release from martyrdom. I depicted Peter according to the tradition crucified upsidedown but when I had finished his portrait I found that I had depicted myself, twisted about on the cross being raised and staring cataleptically at the witnesses of my crucifixion who are all of you. And the longer I worked at that fresco, the more my own image reappeared, at least ten times it emerged out of the damp plaster and drench of colors—and I became frightened. I was St. Peter crucified upsidedown, I was the old man at the arm of the cross, I was another at the foot, I was behind the centurion on his horse; I was crucified, I watched myself being crucified, I wept or took pleasure at my own crucifixion. I became frightened, I tell you, some devil of Self was in my brush. The world was populated with multiples of Michelangiolo!

And this was indeed strange, as strange as a Holy year without a Holy Father. For all my life I have avoided portraiture, or self-portraiture, unlike Ghirlandaio or Raffaello who populate their frescoes with a portrait gallery of themselves and their contemporaries.

But the same thing was happening then with the new Deposition which I had recently undertaken and intended for my own tomb. There, in the guise of Nicodemus, I was also depicting myself—but this time I knew exactly what I was doing: the hand that grasps the cold chisel obeys the intellect: a marble portrait does not flow unbidden from the brush, as it was flowing in the Pauline.

Only once before have I depicted myself—and that was a kind of foul joke—my face in the flayed contorted skin held in Aretino's hand in my Judgement of the Sistine, a foul joke against myself in that skin, and a foul joke against a slanderer depicted as a Saint. For he can, the ambidextrious Aretine, write whorishness with one hand and pieties with the other. At the same time, too.

Now, all this time, from the 29th of November 1549 until the 8th of February 1550, the Conclave was going on—the longest conclave in the history of man. Wooden booths for the Cardinals had been erected in six of the greatest chambers of the Vatican, and of course among them was my Sistine where the new thundering nudities of my Judgement hurled down at them. I wondered often whether their judgement was in any way affected by my Judgement? Those Cardinals elevated by the late Paul wore violet, the others green, so that against the rainbowed harmonies of my vault and the sepias and flesh tones and lapis lazulis of my Judgement, there was indeed an irridescence of color in the Sistine which would have pleased any of the Venetians. It must be an emblazonment of parrots I thought; I wondered whether any booths had been set up in the Sala del Papagallo where a parrot was kept in the audience chamber by the Holy Father. That would have been a suitable place for those French Cardinals who were indeed eager for a Pappa Gallo!

And although, as was customary, the doors of the conclave were locked from without and within with six bolts, the truth was that this closure was applied with so little rigor, and there were so many agents of the various parties receiving messages and distributing them all over Roma, that this was not only the longest conclave in history, but also the most open.

How Pasquino chortled through it all!

And through all these events, through dreary November and a joyless Christmas, and a blustering January, I was supposed to be completing my Crucifixion of St. Peter—the winter months are always difficult for fresco painting, the plaster freezes in the vats and I am seventy-five years old and weary of climbing scaffolds and wielding the heavy brush. I had hoped indeed that booths might be set up in this yet unfinished Pauline Chapel as well (as they were in the adjacent Sala Regia), thus affording me a perfect excuse for not even attempting to work through the winter. Yet even without such excuse, I did little or no work, following instead the events of the Conclave.

I was particularly interested in that Conclave because from the very beginning the talk all over Roma was that England (by which was meant the Cardinal Reginald Pole) had the tiara already in his grasp. At the first scrutiny, I learned, he already won 20 of the necessary 28 votes that would give him a majority. And I was well acquainted with the Cardinal and enjoyed his esteem and he had acquired several of my drawings through his disciple Vittoria Colonna. I was proud to have been the friend of his great friend, the Marchesa of Pescara, and I knew the Cardinal wished me well. For this Englishman was universally admired for his zeal for reform; he was one of those within the Church (among whom I counted myself) who believed that the best, indeed, the only way to combat the heresy of the Lutherans was to cleanse the Church of all the corruptions the German reformer had justly pointed out. Of course, we needed no German heretic to point to the filth in our own house; Fra Girolamo had already done so, and preached his last fiery sermon from a blazing pyre for having done so. But I could bear witness (and so could many others) that this English Cardinal (like Fra Girolamo and unlike Fra Martino Lutero) knew that cleansing the Church did not mean cleaving it; but (unlike those other two intemperate ones) Pole's patience, kindness, his willingness to parlay with the Reformers and bring them back into the fold, won the admiration of all.

So we all thought Pole's election was assured. The universal voice— by which is meant the voice in the streets—was that Pole could seize the tiara from his closest rivals the Cardinal Salviati and the Cardinal Santa Croce any time he wished by his zeal for reform alone. On the second day, his votes already rose to 24. He needed but 3 more to become the Vicar of Christ.

Everything that was happening at the secret sessions was known almost immediately all over Roma. By decree of Gregory X, each Cardinal was entitled to two conclavists, and since relatives of the Cardinals—nobles and barons—usually obtained these posts, the supposedly secret votations were as open as the wide mouth of the Colosseum. Cracks were opened in the walls through which the imprisoned Cardinals might infiltrate messages and letters to the outside world. The booths of the conclavists were stuffed with such letters.

It amused me in a way to think that much of this was going on under the gaze of my thundering Judgement.

So on the second day when Pole won 24 votes, the Cardinal d'Urfé, representing the King of France, who was fearful of the English Cardinal, rose and threatened a schism unless the conclave suspended all voting for at least a week till the arrival of the French Cardinal delegation who were then in Corsica. Later we learned that this was an outright lie; d'Urfé had no idea at which point in their travels the French delegation were.

So now there was much milling about, (under my milling Judgement) and cries that Pole should be immediately chosen Pope by acclamation, and it was already past midnight and the Cardinals had not yet retired to their wooden cells.

Amidst all this perturbation, the Cardinal Pole never lost his poise. Not wishing to accede to elevation by way of homage—that is, ovation— he told his friends (an old friend in Vittoria's circle brought the news to me) that he wished to arrive at the Papacy through the door and not through the window.

By early December so certain was the Conclave of Pole's victory that his pontifical robes were already prepared and he had already written a draft of his speech of acceptance and gratitude.

In the Region of the Banks—where there is a concentration of Florentine merchants and bankers—and where I was wont to wander out of homesickness for familiar cadences and faces—they were no longer taking bets on the results.

But the French party were not so prepared to yield without a struggle. The agitation and the irritation rose to an ever higher pitch. The Magister Caerimoniarum even failed to ring the usual bell for Mass. He said he would wait until all the Cardinals had met. There was talk of schism in the air. I recalled my brother's account of the last days of Fra Girolamo.

And then a strange thing happened. All those for Pole gathered in the Pauline

Chapel; those for his adversaries in the Sistine. Thus the two chapels I had decorated became the battlefields of this ecclesiastic warfare!

Now the battlefield of my soul was occupied. I could not paint even had I wanted to.

Yet, on the following scrutiny, the election of Pole seemed assured. After he obtained 23 votes Carpi reconsidered his vote and publicly declared his adhesion to the Englishman's cause, then rose Farnese to make a similar declaration, following which there was a sepulchral silence. Pole now lacked only a single vote to become Supreme Pontiff. For if he had obtained the 26th vote, the 27th was already assured him according to the agreements of the night before, and then he could have given himself the 28th, the final tally needed.

Full of expectation Pole's electors glanced at his adversaries and with nods of their heads sought to obtain that final vote.

But no one moved.

After a pause, the deacon demanded if anyone intended to yield. Profound silence. After which, the Cardinal de Cupis declared that day's voting closed and all rose and left their booths, the Imperials greatly depressed, and again the black smoke rose from the chimney, and the mob in St. Peter's Square groaned.

No one had expected such an outcome. Some opined that only by divine intervention was it possible that a Cardinal so eminent as Reginald Pole should have arrived so close to the tiara only to have it plucked from his hands before he took it.

We knew—we friends of Pole (and I counted myself among them, although I didn't like the Imperials who backed him for they were also backing the Medici tyrant of Fiorenza)—that the fundamental explanation lay in a more terrestrial plane: the reluctance of the Italians to elect a 'foreigner.' (I shared that feeling too. The last foreign Pontiff—the Fleming Adrian—had been no friend of the Arts.) Besides, the English Cardinal was only 45 years old, had little knowledge of affairs and messer Donato (whose nose is as keen for politics as the late messer Niccolò Machiavelli to whose post he succeeded in the last Florentine Republic) told me that many feared to embroil the Italian States in a war with England since the reigning King Henry there (who had separated his country from the Church on an issue more biological than theological) was enemy to Pole's house (although closely related to him) and had even beheaded the Cardinal's old mother.

Those beasts of Englishmen!

But more than anything else, there was the suspicion that especially with regard to the doctrine of justification, Cardinal Pole's ideas leaned toward the Protestants.

I know all about such suspicions. Have not the same charges been leveled against me? (who is merely the decorator of those rooms where Popes are chosen?)—especially after my Judgement, (and the cries of heresy still swirling around my head then at the time of England's failure, nine years after I had completed it, and now *now*! twenty-three years after I finally set down my brush, the Council prescripts poor Daniele to mar the purity of my nudes with the impurities of their loincloths. And has not even my just-completed Conversion of Saul been adjudged by some shrewd-eyed theologians as a painted demonstration of justification by faith alone (which indeed it is) and so I am being battered by the same ram that destroyed the English Cardinal's hopes for the Papacy.

That was the nearest he came. From then on, other factions arose. The efforts of the Imperial party to revive Pole's candidacy was rendered ineffective by the arrival of the French Cardinals which shifted the balance. And so the conclave continued inconclusively, and the eve of Christmas came and it was time for the opening of the Holy Door in preparation for the year of Jubilee 1550.

And there was no Pope!

And I was still girding my loins for the completion of the Pauline once the weather, both meterological and theological, cleared and the chapel was disencumbered of these factious Cardinals; and Tommaso's wife was nursing his new second son Emilio who cried with the most musical cry I have ever heard, an ascension of pitch and a descension of volume like a bird obliquely in flight, and hearing it, Tommaso's face took on an expression of paternal pride and wonder.

And Roma was already teeming with pilgrims from all over Europe but everyone was still doubting whether without a Pope and without the usual ceremonies the Holy Year could be initiated with its usual (and longed-for) indulgences and facilities for absolution. And so now arose a roar of complaints and accusations and lamentations from barons and innkeepers and small parish priests directed against that wild plumage of ecclesiastics in my two rooms and elsewhere, that they come to some conclusion and select, without any further undue delays, a new Vicar of Christ for the Holy Year of Jubilee, so important for the flesh as well as the spirit of the city of Roma, Caput Mundi.

Now the barons claimed that to them should be confided the custody of the door of the Conclave because the prelates were too indulgent in carrying out that office. One can well imagine what the barons had in mind! Would they have employed force to bring the conclave to a conclusion? Thus the Holy Ghost would have made its entrance on the wings of lances and halberds.

But though they did not yield to the barons, the inconclusive conclave went on and it was past Christmas and the opening of the Holy Door would have to await the selection of a Pope.

A reform of the procedure was undertaken and we were in January of what was supposed to be the Holy Year but was not yet so proclaimed and now there bobbed to the surface the candidacy of Salviati and now Ridolfi, and now Caraffa, the while Pole always remained high on the surface but never high enough. Every day the Cardinals dropped their ballots in the gold chalice mounted on the altar and every day the votes were counted and every day the black smoke issued forth.

By the second half of January the Cardinal Ridolfi (to the delight of his secretary messer Donato Giannotti and all the Florentine exiles, including myself, if less blatantly, for I had to think of my family in Fiorenza and guarded against being too closely identified with the overt enemies of Duke Cosimo) seemed closest to the Fisherman's throne, although he had already left the Conclave because of illness. It wasn't more than a week or so after this when messer Donato suddenly appeared at Macel de' Corvi, his face ashen.

"Ridolfi is no longer in the running," he announced.

"*Come?*" Like Pole in November, the Florentine Cardinal seemed on the very verge of election.

"The potential Fisherman has been plucked away by the big fish, Death. He has probably been poisoned."

"But who—?"

"His servants corrupted by Mendoza who has, as his hand in the play, Duke Cosimo's *uomo di fiducia* the ill-famed Giovanfrancesco Lottino. So there we are," he added bitterly, "the Holy City has undoubtedly changed since the infamous Borgia, but it's not without its Borgian reminiscences and revivals."

"What are you saying? Now in the midst of the Council of Trent? Are you suggesting that that purgative operation has still not deprived the Lutheran heretics of more nourishment?"

"I'm not suggesting anything. I merely came to tell you that the Cardinal Ridolfi is dead."

So the Fisherman's throne was still vacant and now began a mad running to and fro in the corridors by the leaders of the Imperial and French parties, and an accord was worked out between them, and finally as if by chance, the Cardinal del Monte whose name had been sporadically mentioned before, was chosen by acclamation. I must say the *Habemus Papam* on the 8th day of February of the Holy Year of 1550, astonished Romans and foreigners alike and thus it was that the intervention of the Holy Ghost was called upon in explanation, as had occurred when Adrian the Fleming succeeded Leo X.

What other explanation was there?

For all that everyone knew about this Cardinal Giovan Maria del Monte was that he was esteemed for his humanist education and his courtesy, but it was felt that his propensity for pleasure detracted not a little from his management of his offices. I suppose His Holiness loved life so much because during the Sack he had been so close to death. Taken hostage by the enemy, Clement had been unable to raise his ransom and so the Landsknechts were about to take del Monte's life. Twice he had been led, bound, to the gallows erected in the Campo de' Fiori and threatened with death. Only later had he succeeded in getting his guards drunk and thus escape. He never forgot that, erected a church outside the Porta del Popolo to Sant' Andrea since he had escaped on that Saint's day.

His aspect I must say offered little hope to his portraitists among whom, I knew, I would not be numbered. His face, from which descended a long gray beard, made me think always of a rough contadino, from the hills about Monte San Sovino where indeed his family came from, though he had been born in Roma in the Quarter of the Parione. His nose was a peasant's axe, disproportionately large over the tight compressed lips, his gaze sharp and penetrating like the eyes of farmers striking bargains at Piazza Signoria on market day.

He was a vigorous tall man (younger than Pole whose youth had been held against him), a heavy eater but not very nice in his choice of food, such as had been the gourmet Leo X who had imported lark's tongues from the Bosporus. This holy father was content with substantial fat dishes, strongly seasoned with garlic. His favorite food were onions, and he imported the most extraordinary-sized ones from Gaeta.

But together with these contadinesque manners, he was good-natured, brimful of jokes, sometimes to a degree ill-befitting his dignity. Not only did he give little heed to the ceremonial to the despair of his Magister but created scandals by his frivolous and unsuitable jokes, with which he spiced his banquets, to the embarrassment of the entire Papal family. If the polpetta of veal did not contain sufficient garlic, he would order it taken away as if he were a boy of fifteen and had the stomach of a goat.

I indulge myself in sketching the man's character because he loved me greatly and defended me against my enemies, and said publicly that he would gladly give up some of his own years to add to my already dwindling score. And thinking of these lineaments of Julius III (for he took his name in honor of the Second Julius who had created him Cardinal so that we shared, so to speak, a Julian past), the question of garlic and ill-chosen jests seem very much part of the picture when I think about him but were I to paint him not only would I leave out the garlic but I would care little for rendering with exactitude the eagle-curve of his nose or the boring-in eyes or his ruddy food-crammed complexion. I leave such matters to the followers of Raffaello. The soul I try to paint is revealed in the gestures of the nude body rather than the face reflected as one might see it in a mirror.

But one can hardly paint a Pope nude.

And so I leave portraiture to the others. Fortunately all the Holy Fathers I have known—no matter how much they might have differed one from the other—have respected my lack of sympathy for perpetuating their lineaments. Not a single one has ever asked me to paint his portrait.

Whereas when Titian came to Roma the first time in 1543 it was at the express invitation of Paul for this purpose. And I was seeing the Holy Father almost every week then but he never asked me to do his portrait.

How tactful for a Pope not to risk a refusal!

So on the 22nd of February 1550 with festive pomp and a great concourse of people was crowned the new Pontiff and two days later, with the opening of the Holy Door, the Jubilee year was solemnly inaugurated. The solemnities were to last until the next Christmas eve and amongst the thousands of pilgrims shivering and drenched under the cold winter rain at the opening ceremonies was I, Michelangiolo Buonarroti di Simone, Florentine, then in the seventy-fifth year of my life, and erecting the new House of God for no pay and daily meals far less sumptuous than those consumed by the figure in white under an umbrella wielding the golden mallet at the Door.

For this attendance I received, as did all the thousands present, a Jubilary indulgence.

So the Pontificate of the third Julius began and I was to serve this man for five years.

✳

In the Spring of that Jubilee Year of 1550, Giorgio Vasari and I made the round of the seven basilicas on horseback to earn, by special dispensation of the new Pope, a double indulgence, and to liven the dreary succession of days with the stimulation of new sights and sounds.

I had known Giorgio Vasari since he and Francesco Salviati had gathered up the three pieces of the shattered arm of my David during the civic disturbances at the Palace of the Signori during the revolution of 1527. Defenders of the Palace had dropped stones on the heads of some Medici troops storming the gate and they smashed some heads indeed but also shattered the left arm and hand of my David in three places.

Giorgio was only sixteen then, having arrived in Fiorenza three years earlier from his native Arezzo. Now he was a bushy-bearded, very intelligent and multi-talented, ferociously energetic man of almost forty, but I always thought when I saw him, of that boy then studying in the bottega of gentle Andrea del Sarto and obnoxious Baccio Bandinelli, how far and fast he had risen! I thought of how eager were those two boys that I repair my maimed Giant which indeed I could have done within a few weeks gluing together the crippled left hand and arm and securing them with bronze dowels. But the Signori of the new Republic that had resulted from the anti-Medici uprising were either ill-disposed or too busy to bother about providing minimal funds for the repair or even to ask me to attend to it. At any rate they showed so little interest that I took offense and determined to let my crippled David guard the Palace until I was bidden to repair it. I kept the pieces in my studio on Via Motta, and then came the plague and Buonarroto died in my arms and most of the citizens fled and cobblers and blacksmiths were performing quackeries upon the dying since all the doctors had also fled and the remaining tradesmen receiving payment in wooden bowls stuck through iron grills and immediately casting the money in jars of water to prevent contamination. And I sent my father and Buonarroto's son, Lionardo, off to Pisa, and like the few remaining Florentines, only went out by night, holding balls of ill-smelling disinfectant against our noses.

And who could think of repairing David then?

And then upon the heels of that plague came the greater plague of war, and instead of repairing Davids I was building fortifications up at San Miniato and after the war working on the Medici tombs and warding off the menaces of Duke Alessandro. And every day I saw my David tall and white and balefully beautiful in front of the Palace, guarding those Guardians of our Civic Virtue who cared not a scudo that my White Giant lacked his left arm and hand. And my anger brewed more bitter with the days, and they were bitter days withal, and then I went to Roma never to return, and when I left, David was still crippled, and my anger now—even against a republic which I had served and still supported—was not assuaged but had if anything, increased.

Only nine years after my departure, when Giorgio Vasari made his first visit to Roma to deliver his Venus and Cupid at the home of my friend, messer Bindo Altovito, counsul of the Florentine community in Roma, did I learn that boardings were being set up around "your colossal David" (that megatype Vasari can hardly speak a sentence without at some point pronouncing or suggesting 'colossal') . . . your colossal David by orders of Duke Cosimo" ('Duke Cosimo' splutters as frequently from his lips as 'colossal'.) "People think he's going to have his face washed."

"Who? Duke Cosimo?"

"O Maestro! Your David. But of course it's being done so that the old arm be mended and secured. With bronze dowels too. Just as you suggested."

"Yes. Sixteen years ago!"

But Vasari heard no trace of scorn. He is the perfect diplomat. He hears what he wants to hear and reports to his Prince what he knows *he* wants to hear. The perfect accommodator, he copied my Giuliano of the Medici tombs, and substituted the head of Duke Alessandro, setting it all against a Florentine background. I found all this amusing. My Giuliano was not Giuliano de' Medici anyway. He was Giuliano di Michelangiolo. Who would know or care what the real Giuliano or Lorenzo would look like in a hundred years? So I made *my* Giuliano and *my* Lorenzo: my Giuliano clean-shaven while the real one was bearded, my Lorenzo a melancholic philosopher while the real one was just a young fool. Art climbs Plato's ladder from the senses to the Ideal. That is the only reality I care about.

So Vasari made his reality of my reality.

La Vita Attiva.

Giuliano de' Medici.

Duke Alessandro.

Of course after Alessandro's assassination, Vasari was bound to become the new Duke Cosimo's chief factotum of all the arts. His range of activity is astonishing: painting, architecture, diplomatic missions (such as seeking to seduce me back to my native nest—he, an Aretine!—) and all these projects, missions, assignments, pouring out of his full lips churning endlessly as a millstone in the black wavy waters of his rich beard. Words words words. Indeed his facility with words was easily as great or greater than his accomplishments in the art of painting. And the proof of this was the book of *Lives of Eminent Painters* which he had just sent me for my seventy-fifth birthday on March 6th; in which book I have the honor of being the only living (to my astonishment) artist of a series of biographies that begins with Cimabue, teacher of our Giotto.

I had read his book immediately, of course, and was delighted with Giorgio's lively style and his truly astonishing amassing of materials. Since he begins with artists dead almost two hundred and fifty years ago, one can only admire his zeal, his energy, his efforts to describe all the works all the other masters had done. But when I read the *Life* which concludes his volume—that is, his life of me, Buonarroti—I was not altogether happy. He begins my *Life* with a trumpet blast beyond all the trumpeting angels of my Judgement.

> While industrious and choice spirits, in the light of the most famous Giotto and of his followers, strove to show the world those talents which their happy stars and well-balanced humours had bestowed upon them; and endeavored to imitate the greatness of nature with the excellence of art, and to arrive as closely as possible to that ultimate cognition which many call intelligence, while everywhere they were still striving in vain, the most benign Rector of Heaven kindly turned his eyes to earth, and seeing the vain endlessness of all those efforts, the fruitlessness of all those ardent studies, and the presumptuous opinions of men, farther from truth than darkness from light, in order to save us from so much error, decided to send to earth a genius universal in every art and profession, to demonstrate single-handed what is meant by perfection in the art of linear design, contour, shading, and lighting in order to create relief in painting; and to work with sound judgment in sculpture, and in architecture, render habitations commodious and safe, healthy, pleasant, well-proportioned and enriched with various ornaments.
> And furthermore he wished these gifts to be accompanied with true moral philosophy adorned with sweet poetry, so that the world should look upon and marvel at him as a most unusual mirror in his life, his work, the holiness of his manners, and in all human actions, so that he might be termed celestial rather than terrestrial.

How could one take offense at any biography that began like that? And yet I did. I was particularly irritated by frequent misstatements and misinterpretations. The Aretine writes that my quarrel with Pope Julius and subsequent flight from Roma arose out of my reluctance to let the Pope see the Sistine Vault before it was completed (as if I could, even had I wished, forbid the Holy Father—especially a

Julius!—ingress into his own Chapel!). And Vasari also claims that the execution of the Tomb in its present form was made possible by the munificence of the Duke of Urbino. Obviously the Aretine was cozying up to the Duke for some commission, for never had he been munificent with me; rather he accused me of thievery and threatened to slander my name in the courts as having taken money under false pretences.

But I determined to say nothing to Giorgio Vasari, who notwithstanding these distortions, had written a biography of me so full of love and admiration that he made me blush for shame. I was the only living artist numbered among his 'Lives.' And the other *Lives* in his book were, I thought, admirable indeed, a remarkable gathering of materials, wonderful insights into the accomplishments of hundreds of the great artists Italy alone has produced, and clear evidence that Giorgio had run up and down the peninsula to see with his own eyes every work of which he spoke.

Consider that this book was a voyage into unknown waters for Giorgio. Until then he had been a painter and an architect. Now he proved he was an accomplished writer as well and I certainly could not but respect his intelligence.

So I decided, before I saw him, to make no mention of his errors. Perhaps I would rectify them in time with a little book of my own.

I had just received his book by special messenger several weeks before he himself returned to Roma in his usual millrace of a dozen varied commissions and rushed off to see the new Holy Father and arranged to accompany me on the pilgrimage round (which also secured a double indulgence for the Aretine himself). That was typical Giorgio. He had been the official *cicerone* for old Titian when the Venetian came here on his second visit; now he was ciceroning me. I suppose he was supposed to see to it that I did not fall off my horse.

Since a visit to the seven prescribed basilicas had to be accomplished within a single day, Giorgio came to my studio very early in the morning just after dawn, mounted on a handsome bay. I rode my spotted mare, very reliable, whom I have ridden for several years and whose gait is gentle to my old bones, and yet nimble-footed enough for all the hills and brambles that this day-long ride throughout Roma would inevitably involve.

Before we set out I thanked Giorgio with full courtesy and genuine admiration for the book he had sent me for my birthday. I observed somewhat wryly that though amongst all the artists he had included in his gallery, I was indeed the only living one, yet Death was my constant companion, that I never cease to think of Death and this thought is a great comfort, putting all tribulations into their proper proportions.

The true and proper pilgrimage to the seven basilicas to which were attached copious indulgences had to be accomplished in a single day on foot. But since Julius III, out of gentleness toward me, had made special dispensation that we might make this round on horseback, (doubling the indulgence as well!), this involved hard riding over great distances not only within Roma but without, particularly wearisome for my old bones.

And we were just under way, jogging past the Column when Giorgio's horse slipped on an outcropping of rock in the unpaved road and almost threw him. "Ahi! In our Fiorenza, the roads are better paved than this!" exclaimed Vasari, skilfully pulling back on his bridle. "The Duke has set underway ambitious road building projects all over Tuscany. . ." This encomium of the Duke was to be one of Giorgio's recurrent themes all that pilgrimage day. Nor was it a mere song to his patron. Fiorenza truly had had more paved roads than Roma even when I had left it twenty years before.

Perhaps Giorgio had been staring at Trajan's magnificent column and failed to see the rock in his path. Every visitor to Roma is enchanted by the monuments of antiquity with which the Urbs is bestrewn. *Mirabilia Romae.* And indeed it is a City of Marvels especially for those pilgrims who had thronged to Roma for the Jubilee Year, and were sleeping on straw paillasses in inns, and confessing in special booths set up for them in their own languages in the major churches and churning up the mud of the unpaved streets, as they visited antiquities or made the rounds of the basilicas. The Urbs was jammed with these gaping-jawed visitors— many of them barbarians from outside of Italy—and we heard their exclamations of wonderment in every language of Europe.

But of course those of us who had come from such great cities as Fiorenza or Venezia were more subdued in our admiration. For despite its numerous palaces and churches this city of the Popes cramped in its valley between the Tiber and the Pincio and the Campidoglio consisted for the most part of small old houses on tortuous unpaved lanes. But it is the residence of the head of the Church, and if it is smaller than Paris or London (according to the pilgrims from those cities) or our own Fiorenza which is not only more populous but has a proper center and more paved streets, nonetheless Roma is still everybody's patria because of its historical past, its magnificent ruins.

Since my permanent arrival in 1534 I had observed the Urbs slowly revive after the terrible Sack, and for this the Farnese Pope deserved all our admiration and gratitude.

Usually, the visits to the seven basilicas commenced with the sepulchral church of the Apostle Paul situated at some distance outside the Gate, followed by a visit to San Sebastiano sull' Appia, reached by the Via delle Sette Chiese. On this occasion the pilgrim usually visited some nearby catacomb.

But since we had begun at Macel de' Corvi we initiated our ride heading round the engraved white column of Trajan toward Santa Maria Maggiore, nearest of the seven basilicas. It was a beautiful morning in May, and although we had started out at the 12th hour, shortly after sunrise, the sky was already deepening into that clear cerulean blue by contrast with which the sky of Fiorenza is as changeable as the moods and manners of our citizenry and our constitutions. Against this blue rose the Tower of the Militia brown and grim. We jogged along past kitchen gardens, open fields, past Santa Quirice, conversing as we went in the sweet morning air.

Although this was not his first visit to Roma, Giorgio told me a fantastic story of what had brought him to the Holy City on this occasion.

"Since Duke Cosimo was pressing me, I had already given my book of *Lives* to Lorenzo Torrentino, the Ducal printer, even though the theoretical sections were not yet completed, when news came that Pope Paul III had died, and I began to suspect that I would have to leave Fiorenza before the completion of the printing. Therefore, when I learned that the Cardinal del Monte was passing outside of Fiorenza enroute to the Conclave, I rode out to meet him, and no sooner had I knelt to him and we had talked a bit, when he said—'I am going to Roma and undoubtedly I will become Pope'."

"He said *that?*! The talk at the conclave was that del Monte's election came as a complete surprise after months of deadlock. Indeed it was so unexpected that it has been attributed to the agency of the Holy Ghost.

Giorgio's laughter was a gleam of white square teeth in a blueblack bushy beard.

"Mayhap the Cardinal had advance notice from the Holy Ghost. At any rate, I swear to you, Maestro, he made that prognostication to me *before the Conclave opened!* And he advised me to hasten to bring to completion whatever tasks I had in hand and be prepared to come to Roma immediately without waiting to be called. And while I was in Arezzo during Carnivale, working on designs for the festival there and the masks, came the news that del Monte had indeed become Julius III. So you see it was no vain prognostication."

The great Basilica loomed ahead, second only to St. Peter's. We turned toward the front facade gleaming with mosaics of the balcony, and tethering our horses, entered the golden echoing space of the Basilica. Giorgio never stopped talking except during the necessary silence of the necessary jubileum prayers. Even at this early hour the great nave—golden with mosaics and a stately procession of ancient columns leading to the main altar—was thronged with worshippers, and one could hear all the tongues of Europe amidst the single language of prayer.

So we were out again in the great piazza, and back on our horses heading northwest now toward the city walls. Already immediately beyond the Basilica, although we were not yet outside the gate, we were in open country, broad cultivated fields dotted with occasional ancient ruins, viaducts, crumbling towers, and small churches.

"Of course as soon as I heard the news, I mounted my horse and galloped back to Fiorenza where I was solicited by Duke Cosimo to be present as his representative here at the Coronation and *Possesso.*"

As *his* representative! I thought. Giorgio, you know full well you are primarily Giorgio's representative. Most likely the solicitation was all the other way . . .

"So I came down to Roma posthaste and rode to the palazzo of messer Bindo Altoviti . . ."

"I have seen several of the new pictures you have done for messer Bindo. There are many fine inventions in them."

"O thank you, Maestro. I value your praise more than anyone else's. Did you see my Our Lady?"

"Yes, the big one, you mean? Yes, that is precisely the one wherein I speak of 'inventions'!"

"Well, I seek to add my new caprices to old themes . . . Did you notice that messer Bindo has hung it across from the Venus I did for him according to your cartoon?"

"Yes. I thought the colocation was not unseemly."

"And the lifesized deposition of Christ with Phoebus darkening the face of the sun and Diana that of the Moon? And in the background the scenes of the earthquake that accompanied the crucifixion and the dead bodies cast from their graves?—"

"Yes. Yes. I saw all that, Giorgio mio . . ." We were approaching Porta Lorenzo now, a double-towered gate manned by soldiers of the Papal guard in glittering armor and long spikey halberds, examining a trail of farmers' donkey carts which had been passing through here since before dawn, when the gate was opened to permit produce into the city. Some were leading pigs, squealing in anticipation of the fate that befalls us all; others had loads of hay; a shepherd was bishop to a flock of sheep.

"Your documents, messers," a country lad in uniform asked respectfully; and though he had looked sarcastically, or at least attempted a sarcasm foreign to his simple nature, when we said we were pilgrims making the rounds of the seven basilicas, ("on *horseback*, Messers?"); he obsequiously waved us through the gate, almost knocking over a sleepy oncoming donkey cart to make way for us, as soon as we displayed the Papal dispensation.

And all at once I was seventeen years old and coming down to Roma for the first time, and a country-lad just like this one, squinting at my sealed letter to the Cardinal Riario, pretending he could read, and asking me whether I was a supporter of Fra Girolamo. O il Tempo che consuma il tutto! O time which consumes all things!

Clamour-shade of the double-turreted gate, blaze of sunshine, smell of cow mule sheep goat sweat and damp vegetables, Ao! of contadini swish of sticks. Now we were on the Via Tiburtina in the open country outside the wall.

" . . . and after the visit to messer Bindo—"

"—Required of all Fiorentini . . ."

"—Required of all Fiorentini. Even Aretini."

One could not help but admire Giorgio Vasari. Quite aside from his multifaceted talents, the ingenuousness of his slyness is so winning.

"Messer Bindo is the very model of a patron of the arts. Very wealthy. Very discerning. And the Florentine consul in Roma. After him, I went to kneel and kiss the foot of His Holiness. Which having done, the first words he spoke to me were to remind me that his prognostication had not been in vain."

"And now that he has been crowned and things are quieting down, the first thing he wants me to do is to satisfy an obligation that he feels toward the memory of messer Antonio, the first Cardinal del Monte, to make a tomb for him in San Piero at Montorio. I have already begun to make drawings and models."

"Well, perhaps this new Pontificate augurs well for all us Tuscans. After all, his Holiness is of Tuscan origin—from San Sovino—though he himself had the misfortune to be born Roman."

I doubted Giorgio's story of the prognostication. He must have made it up to redound to his own glory, having been the first artist to hear such an awesome prediction from the lips of one who was to become Pope.

Out in the open fields now, sharp against the sky, loomed our second Basilica: this was San Lorenzo outside the Wall, and here we found only a few pilgrims, all Castilians, solemn and dressed in black from head to foot, and with a kind of preposterous dignity in their manners. Yet these were, I reflected sadly, the new masters of our Italy; Cosimo's Fiorenza leaned on their muskets and cannon; the French could no longer compete with the flood of gold pouring into Charles' coffers from the new Americas beyond the seas; and even wily Paul III had not been able to oust the Spaniards from their footholds here, for all his skillful maneuvering to keep the balance between France and Spain. For Italian freedom is only the space between these two giants and there is no place to breathe when one giant has taken all. And so it has been with the Emperor Charles who, for all his mixed blood—Spanish Flemish German—and all the vast domain he has conquered by steel and wile and advantageous marriaes, propagating between the sheets not only heirs but more extensive Hapsburg domains— For all that, the Emperor remains Spanish in our eyes and our eyes are black with his Spanishness, as black as the Borgia bulls. When I was a boy, we always considered everything south of Roma as Spanish domain (which it usually was); but with the wars of invasion that began two years after the great Lorenzo's death, the French came and then the Spaniards and now they are everywhere: in Milano, and behind the scenes in Fiorenza, and behind every Papal bull there is the Spanish bull.

This doleful flock of Castilians set these thoughts racing through my mind so that I did not truly attend to my prayers, and said them over to be truthful to the Jubilee.

I don't know what Giorgio was thinking. He seemed to perform his religious functions with dispatch and total absorption—. But then he did everything like that.

"Speaking of messer Bindo," Giorgio began at once, as soon as we were back in the saddle and on our way to Santa Croce in Jerusalem, "did you know—"

He has this odd way, Giorgio, of beginning sentences in the middle not because he is at all addled, but rather because so much is racing through his mind, so many projects being carried on at once, that he assumes his interlocutor must be familiar even with his unspoken thoughts. His bubbling words are only fish that break surface. And many as there are, there are many more below.

"—that Benvenuto Cellini is now living in his palace?"

I did know. There are very few Florentine artists who come to Roma and fail to pay obeisance to me, (O of course Baccio Bandinelli wouldn't) almost as soon as they pay obeisance to the Holy Father and to the Florentine Consul, messer Bindo. But I pretended that I didn't know, just to hear Giorgio's interpretation which was certain to be entertaining, gossipy, and full of information, some of it capricious as his ornaments.

"He has done a bronze bust of Messer Bindo, life-sized . . ."

"I know. What do you think of it?"

"Oh, a fine work!" said Giorgio heartily. "Fine! Fine!" jumping his horse over a dip in the road. I walked my mare circumspectly around the dip. "He's a madcap but an excellent sculptor withal, don't you agree, Maestro?"

I found Giorgio's praise of Benvenuto a pleasant change from the usual backbiting of artists who for the most part speak only maliciously of each other's work and character. Of course, I reflected, Vasari is primarily a painter and so feels no competition from Cellini the sculptor. They are both in the good graces of the Duke. And then they share common admirations and hatreds—admiration, indeed adulation for me, and detestation of Baccio Bandinelli. And their joint efforts (both speaking in the name of the Duke) to cajole me back to Fiorenza. An amusing pair.

"I do agree. I was passing the palazzo several weeks ago and messer Bindo invited me in to see the bust. He wanted my judgement. An admirable work. That fellow for all his madcap ways is a skilled craftsman and as elegant in his work as he is crude in his manners. It's set up in Bindo's study which is richly adorned with antiquities and other works of art, and I must say Benvenuto's bust pleases me as much or even more than those antiques. But it is very badly placed. If the windows were above instead of beneath, the whole collection would show to better advantage."

"Benvenuto is already grumbling that messer Bindo is cheating him. He claims that of the 5,000 golden scudi Bindo lent the Duke, 1200 are his, Cellini's and he's beginning to raise his usual clamor about ducats and deceit . . ."

I laughed. "Crazy Benvenuto! He is hardly the one to talk about deceit. Has he already forgotten the terrible dungeons of the Castello?"

While I was working on my Judgement, Cellini had been imprisoned in the

Castel Sant' Angelo under the charge of having stolen from the pontifical treasury at the time of Clement VII jewelry valued at 80,000 ducats. He had been a gunner at the Castel during the Sack and claimed Pope Clement had lent him the jewels to sew into his doublet for safekeeping. But everyone knew Cellini was a liar, and so he was arrested; and after his daring attempt to escape had failed—leaping to the moat and breaking a leg and being recaptured—he served many terrible months in that dungeon until he was released through the efforts of the Cardinal Ippolito d' Este and François Premier. When he returned to Fiorenza, he told the story so many times that it became a bore: the Castellan who thought he was a bat and wanted Benvenuto to fly off the ramparts with him. The angel who entered his cell, illuminating the darkness, and Benvenuto's devout poem of praise . . . Why do angels always visit such scoundrels? Even charming and talented scoundrels like Benvenuto Cellini?

Santa Croce in Jerusalem, our third basilica, was rising up before us, leaning it seemed against the ruins of the Amphitheatrum Castrense, a sort of smaller Colosseum, being built right out of that ancient structure. The Church itself grows out of an ancient Roman court and was erected by St. Helena in honor of the cross she found in Jerusalem. In the gray shade of antique granite columns, many pilgrims were reciting their prayers,—a veritable Babel of tongues this time—and we added our orisons to theirs, and then proceeded eastward, following the viaduct down to the Porta San Giovanni and the Lateran.

It was now the 16th hour, four hours after daybreak, and the sun was approaching meridian; the long lean early morning shadow of horse and horseman were condensing into a shapeless ball, we were treading on our own shadows. I felt not at all weary yet, despite my seventy-five years. Riding is always a joy to me, the sweet rocking in the saddle, the smell of horseflesh in the hot sun, the sights and sounds of Roma floating past my rocking observation post, voices rising as it were from somewhat below. A man on a horse feels privileged toward his pedestrian fellows, and we were indeed privileged to be permitted to make this pilgrimage round on horseback rather than on foot.

"Tired, Maestro?"

"No. Not yet."

"I would propose, that after we have made our prayers at the Lateran, we stop at the Sign of the Sacred Footstep just the other side of Porta Sebastiano and have our midday meal there and rest a bit before continuing."

"D'accordo."

We reached the Lateran perhaps a quarter of an hour past the touch of noon. Entering the huge holy space we stopped a moment at the Holy Staircase thronged more than I have ever known it with worshippers. Every step of the twenty-eight marble steps was occupied from edge to edge, and the slow swarm—an enormous black caterpillar—was making its way upward upon its knees, heads bobbing at certain steps to kiss the drops of our Savior's blood. The tail of the swarm extended out halfway across the Piazza with those waiting to ascend, and another swarm—butterfly-swift now, fluttering—was pouring down the flanking staircase for those who had completed the ascent.

Since the Lateran is the Cathedral of the Bishop of Roma, it outranks in ecclesiastic dignity all the other churches, including St. Peter's, in the Holy City. This had been explained to me, to my surprise, at the time Pope Paul had decided to move the statue of the Emperor Marcus Aurelius from its original post here, alongside the Palace, to its present place in the center of the Campidoglio where I am now designing a suitable pedestal for it. I had objected to that transfer, but the Pope overrode my wishes as Popes do, and it was on that occasion that the Holy Father explained the special status of the Lateran for my benefit, and the unsuitability of keeping the great equestrian statue of a pagan emperor there. For many centuries it had been believed to have been the statue of the first Christian emperor Constantine who had presented Pope Sylvester with the huge Palace which he had fitted up as a church, calling it the Basilica Constantiniana after its founder.

It was huge indeed, but the ancient basilica was sadly decayed. Almost simultaneously Giorgio and I remarked, as we dismounted, and left our horses in the care of one of the hundreds of hostlers begging for trade in front of the twin-towered narthex— "This needs rebuilding even more than San Pietro!"

"Work for you, Giorgio!"

Certainly so venerated (and venerable) a pile cannot be left in its present condition. The huge dingy moldering mass of ancient brick and stone was carious with the centuries. I could still see the old base from which Marcus Aurelius had been removed; in front of it, on low *cippi*, were two lions. The gracious gothic Loggia of Benedictino was half toppled; the octagonal Baptistry to the right of the main edifice was like a round cheese crumbling. Il tempo che consuma il tutto, I thought, the same gnawing teeth of time that I had dreamt of depicting in the form of a rat eating away the unshaped matrix of my figure Night in the new sacristy of the Medici.

Only five years ago had Maestro Bartolomeo Ammannati finally set those statues—which I had left helter-skelter in the Sacristy, the male allegories undone, when I departed for Roma in 1534—into their niches, and although I have never seen the works installed, the waves of praise that were set underway at their presentation to the public—the sonnets, God save me, the hosannas—have rippled all the way down to Roma. Every visitor from Fiorenza has something to say about my sepulchral monuments for a family I distrust, if I do not entirely detest them. The Medici have, after all, been good to me all my life. The great Lorenzo took me to live in his palace, and his son Leo X probably wished me well even if he failed to fulfill his contracts with me and caused me to waste four years of my life for a facade that was never done, and always demonstrated more love for Raffaello of Urbino than for Michelangiolo of Fiorenza.

And as for Clement—how could I very well complete the tombs of his family when I was directing cannon fire against his very own armies?

So now, as I looked at the crumbling Lateran and thought of the teeth of time that gnaws all of our creations to oblivion, my thoughts surfaced into words as thoughts sometimes do, and our interlocutors who do not know the subaqueous swim that brought us there are surprised, sometimes left gasping, by the abrupt inconsequence.

"Were you present at the opening of my Medici tombs to the public?"

"What? What?"

"My Medici tombs."

"O yes, of course, Maestro. A triumph. A triumph. I must have written to you. I must—"

"Perhaps you did. My old brain forgets. I am losing my memory, Giorgio. In fact, there are those (I was thinking of Nanni and his clique at the Fabbrica) who say I am entering my second childhood."

"O nonsense!" It was amusing to see the sudden anger in his eyes, the blood flushing behind and above that great bushy beard which seemed to bristle, the hairs erect as the hairs along the spine of a dog about to give battle, the hand automatically reaching for a sword which was not there. Giorgio is a loyal friend.

He was embarking on an account of that public opening of the Chapel, but I cut him short.

What lay behind my question (I realized no sooner had I spoken it) was a father's concern for his abandoned children. I find myself questioning anyone who has recently come from Fiorenza—And how betides my David? Have you seen my Allegories? Does messer Doni still hang my tondo in his grand salotta?

It is as if I were to ask—How is my nephew Lionardo? And my brother Gismondo and lovely Francesca?

For though I have never married, my art has been mistress enough and she has borne me many children, and some of those I will never see again, and this sometimes sets me bewailing of nights though no one knows of that. How little we know of each other . . . "Later. Later, Giorgio mio. Now let us attend to our prayers."

We were at the main facade of the basilica, the only part practically intact from the times of Fausta, wife of Constantine, with its portico of six columns on the architrave of which was inscribed (and repeated on the inner fabbrica) that San Giovanni Laterano was "mother and chief of all the Churches of the world and of the city."

Silently, I vowed to supercede that inscription with my new San Pietro.

We entered.

Five huge naves, glittering with multi-colored mosaics; a magnificent rich inlaid pavement shining like a mirror, but darkened here and there by traces of fire in an adjacent chapel.

Now at noon the great pentacular space echoed with the new chant of Maestro Palestrina. At the distant altar catechumens were swinging the censer, clouds of perfumed smoke obscured the mosaic'd apse.

We joined the Mass and made our jubilary prayers; and remounting, cast some denari to the hostler, a bucktoothed bumpkin who snatched the coins midair with hands like shovels and waved us on while beckoning his new customer almost before we had gained the saddle.

The piazza was dense with pilgrims and we had to pick our way carefully through the noisy roiling crowd, past the Hospital, along more aqueducts and ancient ruins until we reached the highway leading to the city gate of Porta San Sebastiano. The gate was preceded by the triumphal arch of Drusus, May weeds and grasses grew out of the old stones, the Roman clangor softened with that fuzz, here and there against the yellowish eaten-away stones the first poppies glowed in their fragile rednesses. The huge gate itself was flanked by twisted semicylindrical medieval towers.

Our inn was situated just the other side of the gate. It was crowded with a roaring mass of soldiery, farmers, pilgrims: a bewildering mosaic of costumes of all lands and many tongues. There were Germans who had not succumbed to Luther's heresy, but spoke nonetheless his incomprehensible barbaric language. There were ruffled French and haughty Spaniards and Slavs who had somehow managed to make their way here from the Grand Turk. And there were Dutchmen and converted Moors and other dark Christians who daringly crossed the Mediterranean in Arab feluccas. And there were English and Irish pilgrims from those gloomy isles, quite drunk now with piety and good wine. Indeed, all Roma, once the year of Jubilee had been proclaimed, was just such a combination of carnival and repentance; an air of riotous holiday and of rueful holyday. Thousands of pilgrims were making the rounds of the basilicas on foot singing and shouting and exchanging gossip and stopping at inns like this one along their route and praying before the precious relics to reap the reward of the copious indulgences.

So amidst that throng, Giorgio and I sat at a rough board table and chewed the hard contadino bread and salty cheeses, tripes and fig bread— all washed down by the white gut-strangling wine of the Castelli, not smooth as our Trebbiano; and Vasari all the while managing to chew and eat and talk all at the same time.

For the most part his talk was about his work—work accomplished and work hoped for. And then he was chattering away about the marvels of Duke Cosimo, insinuating now and again the diplomatic feint of a request that I return to my native city where I could enjoy the honor I deserved rather than the hatred and villany of my detractors here in Roma.

"Especially Nanni," I said, ignoring the first part of his request. "Do you know Nanni di Baccio Bigio is spreading the rumor all about this city that I am in my second childhood and the Pope's Cardinal-of-all-tasks, Monsignor Pier Alioti of Forli, the Cardinal Tantecose . . ."

Giorgio guffawed. He had heard about but never heard from my own lips the name I applied to this officious busybody and meddler: Cardinal Tantecose— 'so many things.'

" . . . is inclined to give ear to him. But Nanni has been my enemy since he was a boy in Fiorenza. Do you know that he crept into my studio and stole the drawings I had given to my servant Antonio Mini?"

"Yes, I understand the Magistrates of the Eight ordered him to return the drawings, and if it weren't for the intercession of his friend the Canonica of San Lorenzo, he would have been put in prison—"

"He should have been put into prison."

"Oh well, as for that escapade, Maestro," Vasari laughed, spraying crusts of peasant bread as he did so, "I must admit I cannot blame Nanni for that theft. If I were the culprit I would have stolen not only the drawings but I would have lifted everything of yours I could lay my hands on. Just to learn art, you understand. One should really admire a boy so resolved to learn the secrets of art, and from whom can one learn better than from you, Maestro? Such thievery is a sign of virtù, Maestro, don't you see? Such a thief should not be treated as if he were robbing money or goods . . ."

"I see. And if now he seeks to rob me of San Pietro? . . ."

The smile disappeared as when the host wiped a damp rag across a littered table.

"He should be garrotted. I will draw the ropes myself."

I grunted. I didn't care to have Nanni garrotted though he surely deserved it. But I didn't care to be strangled myself either. Nanni wasn't alone among my enemies. There were Cardinals, Deputies of the Fabbrica, especially Cervini, who were on my back all the time spurring me more savagely than I spurred Matilda, my mare. I knew that soon I would have to confront all these enemies and let the next Holy Father decide whether I should be left free to complete the Basilica or return to my own patria to die.

After the inn, we rode down the Appia Antica lined on both sides of the road with ancient Roman sepulchral monuments between feathery silvergreen olive trees and black umbrellas of pines. We had to keep our eyes on the pocked ancient road gutted with holes, carefully picking our horses past the dangerous pits. Besides, the road was crowded with pilgrims. The sky was brilliant, blue, cloudless. Many of the pilgrims were singing—some pious chants and others not so pious. Some had staffs and wore rich woolen cloaks, others were in rags. There were boys and bearded old men, there were wealthy ladies in fine embroidered cloths and poor ladies wearing simple hoods and scarves.

With all these pilgrims we crowded into the basilica of San Sebastiano and then holding flickering torches, we made our way down crumbling steps into the catacombs of so many martyrs over which the church had been built. Some of the cubicles were inscribed in Greek characters, but the most of them were in Latin; and again I regretted ruefully my deficiency in that tongue of our forefathers.

Traces of graffitti and flaked mosaic could be seen in the flickering torchlight. It was hard to breathe there in the damp dark.

A monk showed us the precious relic of Christ's footprint impressed on a piece of marble. The print was enormous—almost twice that of a normal man—and I was reflecting upon this miracle, when Vasari's stentorian voice rang out, innocent and bold at once:

"Padre, is that really the Lord's footprint?"

According to the legend, St. Peter, fleeing from a martyr's death, met his Master on the Via Appia and inquired of Him *Quo Vadis Domine?*, to which he received the reply *Venero iterum crucifigi*; whereupon the Apostle, ashamed of his weakness returned to Roma and martyrdom. So I have often been ashamed of my weakness, thinking to flee my martyrdom when Giorgio, having received no reply, repeated as loudly as before:

"Padre, do you mean to assert that that is *truly* the Lord's footprint?"

"By Bacchus, only heretics would doubt it?" replied the monk.

There was a resentful murmurous echo from the crowd of gazing pilgrims. Many of them had traveled enormous distances and suffered sickness by sea and brigands by land to come to this Holy City, and they did not like being deprived of the miracles and relics for which they had come. My own meditations in those damp underground passages, lined with closed cubicles and occasional tombs broken open to display grinning skulls and a clutter of bones—my own meditations were, as so often they are, on Death and the vanity of human wishes; but Giorgio's impertinence caused me to smile. He can cause even a stone to smile. He is a curious blend of diplomacy and bluntness, stiletto and broadaxe.

Indeed, after we had left the church and began the long ride to St. Paul's Outside the Walls, Giorgio was still searching for a theological explanation of how so huge a footprint could belong to a man (for Christ voluntarily took upon himself all the attributes of a man, even death) and further how it could have been impressed into marble? I did not attempt to answer. Each to his own *mestiere,* and notwithstanding that I have frequented many a theological discussion in the Marchesa of Pescara's circle, the Oratory of Divine Love, and I have heard Contarini and Cardinal Pole and Vittoria Colonna herself—all minds honed as razors—disputing the finest points of doctrine. I prefer not to enter those lists myself.

My mestiere is to liberate my spirit from a block of marble.

My silence finally silenced messer Giorgio. And we rode thoughtfully along the wall, welcoming its shade because now the sun, though beginning its decline, was hot, and my old flesh was sweating in the woolen cloak. While riding, I unstrung the laces at my throat with one hand, and flung the cloak across the withers of my horse; and Giorgio complimented me on my horsemanship which praise I found sweet. Indeed, I can accept such praise more easily than praise for my works, which always embarrasses me, especially when the incense is as thick as Giorgio wafts it. But to be praised for simple things is always a great pleasure: to be told that I sit my horse well, that I can draw a straight line without dropping a plumb, or draw a circle freehand as perfect as those who inscribe it with a nail and a piece of string, that I have the compasses in my eyes and respect my craft as any good artisan must do, as in my boyhood, I walked the streets of my beloved Fiorenza, and had gazed into hundreds of shops and watched wood carvers and goldsmiths and silversmiths and hammerers of metal and pottery makers and layers of gesso and scaffold-builders, and cutters of brick and haulers of great stones being piled up in rustico palaces and color—grinders and beaters of wool and dyers dipping cloths in the great bloody-colored liquids of the vats,—I had grown up in this artigiano Fiorenza. I had indeed suckled the dust of pietra serena from a stonecutter's wife at Settignano, who was my wet nurse; and spent my boyhood in that artisan-humming hive between Palazzo Vecchio and Santa Croce. So I respect craft wherever and whenever I come upon it; and I am more at ease with stonecutters than Popes. I like their humor and I even like their broken ragged nails.

We returned to the city gate, then cut along the Tiber subsidiary called the Almo; although within the city walls we were in open country— tilled fields mostly, dotted here and there with little churches or ancient ruins, then our road crossed the swamp of the Maranna until we cut into Via Ostensiensis, and rode westward toward San Paolo, our penultimate basilica. It was a long ride—many many leagues—and I was more winded than my horse when we reached the Sixth Pilgrimage Church, the Basilica of San Paolo near the Tiber.

After San Pietro this was the vastest church of Roma. Here Constantine had transformed the cell of the Apostle to the gentiles (whose image I had just set upon the wall of the Cappella Paolina in a mode not entirely to the satisfaction of certain pedants who found my figure of Saul becoming Paul old and bearded when he should have been young and presumably cleanshaven when he was struck by the light from heaven, but I was less interested in illustrating stories than finding some fitting outward guise for my own soul.

With hundreds of other pilgrims, we crossed the enormous columned portico and entered the splendid basilica of five naves divided by eighty columns, the greatest church of Christendom until my new San Pietro shall have been completed but I shall not live to see that; I shall be lucky to see the walls arise at least to the level of the drum. What first strikes the pilgrim entering San Paolo is the enormous triumphal arch scintillating with mosaics and the ancient frescoes and mosaics of the transept and semicircular apse. Many of the frescoes are by Pietro Cavallini, one of the very few native artists of Roma, his manner obviously much influenced by our great Giotto. I can think of few other Roman Artists—Giulio Romano, perhaps (but he was in a nest of Umbrians: his master Raffaello of Urbino who served apprenticeship to a fellow Umbrian, Perugino, and was in turn aided by his kinsman, Bramante); some few Venetians have come here, my dear gossip, Fra Sebastiano Luciano of the Piombo, whose melodious tongue is sealed now, alas, but all the rest?—from the distant days of the great Giotto and his followers, and amongst the moderns too: Peruzzi of Siena, and Giorgio Vasari of Arezzo, and Botticelli and Signorelli, Rosselli and Fra Angelico, Chirlandaio and Filippino Lippi, Donatello and myself—all Florentines, all Florentines. We come here and embellish this city and place ourselves and our arts at the disposition of these Popes and Cardinals and great Lords, and ever since the time of Leo X, especially, we Florentines have been the spur of Roma, to make this lazy steed leap; we have been their artistic conscience and their bankers, and there are sections in this city where I love to walk whenever I feel a nostalgia for the Cupolone, in the Rione of the Parione or the Banche, where the faces are lean, the lips sharp, the wit sharper, and the cadences are the familiar cadences of my Lily on the Arno. With every swallowed "c" and thickened "t" I am back home. At the time Giorgio and I were making this round I had already been in Roma, Caput Mundi, for sixteen unbroken years and the halls of the Vatican were more familiar to me than the Palazzo Vecchio and my labors on the Judgement and now the Pauline Chapel were devoted to the great Farnese Paul III, Roman of the Romans.

But I remain a Florentine.

I can no more dispense with that than the color of my eyes.

Fiorentinità is the color of my soul.

We passed through the quadriportico and then the portico and the huge bronze central door from Constantinople and entered a great courtyard all paved in shining manycolored marbles.

The columns of the naves were of the Corinthian order, at least thirty-eight palms high and led to an enormous arch through which one passed to the crossing. The floor on which we trod was a graven marble book of inscriptions. A series of mosaic'd popes ran round under the roof. Porphory, granite, marble, a forest of columns and Giorgio and I kneeling in the forest amidst a murmurous chanting throng.

So we said our orisons and departed. The sun was halfway down to the West now, a slight golden haze hung on the horizon. In the distance, to the west we could see the bristling towers of Roma, huddled within the walls. The fields about us were scattered with ruins, fragments of viaducts and aqueducts, occasional columns and round towers of tufa, crumbling walls of that ancient Roman brick, so much thinner than ours but worked and patterned with great subtlety.

A sense of brooding solitude and irony emanated from these ruins in the open fields; goats and sheep grazed indifferently amidst this antiquity, and left their droppings on single breasted Venuses and prone Jupiters with broken penises. All the gods were fallen and the sun was going down. "We had better hurry," I said, "I want to arrive at St. Peter's by the twenty-second hour at the latest. That will leave us time to make our jubilee prayers and yet arrive back at Macel de' Corvi before nightfall."

We spurred our horses and jogged down to the road along the Tiber but since there was no bridge here, we had to return via the Ostensis Road, past open fields and an occasional church and the ever-present silent-speaking ruins, In the golden haze, the ruins seemed softer now, the tufa and bricks were laved with amber dust, the pines seemed blacker against a deeper blue. This stretch now to St. Peter's, the longest leg of our journey, would take us across the entire city from South to West and we rode harder now to arrive at the Mother Church of Christendom—the culminating Basilica of our pilgrimage—before the evening Angelus bells.

Just beyond the gate was the Pyramid of Celsus, and at a spring there we rested a bit, watering our horses before setting forth again, riding in a pleasurable jog, not too ardent for my old bones but fast enough to be pleasurable, the rocking rhythm of it that sets the blood flowing and sparkles the eyes. Vasari was thoughtfully (and thankfully) silent now. We were inside the city walls again, but we were still in a sparsely populated area.

Giorgio broke his silence when we came to the extended meadow that lay below Mons Testacius.

"Have you ever seen the carnival from here, Maestro?"

"I have."

"I am told it is a bestial spectacle."

"It is indeed. Perhaps we might better call it a *human* spectacle for beasts are never as cruel to their kind as we are to ours. Cartloads of live pigs pushed off the cliff and then the obscene sight of those Romans running with pans to catch the live hot blood issuing from the mouths and eyes and ears and open wounds of those shattered beasts so that one cannot distinguish the screaming of the pigs from the screaming of their tormentors. After such a spectacle the mere sight of fried pig-blood sausages makes me retch."

Vasari grimaced. "There is much in Roma to make one retch."

"Già"

We continued silently through the great grassy meadow under the Testacian Hill past more open fields until we reached the Tiber again at a point called Marmorata. Here countryside had modulated into city again: people in the unpaved streets (our Fiorenza has many more paved streets than this Capital of Christendom), small houses, sometimes leaning against ancient ruins like mollusks attaching themselves to rocks. So we attach ourselves to our past: lean against it, build upon it.

A number of the streets have had arches across them. We continued past the Greek school, past the round church of St. Stephen, similar to the temple of the Vestal Virgins. Now the streets were crowded again. At the river bank just ahead we could see the island in the Tiber and on the right bank the huge great round brown pile of the Theatrum Marcellus onto which the Savelli have grafted their palace.

We might have continued to the Vatican on this side of the river but I was curious to see how well Nanni was coming along with his repairs on the ancient bridge Pons Amelius, renamed in our days, Santa Maria, built of round arches of blocks of tufa.

I pulled my horse to a stop at the bank and tried to see through the forest of scaffolding what further work had been accomplished since it was wrested from my hands.

Giorgio suddenly realized I was not with him and he wheeled about and asked "What is it, Maestro?"

"Another example of the malice of my enemies," I said. "Originally the reconstruction of this bridge had been entrusted to me by Pope Paul of sainted memory. It surely needs repairs. Fifteen hundred years the river has flowed through it, fifteen hundred years have eaten away the old stones. Look there, like rotting teeth, brown decay, the foundation stones are crumbling. Several years ago I gave orders that new foundations be sunk and diligent repairs be made on the piles. And these works were already well under way, goodly sums of money expended for scaffoldings and new blocks of travertine to be set into the structure. But just last year the Congregation of the Clerics proposed that the works be handed over to—"

"Nanni di Baccio Bigio."

"*Preciso!* Nanni di Baccio Bigio. Architetto they call him. The very one. It seems Nanni claimed he could complete the works in much less time and with much less money than I could do it; and that stupid committee of clerics alleging they were acting for my sake since I am an old man and should be spared further aggravations, (San Pietro being a sufficiency) and forgetful and so on and so on . . . And the good Holy Father, not wanting any trouble, handed all authority over to the Clerics of the Camera nominally in charge of these works here, and without consulting me any further—without even informing me—they turned the whole thing over to Nanni last year . . ."

"Shameful shameful."

"Già." I said no more but started my horse across the bridge and Giorgio followed. We were almost half way across when I cried out: "Giorgio! This bridge is trembling! Gallop! *Via!*" And we flew across to the other shore, fearing at any moment we would land in the river together with planks of the roadbed and a heap of moldering Roman stones.

As it was the bridge did not collapse. Not then. But seven years ago for my mind now remembering is a labyrinth of time forward, and time backward, so that often here in the night, hammering at this Christ, I feel that time has ceased to flow entirely, that everything I remember is Now, this very Moment, there is no past and surely no future (on this earth), a continuous Now, carving these figures to further emaciation in the night and crossing that bridge with Giorgio fourteen years ago as I am crossing it even now as I say it, and feel the timbers of the temporary roadbed trembling with the trembling foundations that were supposed to sustain it and I am shouting Giorgio! Giorgio! Gallop! *Via*! This bridge is going to collapse! . . .

But it didn't and we were on the other bank and I loked carefully to see what I could—which was little. Nor did I care to descend through that forest of timbers to examine the situation more closely. Later I learned that Nanni had simply set aside my plans for his own profit, selling off a great number of the blocks of travertine I had ordered, so that the bridge might be flanked and supported as it had been in ancient times. Instead of travertine Nanni substituted pebbles and other fill inserted in such a manner that from within no one could see any faults, the bridge looked entirely rebuilt. The upshot of it all was that Nanni was doing the work in such a way as to redound more to his earnings than to the solidarity of the bridge.

So we escaped that peril and I decided to light as ex voto a special candle in Santa Maria Sopra Minerva which is my church in Roma and where the Christ I made (and Urbino almost ruined) for messer Varo, still stands although as much scandal is being murmured about his nudity as about the nudes of my Judgement, and inasmuch as one cannot very well paint britches over the loins of a marble statue, some new form of bracche will have to be devised, should the Council of Trento so decide, as it probably will.

But I was so shaken that we did not proceed to San Pietro through Trans-tiberium which is on the same side of the river below the Janiculum Hill, the sun being now more than halfway to its rest, and I feared the treacherous muddy road along the Tiber. So we crossed the Tiber again a league further downstream on the Ponte Sixtus and now we were in the Rione of the Banche and I felt at home seeing all about me those familiar faces. For although I did not know them all personally, they were for the most part Florentine faces: those long sharp-honed visages, somewhat equine in the protruding cheekbones and temples, stony fields in which the eyes were mica-sharp and ducat-gleaming and the lips long and sensual, set tight, ready to spring, traps. O I can spot my countrymen even from a crossbow-shot away; I know their gait and I know the hang of their luccas and there are plenty of them here in Roma so that though I have been physically here now for thirty years, there has never been a paucity of Tuscan faces here; I can walk along the banks of the Tevere and be Lungarno, Brunelleschi's great brickred Dome contains me ever in this hotter sky; and especially when I wander about the Rione Ponte and Borgo, that is, the centers of mercantile, financial, and ecclesiastical power, I am quite at home. When I came back here definitely, I found that though the Sack may have diminished the power of the Red Lily a bit, yet we Tuscans were still powerful, even if Paul soon changed our domination of the Papal family which had continued from the time of Leo X, Lorenzo's son. We entered Via Giulia named after the late Pope Julius II who in his *furor edificans*—rage for building— did not hesitate to destroy medieval quarters for modern streets. A short way down from the river was the extension of Bindo Altoviti's palace where Benvenuto

Cellini was now lodging. Giorgio thought to knock at the door; he always found Benvenuto amusing. Perhaps he might join us . . . But I dissuaded him. I too considered Cellini amusing, but I was wary of the man: he was an odd fellow, explosive as a blunderbuss, an assassin several times over (by his own account)— and yet, incongruously from such a roiling boiling man there issues forth the most exquisite work, whether in large or small. I had seen his Ganymede in Fiorenza and his portrait head of Alessandro, and here in Roma the Altoviti portrait— admirable all of it. I feel he is a goldsmith even when he works large but the elegance of his work in no way detracts from its power: a rare combination of strength and great control. But as a man, I would as lief trust a bull: some inadvertent remark would be the rag that sets the bull charging.

"As a matter of fact", I said, "Benvenuto came to visit me only two days ago. He repeated in full what he had already written to me from Fiorenza in the Duke's name."

"Ah?"

"I told him that I was engaged upon the fabric of St. Peter's and this would prevent me from leaving Roma. To which he rejoined so quickly that I had the impression he was acting from instructions, that I might leave the execution to my man Urbino who would carry out my orders to the letter."

"He said that, did he?"

Vasari was altogether too innocent in his attempt at slyness. I know very well that they are all in this together—Vasari and Cellini and even my nephew Lionardo—to entice me back to the Duke.

"He did indeed. As well as a cornucopia of future favors in the form of a message from the Duke."

"And how did you respond to that?"

"I looked Benvenuto straight in the face and said: 'And you? To what extent are *you* satisfied with the Duke?'"

And I smiled the same sarcastic smile at Vasari which I had smiled at Cellini.

With that smile we continued riding down the street of Papa Giulio, my Medusa and Maecenas. Close by, we could see the back of the enormous Farnese Palace on the Campo dei Fiori which the Roman plebe called the "die" because of its cubic shape. It dominated this entire quarter and as we jogged past, Giorgio began an encomium on my architecture: the "cornice of all cornices" which I had designed for it, as well as the top storey, the loggia of the main door, the arms of the Pope, and the regal inner cortile.

"I intended to place the Dirce group—the Farnese Bull—in a back portico," I said to Giorgio, "and build a bridge to join the Farnese vineyard with the main palace. The perspective through the courtyard across the river would be beautiful. But Paul's death has undone that dream as it has undone much else."

Like myself, Vasari was becoming more and more involved in architecture; in this art, which like all the others derives its true proportions from the human body, I have discovered, ever since I built the New Sacristy for the Medici, that the shapes and proportions and decorations of buildings are as human as limbs and torso and facial expressions; that my columns recessed in the wall of the Ricetto of the Laurentian Library express the same concept of imprisonment as do my Prigioni for Julius' tomb; that an agitated cornice is my Lorenzo's twisted wrist, that a pale shallow niche stares blankly as my forerunners of Christ in the spandrels of the Sistine Vault; that a broken pediment, an invert baluster, a soaring dome—all these are lurking messages of claustrophobia, of strain, of weight, of yearning, of suffering, of torment and of grace—I discovered that I had at my command a secret handwriting (and these are times for secrets and codes: clear enough for those who clearly wish to decipher them). What I had said with the human figure I could say with the forms of architecture.

And no one could paint britches on my most sensual volutes!

Just a few blocks away, across the Campo dei Fiori caterwauling with its market vendors and screeching mules and vivid with its living mosaics of fruits and vegetables, we could see the only other structure in Roma that might vie with the Farnese Palace. This was the Chancellery, and I was not surprised that Giorgio should now embark on a long discourse on the art of fresco painting. He wanted to know how close I was to completion on the Crucifixion of Peter in the Pauline Chapel.

"A month or more" I replied hopefully. "But it goes slowly, Giorgio; terribly slowly, and I have been ill several times since Paul forced me to paint in the Pauline. Fresco painting is not an art for old men." (I said that for Giorgio's benefit. I suppose I was pulling his leg. For if painting al fresco is not an art for old men, surely the hammering at obdurate marble is even less indicated for the old. Yet I seldom let a day pass without hammering at marble and if I pare away that bulge I might reach the very core of Christ. Giorgio didn't know then (nor did I) that the first thing I would do yet within a few days after completing the Pauline paintings at the age of seventy-five, would be to secure that great column of Diocletian I had already decided upon and begin to hammer out a Deposition with four figures in it, including myself as Nicodemus for my own tomb. And hardly a day went by when I wasn't hammering at that block and when I finally smashed it I did not wait long to begin another Deposition, and here it is before me now, reduced after ten years to a column of pure Idea.

So I think that when I told that vainglorious Vasari that fresco painting was not an art for old men, I simply meant that I was bored with painting after fifteen years of the Judgement and the Pauline and I was eager to return to the only art I have ever considered truly mine own: carving in marble.) "I have been at these two frescoes now for nine years. Yet in my youth I completed the Sistine Vault in four."

"And do you know how long it took me to do the great hall of the Chancellery over there?" He pointed through an orchard where one could now see more of the Palace.

"Yes, Giorgio, I know," I smiled. He never failed to boast of this accomplishment.

"One hundred days! Exactly one hundred days!"

"Yes, one can see it."

He failed, as he had failed the first time I made that remark, to catch the irony. He is so proud of his speed of execution, Giorgio, that my barb just whizzed by imperceived. He wasn't wounded in the least, not even a scratch.

"One hundred days, the salone almost as big as the Sala del'500, more than 200 figures." With each tally, he slapped his horse's neck in jubilation and had to pull the bridle to prevent him from galloping off down the crowded thoroughfare.

Of course Vasari doesn't work alone, as I inescapably must. He employs teams of assistants as did Raffaello in the Stanze, and indeed as does any artist confronted with a major project.

But fresco painting is not my craft. I have always been forced to do that which I do not want to do.

Not only does Vasari employ teams as did Raffaello, but he has another quality which reminds me of the Urbinate notwithstanding his manner is considerably more rhetorical.

When he had ushered me into the great hall of the Ufficio of the Chancellery four years before our pilgrimage ride, and with a proud flourish unveiled, so to speak, his painted accomplishment of a century of days, I noted at once that not only was the fresco teeming with almost as many figures as my Last Judgement, but conforming to the new rigid spirit of the times, all his female figures were clothed. And needless to say the males were not only clothed but (and here was the resemblance to Raffaello) almost all portraits of his contemporaries.

"—And there *you* are, Maestro! Next to the Pontifex Maximus!"

And indeed it was a portrait gallery. There was the Holy Father himself, Paul III garbed like a Pontifex of the Old Testament—putting Jerusalem in the shade with his new St. Peter's. Giorgio had even painted the new constructions of the Fabbrica! There was the Cardinal Alessandro Farnese, the spirit and the goad behind this commission. There was Charles V and Francis I, and all the greatest humanists and theologians of our time: Guidiccioni, Contarini, Sadoleto, Bembo, Pole, Giovio. There they were all on the wall, their speaking likenesses forever fixed on that wall. And I could not but admire Giorgio Vasari for the skill with which he had siezed these personages, myself included, without idealizing them, but presenting them as a looking glass reflects a face. His rhetoric was reserved for battle steeds with enormous buttocks, and golden and silver manes streaming like the hair of Botticelli's Venus, and the exaggerated posturing actors of his fable.

But we, portrayed there, who looked on, spectators at a play, were staid and respectable, unidealized, as straight-forwardly realistic as any of the portraits of the Tornabuoni and Sassetti, and Medici in Master Ghirlandaio's frescoes in Santa Maria Novella or Santa Trinita.

All these painted compliments, I thought, this scraping of the foot, this courtly bow, this sweeping of a feathered hat below the knees.

His art serves his diplomacy.

His diplomacy serves his art.

So I duly thanked Giorgio for ranking me with those immortals he had set upon the wall, and lauded his work in full honesty and without reserve, for doing so well and so craftsmanly and so swiftly what he had set out to do, knowing all the while that this is not what I have ever set out to do. As we walked about the great hall, the marble pavement clicking underfoot, the courtly figures of his painting seeming to speak with us, I thought of my tormented swarm of the saved and the damned of my Judgement, in which the only portraits are of myself as a flayed skin, and Aretino as a saint, and Biagio as a devil.

My only portraiture is of the soul.

We passed the foundation stones of the colossal mint Pope Julius had commissioned Bramante to build on this new street. There were but the corner stones jutting from the street, like worn down molars of a toothless old man. Nothing else. Judging by the extension of the stones, the mint would have been colossal beyond anyone's imagination, colossal like all of Julius' dreams: like the tomb he wished me to make, like the church in which I was still engaged. Aborted, I thought like so many of Julius' colossal dreams.

Like so many of mine.

Julius' street ended (as it had started) at the river where the new Church of the Florentines was to be built, and now directly to the right loomed the colossal round mole of the Castel Sant' Angelo with my namesake atop glittering his sword in the sun, deeper gold now, soon to plunge hotly into the river. We spurred across the bridge and up Via Alessandro toward our goal: San Pietro's basilica across the huge Piazza.

The Piazza was so crowded with pilgrims, that we had to dismount at the rim; we had difficulty finding a hostler though there were hundreds of them serving the throng, but finally near the Foundry behind Sant' Anna we tied our horses, and walked toward the greatest church of Christendom, which God willing, I hoped to transofrm into a greater church still. The approach had not been affected at all by the works we were engaged in which were all concentrated in the apse and deep interior of the basilica. But from here, as we walked past the beautiful three-tiered fountain erected by Alexander VI, buffetting our way through the polylingual crowds (and though I was tired after the long day's ride, I was jubilant too that I had accomplished such a long round, at my age, and the slight twinge in my left side and a slight headache seemed a small price to pay for that pardonable pride).

Constantine's basilica was not unlike San Paolo Outside the Walls or Santa Maria Maggiore except that there was no great portico'd narthex. The westering sun was now setting behind the Basilica; the mosaics of the facade pricked out in stray beams. We walked in a throng of pilgrims up the broad staircase leading to the church. The simple quadrangular vestibule and atrium contained a fountain decorated with a bronze pine cone and gilded peacocks. This inner court was littered with fragments of ancient statues and in the portico of Constantine's venerable basilica what first struck the eye were the marble statues of St. Peter and Giotto's Navicella.

Filarete's bronze central door as well as the Holy Door to the right were open.

So we entered that holy space—a long five-naved ancient basilica, gleaming with mosaics and whatever ancient marble columns had not been destroyed by Bramante. As we passed the Chapel of Santa Maria della Febbre, outside of which stood an obelisk crowned with a ball, I glimpsed within, as I always did, my earliest marble Madonna with the dead Christ in her lap, glowing in the warm ivory of a full moon and bringing back to me my first sojourn in this holy city more than half a century ago. It was the silent colloquy I always experienced when I saw again a work I had long done with: this Pietà or the Bacchus still in messer Gallo's courtyard (missing a hand, cut off like so many living hands during the Sack of '27)—seeing those old perpetually-youthful children of my youth, the silent questions the silent answers—And how do you fare?—And you, Maestro?

—Badly, but I fare.

—I change but little. My flesh darkens a bit. My hand has been chopped off by a German lance-knight.

—Mine not. My soul . . .

—My soul is my body. I still glow . . .

O she does still! Smooth and elegant, my aristocratic Lady, her solemn monstrance—Here is my Son—and the son, dead, stylish-dead, his decorative beard.

Giorgio would gape still, and pour too many words of praise. He intruded on my private colloquy, the silent colloquy of sweet forms, his words were boots trampling over our dialogue.

Impatiently, I walked away, down the main nave, Vasari after me, down toward the main altar where we could see the gigantic piers raised by Bramante and the altered tribune which I have initiated. When we arrived at the back of the church where the new constructions could be seen, Giorgio exclaimed in praise of what I had already done. Around the piers I had constructed spiral ramps up and down which could be seen mules laden with building materials and men on horseback right up to the top of the arches. And it was a strange sight to see those living men and beasts riding up and down those two spiral ramps right in the church, while below, worshippers knelt and choruses intoned.

Only three years before I had been placed in full command, appointed architect of Saint Peter's in succession to Antonio di San Gallo, and still the San Gallo pack were hounding my every step.

So I prayed the Jubilee prayer and I prayed for the defeat of these hounds and I prayed for the new Holiness who wished me well it seemed, and I prayed for the welfare of my family and the freedom of my city.

And on my knees beside Giorgio Vasari, amidst thousands of other pilgrims, in the soft flickering of hundreds of candles and the sunset effulgence of the mosaics glinting in the golden light through the Holy Door, I felt that I had truly made the round this day not merely of the seven basilicas but of the more than fifty years since I had first come as a boy of seventeen to this most holy city of Roma, Urbs, Caput Mundi.

V

Messer Tomao

That round of the basilicas seemed really to invigorate the old man. "Tomao," he said proudly, "I have done it. All day on Matilda and she— povera bestia!—more weary than I when we returned. Giorgio wanted to accompany me home from San Pietro but Matilda knows her way from the Fabbrica to Macel de' Corvi even in the dark. And it was already dark. The Pantheon was black as a blood pudding when we reached it, a pale sickle moon floating just over the oculus. I went in: a shaft of moonlight slanting right onto Raffaello's tomb . . ."

He was unusually talkative, I thought, lively. He chattered on and on about his fellow Tuscan Vasari who had accompanied him: "A talented fellow withal, Tomao, immensely talented. But he deflects too much of his energy into celebrating this Duke Cosimo. And of course, he was fishing for more compliments for his book. But I had already sent him a letter of thanks as soon as I received it and even added a sonnet in its praise . . . All that remains now is to correct some of its errors," he added darkly.

"It's certainly been a Holy Year for books about you, hasn't it Maestro? Varchi's in January, Vasari's in March? While you're writing sonnets of gratitude, have you ever sent one to messer Varchi for his *lezione?*"

"Madonna, no! How can I presume to send sonnets to so learnèd a man who manages to lecture for more than an hour on one of my scribbles? But I did send him a letter." I was flattered when I learned that Varchi had in his lecture explicitly referred to my friendship with Michelangiolo as a noble example of Platonic love. Later, when I learned more about Benedetto Varchi, I was dubious of the savor of his praise).

Varchi's second lecture (later published in a booklet) dealt with the question of the relative nobility of the two arts of sculpture and painting.

He had queried Michelangiolo earlier upon this question, and Michele had replied then that he considered painting good to the degree that it tended toward relief, and relief bad insofar as it tended toward painting and that the relationship between them was that of the sun to the moon.

He had showed me this letter with a shy smile. "That is surely not calculated to gain you friends among the painters," I said. "They would rather be solar than lunar."

"Wishing is not being."

But now after reading Varchi's printed booklet on the question containing Michele's reply as well as that of many other painters and sculptors, the old man felt, I imagine, that he owed Varchi (who had done him the great honor of lecturing on his Sonnets before the new-formed Florentine Academy) the courtesy of a more oblique answer.

"Now that I have perused your little booklet," he wrote (I read the letter in his firm square hand, as beautiful to the eye as to the mind) "where you say speaking philosophically that things, which have the same end are one and the same thing, this has caused me to change my mind (which he had only on the public level) and if greater difficulty and judgement, impediments and fatigue do not make for greater nobility, well then painting and sculpture might well be the same thing." (I burst out laughing. *Why do you laugh, Tomao?* His gray eyes shrewdly assessing my reaction, no trace of a smile on his lips. *I appreciate your nimble swordsmanship.*) "and in order that they be considered equal, every painter should busy himself with making sculptures no less than paintings. And similarly sculptors should busy themselves with paintings as well. By sculpture I mean that which one makes by means of taking away. That which one does by means of pushing or adding is similar to painting."

"But enough of all this. Since both sculpture and painting derive from the same intelligence, let them make a good peace pact together, and set aside all these disputes. Because disputing over primacy wastes time that had better go to making figures."

A wonderful letter I thought. Like any good Florentine artisan, he preferred *fare* to *chiacchiera*, making to palavering.

In his booklet Varchi had quoted someone to the effect that painting was more noble than sculpture.

"That fellow uses arguments that my *fante* could have done better."

Yet typically, though the Master preferred to embody his concepts in carven human forms, even considering painting and architecture a deflection, "not my craft," as he so repeatedly said to avoid unwelcome commissions, his literary skill was considerable. Varchi was not alone in praising the rough-hewn sonnets and madrigals which he was forever scratching on the backs of drawings and copies of letters to his family. He may have considered them scribblings but none of us did. The Marchesa of Pescara and messer Donato Giannotti and messer Luigi the banker and I (though I never hazarded literary criticism, especially since several of the poems were addressed to me)—all of his friends found much more worth in his word-carvings, for that is what they were, than he did. Indeed, messer Luigi, just before his death, had gathered a sheet of them together and obtained from Michele a reluctant permission to have them published.

Yet he was always so self-demeaning about his poetry. I recall how comically he scowled when he first heard about Varchi's lecture from Donato Giannotti who had learned the details in a letter from Fiorenza from one of his numerous spies in the Duke's service. Then came a letter directly to Michele himself from messer Luca Martelli, overflowing with lauds, a laurel-wreath of a letter. It was amusing to note Michelangiolo's embarrassment. He is incredibly, I would say excessively, modest in dealing with these learnèd men, always self-conscious of his lack of Latin. But I have yet to meet any scholar who can match our Michele's knowledge of Dante Alighieri: one would think he had made that journey personally with the Divine Poet as he had made his journey this day with the most undivine Vasari.

Varchi's first lecture had treated of Michelangiolo's poem that begins:

> Non ha l'ottimo artista alcun concetto
> Ch' un marmo solo in sé non circonscriva
> Col suo soverchio . . .

treated it, according to messer Luca's letter no otherwise than he would have treated a sonnet by Dante Alighieri or Petrarca. When he received the book, Michele wrote a most delicate letter in reply to messer Luca in Fiorenza:

"The sonnet is certainly mine but the comment comes from heaven. Truly it is an admirable thing—I don't say according to my judgement, but that of valiant men, and especially of messer Donato Giannotti who never wearies of reading it; he sends you his warmest greetings.

About the sonnet, I know what it amounts to; nevertheless, I can't help but feeling a bit of pride for having been the occasion of so beautiful and learnèd a commentary; and since in the words and praise of the author of that lecture, I feel to be someone whom I am not, I beg you to compose in my name some words addressed to him that would be a suitable response to such an expression of love, affection and courtesy. I beg you to do this because I feel I possess little talent in this regard; and when people have formed a good opinion of one, better not to tempt fortune; better remain silent than fall from the heights. I am old and . . ."

How Donato laughed when he saw that note! Donato was at the core of all this Florentine-Roman literary-political activity: I was at the periphery of it; and Michelangiolo was frequently the subject. I liked Donato, but felt at times a bit jealous of the Fiorentinità he shared with the Master. No matter how close I might be, I was out of that.

At any rate, Michele had involved Donato too in that whole silly business of thanking Varchi. Messer Donato was an old friend of Varchi's; they had been in exile together; and though the Humanist had made his peace with the Duke and returned, while Donato remained stubbornly in opposition, yet like others in the Duke's entourage, Varchi served as a kind of spy to Giannotti acting for the exiles in Roma. At any rate, Michelangiolo found letters of gratitude very difficult. He was always asking his friends— mostly Giannotti these days, but it used to be Luigi del Riccio here in Roma and Bartolommeo Angiolini up in Fiorenza, both dead now alas—he was always asking these friends to polish his sonnets—pumice them, he used to say—and write letters of gratitude for him as if he were as illiterate as his Marchigiana cook and did not know how to wield the pen as skillfully as he wields a chisel or a brush. When the Dutch composer Arcadelt set several of Michele's madrigals to music, the Maestro turned to Luigi: " . . think of some suitable present to give him, either silks or money . . ." (Why didn't he send a drawing? I wondered at the time).

And when he received a gift from Monsignore di Todi, Federgo Cesi, again Michele turned to messer Luigi: "Since I know you are a master of ceremonies to the same degree that I am far from being one; and since I've received from Monsignore Todi the letter that Urbino will give you, I beg you enter into the matter; and since I believe you are a friend of his Lordship, thank him, whenever you think best, in my name with that ceremony which is easy for you and difficult for me . . ."

I understood why he never made such requests of me: he always considered me but a boy, even when I had long ceased to be a boy.

He still considers me a boy. I with my graying beard and a wife and two sons! For notwithstanding I am his most intimate friend, he sought someone also to whom he might dictate his memories.

He had set about this almost immediately after he had read Giorgio Vasari's book. "Of course, I didn't tell the good fellow. He is so fulsomely fond of me. But I cannot help but be offended by his utterly false account of my relations with Julius regarding the tomb."

I thought—I hoped—he might dictate these autobiographical rectifications to me. Instead he chose Ascanio Condivi, a simple young fellow who had begun assisting around his studio since he had come to Roma from Ripa Transone, color-grinding and copying Michele's drawings. He was a Marchigiano like Urbino and almost all those in Michelangiolo's service.

When, to Michele's own astonishment, he learned that young Condivi was preparing a Life, he summoned him and offered to cooperate in every way, thus providing him with an opportunity to correct what the Aretine Giorgio had already published. And it was indeed easy to work with Condivi for he was a faithful fellow and by no means a simpleton, and soon Michele realized he was writing his own Life. And since he knew it would all be corrected by messer Annibale Caro who had introduced young Condivi to him, he felt secure that it would be written in buon Toscano . . . It was amusing to see Ascanio struggling with his quill as Michele narrated to him the events of his life. He seemed as clumsy with that tool as with a brush. For though Michelangiolo gave him several cartoons, when he came to color them the results were clumsy and the forms ill-wrought. But I was reluctant to criticize the young man for he was doing our Michelangiolo a good service.

Ascanio brought a bucolic air into Macel de' Corvi with his hay-colored hair, florid complexion spotted with freckles, short-spade of a nose and little greenpea eyes. He was a gentle sweet fellow who revered his Master as a faithful dog might revere him. In many ways, quite apart from their both being Marchigiano, he reminded me of Urbino except that Condivi's voice was soft and murmurous as a

running brook and Urbino could not ask for a glass of water without making you
jump for terror. He was a shepherd bellowing to a comrade across a deep valley. So
he had bellowed the day Cellini came recently to convince the Master to return to
Fiorenza, and Michele turning to him for counsel as he always oddly does (even
more than he turns to me) and Urbino bawling in his rustic way: "I will never leave
my master Michelangiolo's side till I have flayed him or he shall have flayed me!"
The blast was so convincing that Cellini forced himself to laugh and retired.

Only Urbino's wife, Cornelia, never jumped. The more agitation Urbino
created, bellowing and knocking over things, the more Cornelia smiled and
placidly and efficiently went about her household affairs. Urbino had served
Michelangiolo faithfully and lovingly for twenty-one years when he decided to
marry. He had returned from the Marche on one of his vacations, and there was a
new air about him, dreamier and distracted. He had he said, to Michele's
prodding, fallen in love with a beautiful young girl and wanted to marry her.

—Eh, allora?

—I want your permission.

—I am not your father, Michele said irritatedly.

—You are more than my father, replied Urbino. —I would not dream of
marrying without your permission.

So, of course, Michelangiolo gave him his blessing, though he knew nothing of
the girl, and soon after Urbino returned to Castel Durante and married her. He
brought his bride Cornelia back to live with him at Macel de' Corvi. Michele had
given him permission to do so though with misgivings and at first sight this
fulsome young wife became the Old One's loving and belovèd daughter. She
revered him and he adored her. She felt closer to him than to her own parents, and
Michele felt she had brought a needed feminine note into his household.

Well, Ascanio Conivi was a more gentle version of Urbino, and soon as the
Pontificate of Julius III got under way, every time I came to the studio I would find
Ascanio more busy taking down the Master's dictation than grinding color or
making one of his clumsy paintings on a cartoon which the Master had generously
provided him. He suffered from a pictorial disease not uncommon among un-
talented artists: he had to aggrandize even Michele's grand forms, with the result
that the human became gargantuan, elephantine, the noble Sistine forms which
Michelangiolo had provided him—say for a Holy Family—became a convention
of dinosaurs, and Ascanio's mediocre colors did not help either.

But it was obvious that his chief service to the Master was as an amanuensis.
And here he did very well—. I had to admit that to myself notwithstanding my
twinges of envy that I had not been chosen for the task.

"But is the man really literate?" I cautiously questioned Michelangiolo one
afternoon. We were climbing the ramp to the Church of the Aracoeli to cut over
to the Campidoglio. Real work, after all these years, was perhaps soon to get under

way, and Michele wanted to go over the site with me to whom he had handed over the responsibility of executing his designs.

"Of course, he is literate. Why do you ask?"

"Well, I thought . . ." I stammered. "He does seem a simple peasant. Frankly I was surprised to learn that he could even read or write."

"He reads and writes well enough. And after he has completed the text, at any rate, we shall turn it over to Messer Annibale Caro for further polishing, before we publish it."

There it was again! Further polishing. By an expert polisher, I had to admit to myself. Caro was one of the literati most in favor in Julian Roma. Messer Annibale belonged to the household of the Cardinal Alessandro Farnese, and when he wasn't serving the Cardinal he frequented a group of amusing humanists who met regularly in the Vignaioli Gardens under the protection of the Mantuan curialist Umberto Strozzi, who was also the protector of the famous courtesan Isabella de Luna. This circle composed Italian satirical verses of the type of La Fava, Priapus, Il Mal Francese (the French Disease) or Latin compositions like Della Casa's Formica whose subject is an ant which penetrated the pudendum of Venus and the wonders he encountered in those satin corridors. Of course this literary composition cost della Casa any hopes he had ever entertained of becoming a Cardinal. "Poverino!" Caro used to say, "the journey of that ant is mild compared to what is happening in the Vatican these days!" He was referring of course to the scandal of the new Pope's "nephew" Innocenza, who from being monkey-keeper had now at the age of seventeen been raised to the purple as a Cardinal.

Michele acted as if he never heard such remarks. As one associated with the Spirituali of the Marchesa and of the Cardinal Pole, he felt equidistant from the hedonistic Julius III and from the Inquisitionistic Cardinal Caraffa. So he withdrew more and more into his work.

Yet, withal, he liked Annibale Caro. His visits to the studio while Condivi was taking dictation, especially regarding the tribulations of the Julius tomb, were always a source of pleasure to the Old One. He was grateful too, for the assurance that Caro would smoothen Condivi's plowshared rows into a Latinate garden path with clipped hedges and trickling fountains. How well Caro could write a vigorous Tuscan that yet partook of its Latin heritage, and Michele was eager that his new biography, ostensibly by Ascanio, should correct but not antagonize Giorgio Vasari, who besides was still in Roma, and very much a favorite of Julius, working on his new villa. Roma was full of these literati, some of whom took lesser orders, others serving prelates or princes as secretaries or emissaries.

In our Roma, writers and scholars, and artists as well, all sought clerical offices—Sebastiano Luciano was by no means the only one. Even Titian had fished in those waters. But Michele never wanted or took any of these clerical offices, though he had often been offered them. Nor did he ever want to be paid for his work as architect of San Pietro. He hated to think of the Roman curia as a bottega.

Messer Caro was one of Michelangiolo's most loyal friends in the circle of the curia and he served also to finally lay the ghost which continued to rise from Julius' tomb. They had met in the Palazzo Gallo where Caro was lodging for a while and there Michele listened to the amusing flow of Caro's wit whilst regarding again the Bacchus of his youth which still stood tipsily in Gallo's courtyard together with broken-penised Apollos, a headless Venus, several Roman sarcaphagi and Egyptian sphinxes.

Once walking home from Gallo's courtyard Michele remarked about "Those statues of ancient gods, some lacking heads, and some of their male members and some both, which is indeed the case with many courtiers walking around today in modern Roma . . ."

Caro was a tall thin man, his blue eyes brimful of laughter, a glinting chuckle always trickling in the rich foliage of his ambercolored square- trimmed beard. He too dressed in the Spanish style though there was nothing Spanish about him. It was merely a sign of intelligent accommodation to the facts of the times.

But though Michele liked Caro and was grateful for the certainty that he would polish Condivi's text with his diplomatic file, yet the Maestro was always a bit distrustful of literati especially when they presumed to interpret his work.

"Oh those literary fellows!" Michele exploded. "Always seeking for a text from which they think I have extracted my image. Don't they know (but obviously they don't) that the imaginings of an artist are never born from words, not even from the exalted words of Scripture or of Dante? I do not know myself whence these imaginings emerge; they rise unbidden out of the heart of the stone, or should I be painting, as colored clouds in which one sees with every change of light what one has never seen before. Some new radiance, some sheen. Those intangibles! Ah, those intangibles! to swoop down among them and capture them mid-air as a swallow feeds in flight.

"Of course, to be sure, I begin always with a central idea, a major concept, but that is only the skeleton, fleshing it out is an act of love, a voyage among unpredictables.

"Like the mariner Cristoforo Colombo who discovered a New World when he thought he had found a new way to the Old One. So I never know exactly what I will find though I do know what I am searching for and I make the most careful navigation charts of voyage before I set about cutting into the block. Yet I never find exactly what I have been searching for, and that is the glory and the torment of it.

"Now how am I to explain all this to that learnèd tribe of jackdaws?—fluffed with feathers of their erudite incomprehension of how a work of art comes into being? . . ."

All this while we were climbing the long flight of steps to the church of Ara Coeli. Now on the Capitoline Hill flanking the church, Michele caught his breath and looked up at Marcus Aurelius bold and gilded in the sun.

"So though I am embarrassedly flattered when a Varchi lectures on my stammering poems, I am nose-deaf to all the clouds of incense beaten up by the Ariostos, the Paolo Giovios, the Aretinos (who returned to praise me after damning me to hell!) and all those literary fellows when they write about my art. But Caro is, I must admit, *simpatico.*"

Vasari told us that messer Annibale had written to him two years before the Jubilee asking him to make a *figura* especially of Michelangiolo's Leda which the master had painted during the Siege for the Duke of Ferrara, Alfonso d'Este, and then, offended by the insulting price offered by the Duke's emissary, had given it instead to his servant Antonio Mini who took it off with him to France. I've never seen the Leda myself but I am told it is the most sensual thing the Master ever did. Caro told Vasari (who told us, as we were strolling through the Forum where amidst the copulations and hilarities of goats (*Hilaritas pontificis* was the slogan chosen by the new Julius) we had come across two marble lovers of ancient Roma: he deprived of his organ of generation, and she missing her arms. But their love conquered their deprivations.

"Since I couldn't copy *your* Leda, Maestro, since she has unhappily disappeared somewhere amongst those barbarous Gauls, and I don't care to copy copies (of which there are many as you well know), I so informed Messer Caro, and he replied that he didn't care about the subject since, as he put it, 'You're a poet as well as a painter, provided there are two nude figures, a man and a woman, which is the main subject of your art. So choose whatever story you wish . . .' But then Caro went on to give me a detailed prescription for a Venus and Adonis, Venus looking at the dead Adonis with a wound in his thigh, blood on his person, perhaps a dog (if it doesn't take up too much space, . . . and from the blood are born roses and from the tears poppies . . . " And then he came right round about to his original request. 'If you don't want to make more than one figure, a Leda, especially Michelangiolo's, would please me very much . . .'"

So, though Michelangiolo found Caro immensely *simpatico,* he felt nothing but scorn for these literary prescriptions and interpretations of works of visual art.

He is full of these contradictions, our Michelangiolo. A Yes and No move him in all things. So he manages to be humble and self-effacing toward the learned, and at the same time—when they infringe upon his domain— contemptuous.

We walked about the campidoglio talking about the works which Michele hoped would finally get started. But he was not very optimistic. All available funds were now being diverted into the new extravagant summer villa which Julius III was building just outside Porta del Popolo, near the river. Even funds for the Fabbrica were being diverted into Julius' villa, and Vasari was remaining in Roma precisely because he had become very close to the Pope who was always consulting him about the building. Construction of the Fabbrica had practically ground to a halt, and yet there was renewed talk about finally doing something about the Capital. That project dated from the visit of Charles V back in 1536. Paul III had been ashamed of the condition of the hill and decided that the Capital should return as it had been in imperial times, refulgent with the splendors of art. Michele was invited to study the project. Those were still the early days of our friendship, and he discussed his plans with me—me! a mere boy, totally ignorant—and even asked my advice as if I were in any condition to offer anything other than a stricken gaze.

Well, that ceased after a few years. He no longer asks me for advice (and I no longer gaze at him with the same gaze). Instead he depends on me to facilitate carrying out certain of his projects, especially the re-ordering of the Campidoglio. He entrusts me as Conservator of the Urbs to see that certain strings are pulled, certain levers are pushed. Even in the Holy City the mechanism of change is not set into motion by divine hands alone.

Although I am no architect, I am not without some service to the Master since I am a member of the Commission for the recomposition of the Fasti Capitolini and I have been asked for my opinion on improvements to be made at the Porta Maggiore and the Orti Farnesiani. I also have achieved, I might say, a certain reputation as a collector and connoisseur. My palazzo on the Piazza de' Cavalieri contains one of the best collections of antiquities in Roma and has been so duly included in Aldovrandi's and other Mirabilis Romae. I certainly have gathered together more masterpieces of the ancients than has the Master, but I have observed that Makers do not collect and Collectors do not make. Da buon fabbro, messer Michelangiolo absorbs the ancient works in his mind rather than setting them up in his salotta. Besides, this mental collecting takes up less physical space. Michelangiolo's surroundings are really quite barren: one would think he were poor (which he is not) but those statues in his head (for he never forgets what he has seen) engender new statues all his own though the seeds were scattered before the birth of our Lord.

Michele had not only opposed the transfer of the Marcus Aurelius statue but also the idea of erecting on the edge of the newly-leveled piazza the colossal Dioscuri with their horses. But he had to yield to the will of his patron Paul III in this, as well as in the painting of the Last Judgement and later of the Pauline Chapel, as he had earlier to yield to Julius II with regard to the painting of the Sistine Vault. All his life Michelangiolo has been forced to undertake tasks which he did not consider his true and only craft—carving marble statues—and in every case, I have observed, he makes the uncongenial and unwanted commission his own, he absorbs it, he devours it, and once the ungrateful assignment has become digested, it is Michelangioloized, so to speak, it is his, and from that point on he pursues it with a fury and fantasy from which every outside influence is rejected. All we can do is help—when help is asked—him carry out the most tedious aspects of the work. So it was with me and the Campidoglio.

Four years before the Jubilee, the great equestrian statue of the Emperor had finally been transferred here from the Lateran and set upon a block of marble from the Foro Traiano. Now Michele had designed for it a new oval pedestal which would echo the oval form of the piazza which he had already in mind.

"Echoing, you see, Tomao mio," he explained now with an eloquent swing of his arm, "is an essential part of art whether it be the echoing of the interlocking lines in the Divine Comedy or the echoing of the penises of my Nudes on the Sistine Vault with acorns of the swathes of oak branches honoring the house of della Rovere, or the echoing limbs of my slaves or the volutes and curves of architecture. The echo reiterates, binds, all the world is but an echoing of divinity. There is correspondence in all things. The world is an echo in the mind of God."

When Michele was in these incandescent moods I felt that I was in the presence of a divinity. I understood why the poet Ariosto had referred to him as "Michele Angelo Divino," why Giorgio Vasari worshipped him as the culmination of all art. But he was a moody and unpredictable divinity, withal, one moment on the heights and the next in the depths, one moment Jovian and the next Saturnian; fire and ice are the two elements most frequent in his poems.

His broad gestures and elegance that day summoned up the Campidoglio that was to be. But it was only a dream. The actual hill on which we stood was irregular even if very picturesque. In the background rose the ruins of the ancient Tabularium, the Palace of the Senator, similar to a fortress, from whose center rose, superceding greatly the towers at the corners, the main tower crowned with merlins. In front of the eloquent wreckage, a fragment of an ancient marble group, a lion clawing at a horse served as an allegory of punitive justice. A crowd was already gathering there to hear a proclamation being read to a bound criminal soon to be executed. Michele went on discoursing of his urban reconstruction and the criminal was soon led off, followed by a jeering crowd, to the adjacent southwest part of the hill, called Monte Caprino because of the many goats grazing there. We did not wait to see the fellow hung, but after completing our inspection of the Palace of the Conservators ("Across the Piazza we'll build a matching palace") and the two giant fluvial divinities of the Nile and the Tigris, which Michele planned to place in front of his reconstructed Senate house, we did catch a glimpse of the figure swinging in the wind on the gallows erected amidst the numerous blocks of pentelic marble from the celebrated Temple of Jove. The goats were peacefully grazing under the dangling feet of the hanged man. Spectators were lounging on the marble blocks. "We might use some of those for our Senate house," Michele said. "I've already adopted some into Saint Peter's."

※

This new Pontiff made all the Florentines of Michelangiolo's circle think they were back in the days of Leo X, second son of Lorenzo the Magnificent. For although the flames of heresy then lighted were raging now all over Europe, and although England has also been lost to the Church, more it seems because of their King's lust than for reasons of doctrine; and although the Council is still meeting up at Trent after two decades of theological debate on how to strengthen the Church against the spread of heresy—despite all this the Pope Julius III took as his motto HILARITAS PONTIFICIS.

As if these were times for hilarity!

Almost immediately after achieving the Fisherman's Chair, he began planning his new summer villa to be built outside of the Porta del Popolo, a cannon shot up Via Flaminia near the River. It was in connection with this project that he kept Giorgio Vasari in Roma and consulted him often. He even, to the Maestro's anger (which he managed to conceal) consulted Michelangiolo himself on the plans! For Michele felt, once he had completed the Pauline Chapel and laid down his brushes fourteen years ago at the age of seventy-five (nor has he ever picked them up again); Michele felt that all his public energy, so to speak, was to be devoted to the Fabbrica of Saint Peter's. For himself he had obtained a capital of Vespasian's Palace and was carving a Deposition group out of it. So that he felt consultations on the Pope's new villa were an excessive demand on his energy.

And amidst all his other tasks he now began working quite steadily with Condivi who these days was frequently at the studio with pages of manuscript he had already written, and Michele looking them over and dictating revised passages, usually walking back and forth murmuring his account in a deep and yet whispery voice as if he were telling the tale of his own life to himself. I always had the impression at such times that his Florentine accent became more noticeable, he swallowed his C's and thickened his T's and his diction was full of Tuscan turns of phrase and colloquialisms.

The young Marchegiano Ascanio took all this down with a quill grasped in his thick fingers and an air of beatitude that he had been chosen for this task.

I don't know whether Giorgio Vasari, who also came to Macel de' Corvi not infrequently those early days of Julius' pontificate, knew that Michelangiolo was writing a correction to his own *Vita*. Certainly Michele never told him, nor can I imagine anyone else who might have, not even messer Caro who was on good terms with the Aretine. Indeed he was on good terms with everyone. He did not (unlike Giannotti and others similarly impassioned by political quarrels) select and reject friends according to their affinity with one's own ideas. Caro was ecumenical in friendships as in his artistic taste and he served his cardinal (or any other cardinal) with wit and the total dedication required of that moment.

As for Giorgio Vasari, his visits were usually an excuse to secure Michelangiolo's advice with regard to the Villa Giulia, the actual construction of which was soon under way.

"And the work on the Fabbrica is practically suspended!" Michele exploded. "There is no money to pay the workmen! All the funds are being diverted to the villa . . . The Holy Father's passion for this new Vigna of his is incredible. The other day I saw him proceeding down Tiber from the Vatican to the building site in a boat trimmed with flowers and accompanied by musicians! Incredible! There was the Holy Father reclining amidst Tyrian purple pillows with Scythians and Moors fanning him and trumpeters pealing to the rise and fall of the oars like gulls' wings, and you would have thought you were witnessing a Caligula or Tiberius or Nero of ancient days rather than a Vicar of Christ of our day!"

And yet, for all his frivolities, Julius protected the Old One against all his enemies, and they were not few. And notwithstanding the scandals soon circulating all around the City, (and certainly not calculated to assist the clerics up at Trent)—nevertheless the Holy Father more than any other always expressed the greatest love for our Michele and declared that he was willing to give up the remaining years of his life to add them to Michelangiolo's . . .

"Madonna! He even speaks of keeping me permanently by his side in the Vatican—even after my death!"

"O a great honor, Maestro! To be entombed amongst Cardinals and Popes . . ."

"What tomb! He thinks to have me *embalmed*! He told me to my face—and with a smile—that if he outlives me, which is more than likely, he intends to have my body embalmed and keep it ever by his side, so that my cadaver live perpetually, like my works!"

I grimaced. "To say the least, this Holy Father displays bad taste."

VI

Messer Donato

Michele was on such close terms with this Pope that he was as frequently in the ecclesiastical palace as myself, and so he knew perhaps even before those of us who were mere secretaries of Cardinals, the scandals that soon were being trumpeted with glee all over Roma especially by Pasquino, that ancient Roman statue near Piazza Navona. The centuries have worn old Pasquino down to a mere hulk: he lacks most of his arms and legs and everything else, but he doesn't lack a mouth. Pasquino indeed is the chief gossip of this Holy City. Everyone, especially in the circles of the learnèd appends apothegms and rimes to him, almost always of derision and most frequently about the current occupant of the Chair of St. Peter's.

Never did the Pasquinades flutter as during the days of Julius III!

Whenever Michelangiolo and I or messer Tomao or the Maestro's new friend Annibale Caro—like myself a Cardinal's secretary—found ourselves in the vicinity of Piazza Navona we would stroll over to hear what new rimes Latinate or Tuscan, but in any case, malicious and ribald, Pasquino had to offer that day. There was always a group around the statue, smiling knowingly, or sometimes doubled up for laughter. Nor are Pasquino's admirers limited to humanists and patricians (who can read his Latin utterance); the plebe congregates there as well in their rough boots and horny fists, pummeling each other for glee and repeating in Romanesco what Pasquino has said in Tuscan.

But Michele had no need for Pasquinades to know what the hulk was saying.

Since the Maestro had little or no work to supervise at the Fabbrica, more and more of his time was spent now with Ascanio Condivi and soon with my fellow curial secretary messer Annibale Caro, who had promised to oversee the manuscript. Caro was in the household of the Cardinal Alessandro Farnese, whilst I, after many years in the service of the Cardinal Ridolfi, after his suspicious death during the conclave, I had become secretary to the French Cardinal of Tournon. Thus Caro and I had long known each other in curial circles.

Annibale Caro was a most welcome addition to the close circle of Michele's friends. I found his humor delicious. And besides he was a very attentive ear and faithful informant with regard to whatever political plots were being hatched, especially against the Florentine exiles. I observed also that the Old One was shaken out of his melancholy by Caro's sallies and jests. His translation of Virgil's *Eneide* was famous: now he was contemplating a *Noseide* in honor of the celebrated proboscis of his friend messer Giovan Francesco Leoni. Like many letter-writers of our time (Aretino is an infamous example), Caro's letters were written as much for future publication as for their recipients; and one autumnal afternoon, in the garden under the larches after messer Annibale Caro had completed the day's work of revisions with the Maestro and that naive oaf Condivi, Caro read to us portions of an absurd letter he had written to Leoni. The whole household was present in the garden—an audience ranging from Urbino and his pretty wife Cornelia, suckling a babe; a young sculptor Tiberio Calcagni who has been part of the Master's entourage ever since he completed the toga of the Brutus bust Michele had carved for the Cardinal Ridolfi. Nominally for the Cardinal, that is. Actually as a result of my intervention. Immediately after the slaying of Duke Alessandro, I saw the political usefulness of the Brutus-symbol. When I induced the Cardinal to commission the work, I was not yet aware of the Maestro's political ambiguity on the subject.

But everyone's private devil was sent flying by Caro's wit. Even Michele was dislodged from Saturn to Jove:

MOST NOSISSIMO M. GIOVAN FRANCESCO—(began the letter: messer Caro's voice inflectionless and dry, flat as the expression on his face)—After long consideration regarding a suitable subject on which to write to you I have at last decided upon your nose insomuch as its magnitude is so well known and so enormous an impression has it made upon everybody's minds and tongues and pens. So I can speak of nothing else. You are the very King of the Kingdom of Befana and never has there been a crown more glittering than yours, nor a scepter more sturdy than that which you wield, nor a throne more featherbeddy than that on which rests the round fat apples of your arse nor can the Monarch of all Cuckolds find a more curial arse-hole than yours. (by this time Michele was already grumblingly chuckling)

But none of these attributes of your virtue can stand comparison with that which gives you domination over all of us: your NOSE. By your NOSE you make men your vassals, by your NOSE women become your slaves (Cornelia, suckling, tittered) Blessed art thou to bear such a marvel on your face, such a consolation to all who gaze upon it. He who sees it is overwhelmed; he who feels it is intimidated; everyone is tickled by it, everyone smells it, everyone desires it. The Poets all sing of it, the Prosaicists celebrate it, the prognosacists reason upon it. Nor will it be surprising that eventually the Sibyls should not prophesy about it. That the Appeles should paint it, the Polyclitises should carve it and that Michelangiolo in one way or another should immortalize it.

—(And here messer Caro stopped reading, his eyebrows raised, with the stern expression of a schoolmaster whose lesson had been interrupted by Michelangiolo's explosive guffaw. After a moment's admonitory silence, the curial literatus resumed):—Here in Roma since you have departed there has been more fracas about your NOSE than about the Pope's trip to Nice or the

Grand Turk's preparations for further attacks on Christendom. Even yesterday I was told that there was a new Nosaria in the form of a sonnet and indeed it is bruited about that your NOSE is the target of the bow (or of the bowlette) of Apollo, or the trumpet (or the flute) of the Muses since all the Poets put their mouths to it.

—(By now the company—everyone—was a rocking sea of laughter. But Caro continued as impassively as before):—the people are saying this year that Pasquino wants no metamorphosis other than your NOSE. (The old battered statue lacked a nose). And the scoundrel would display great sense to grow such a one if he wants to recover that credit which he's lost with the Muses; because I don't believe there's a turd in Parnassus that would not want to present himself to your NOSE. Perfect NOSE. Chief of all NOSES! Divine NOSE. Nose that blessèd be among all noses, and blessèd be that Mamma who made you so nosified and blessèd be all those things which have be-nosed you. Pray God that he should inspire Brittanio (This was a reference to another writer, Girolamo de Sicigno, a mediocrity who dedicated poems to Vittoria Colonna) to write you a NOSEIDE, greater than his round one and that every book that is composed be Nauseus in honor of your Nasal Majesty, and that there not be so well-furnished a noodle-nose, nor so pinched a needle-nose, nor so majestically overflowing a 'normous- nose nor so elongated a roguish nosish, that would not be vassal and tributary of your Most Nosissimo Nosexcellence Nositude . . .

Enough of noses. The kingdom of Virtue is in decline, Queen Cuntynose is about to pull up her stockings, now she's of healthy body, that is, whatever remains of it . . . My regards to all our virtuous friends in court and I remain

Servant of your Nose,
Annibale Caro

With which conclusion the Curiale took his leave with a solemn bow, and retired into a thick grove to reappear a few moments later, carnival mask of literary learnèd solemnity removed to reveal his smiling shrewd simpatico face to all of us, rolling still with laughter.

Caro's *Noseide* was a delightful bit of nonsense in that period of Papal corruption and Medicean aggression. Some of the scandals of this new Pontificate were quite beyond belief, even to old hands like myself. It seems Julius the Third had a passion for gambling which even those Cardinals of the strictest observance could not always evade. "If you lose," insisted the Pope chuckling, "it doesn't matter. I will teach you to rob for yourself and for me." At these banquets of chance after the noonday meal there were always His Holiness' brother and many Cardinals and the Bishops of Ascoli and Padova. Of course the stern Neapolitan Caraffa and Cervini (who gave Michelangiolo much trouble in the building committee for San

Pietro) frowned on all this. And Michelangiolo frowned too, when Caro or I tried to cheer him up with some of these comic tales:

"It seems as though the days of Pope Leo have indeed returned," the Old One said, "what with all these buffoons and games of chance and the thousands of scudi flying about the gaming table like the swallows over the Cupolone. Thirty-five years since Leo's frivolities were forged into weapons by Brother Martin Luther. And the Church has lost half Europe and nothing has changed. Half a century since Fra Girolamo pricked the Borgia bull with his first bandilleros and nothing has basically changed. Bloodred, the bull still stands . . . under the other Julius . . ." And off he would go, contrasting the two Juliuses—the Pontiff in armor with whom he had fought and for whom he had created the Sistine Vault (inter alia) and this new Julius III whose tenderness was less to his liking than the other's terribilità.

The Pope's hedonism knew no limits. He had no scruples about attending theatrical representations that might well have been considered somewhat un-suitable for a Pontiff, especially in these times of Church reform: the *Menecmi* of Plautus or the *Cessaria* of Ariosto. And evenings there were carousals in the Piazza of San Pietro and bull fights. Eventually some of the smuttier comedies were presented in the Vatican itself. Julius III saw nothing unecclesiastical about all this. After all, what was untoward about *enjoying* the Papacy? Had not Pope Leo enunciated such enjoyment as a personal dogma? *Godiamoci il Papata dato che'l Dio ce l'ha dato.* "Let us enjoy the Papacy since God has given it to us."

Yet, though he didn't laugh as much as Annibale Caro, Michele's attitude toward all this vacillated between Savonarolean judgementalism and what seemed like indifference. After all, he had been on close terms with Holy Fathers for almost half a century, that is, ever since his encounter with Julius II in 1506. And as a good son of Holy Church, he was prepared to forgive them—if not every-thing—much, so long as they did not seek to subvert the independence of his patria or the independence of his art. And so although he felt the arrows of the Protestant heretic did (he admitted reluctantly) strike many true targets and felt himself in his own flesh the jolting justice of their aim, and some of the blood they drew was his blood, yet he feared the consequences even of those criticisms which no one could deny.

It was his cautious father Lodovico speaking in him: it was the caution of the Duchess of Pescara who had immediately suspended all her theological discussions on the efficacy of faith alone, once it was clear that the Council would declare such doctrine heretical.

And besides, how could Michelangiolo criticise this Pope who expressed his love for him in the most dramatic ways, insisting that he sit beside him in the presence of ambassadors so that they paid simultaneous obeisance to the Pontifex Maximus of Christianity and the Pontifex Maximus of Art.

But soon Julius went beyond all bounds. When he had been a papal legate at Parma he had, so to speak, dragged out of the street a boy of humble origin and made him the keeper of his monkey because the boy had displayed courage one day when the beast had embraced him. In a short time this monkey-keeper managed to creep so intimately into the affections of *his* keeper—then the Cardinal del Monte—that the Cardinal induced his brother to adopt the young servant. Henceforth the boy bore the name of Innocenzo del Monte, a name which he dishonored abundantly every day and in every way, as if to be called Innocenzo was a spur to behave as little innocently as possible.

Notwithstanding this, he received a prefecture in Arezzo, since the Cardinal was attached to him with an affection which was as incomprehensible as it was incredible. And indeed as soon as Giovan Maria del Monte had become Pope, nothing was closer to his heart and thoughts than to raise to the highest dignity, honors, and riches, his brother's adopted son. Already the saying went around the Vartican, only three months after he had achieved the See of St. Peter', the Pope had given gifts to his adopted nephew amounting to more than 12,000 ducats.

And now del Monte elevated his monkey-keeper to the dignity of a Cardinal!

Of course there was opposition, outcries against this opprobrious abuse of Papal power. We learned that the Cardinal Pole—Michelangiolo's old companion of those learnèd conversations in Vittoria Colonna's cloister— recalled canonical proscription against such a creation, as well as the gravity of the times. Even more opposed was the Cardinal Caraffa. We heard that the old Neapolitan tried in vain to convince the Pope with whom he had long been on terms of friendship, how harmful was such an elevation to the Cardinalate of an orphan of bad character, and what wagging of tongues it would inevitably bring about. All in vain. On the 30th of May during this very Holy year of 1550 the not so innocent Innocenzo who counted all of seventeen years was named Cardinal and made his solemn ingress into Roma the following day. The nomination of course provoked the greatest indignation and scandal and the new Cardinal had to receive his red hat in a secret consistory. The rumor spread everywhere that Pope Julius was Innocenzo's father. And there were worse sayings than that, the most brutal suppositions. You can imagine the foam of Pasquino!

Perhaps the Holy Father hoped against hope that this neophyte Cardinal Innocenzo might now begin to live in a mode suitable to his new dignity. Vain hope! Rendered more audacious as a result of his unexpected good fortune, the young Cardinal abandoned himself to a life more scandalous than ever before. And yet notwithstanding he continued to enjoy the Pope's favor, was rewarded with rich benefices such as the Abby of St. Michel in Normandy and S. Zeno in Verona and finally became in effect what Alessandro Farnese had been under Paul III—a substitute Secretary of State.

As the reign of Hilaritas Pontificis progressed, it revealed itself as less and less hilarious. Like all Florentines, Michele became terribly disturbed by the growing threats of war in our *patria*. Yet he had in recent years, I noted, withdrawn more and more from direct political involvement: he walked ever more circumspectly around that volcanic rim; he sought, in letters home to his nephew, to have Lionardo serve as message-bearer to the Duke that he, Michelangiolo Buonarroti—not withstanding his friendship with such traitors as myself and the late Cardinal Ridolfi and some relatives and satellites of the Strozzi (the late messer Luigi had always managed adroitly to keep on good terms with Cosimo despite his position as head of the Strozzi bank in Roma)—notwithstanding the Brutus he had carved as a symbol of praise for Tyrannicide (for the statue was as unambiguous as his commentary on Dante's Brutus was not), yet he, Michelangiolo, dissociated himself from active enemies of the Medici such as myself. That's what he wanted Cosimo to hear. But we all knew that his fundamental republican sentiments had not changed, and even though the Duke was taking advantage of the growing criticism of Michelangiolo's direction of the Fabbrica—that he was too old and feeble and senile and had entered his second childhood—to renew ever more insistently his invitations that the Master return to his homeland, yet Michele continued to refuse these invitations, graciously always, the irony of his replies escaping Vasari or whatever emissary the Duke may have employed. I am certain they escaped the Duke himself.

In July 1552 came the news that the Sienese had rebelled against the Spanish garrison which Charles V had placed in that city in 1530, after Siena had appealed for Imperial support against the Medici Pope Clement VII. The Sienese have always feared and hated Florentines, and Medici Florentines most of all. But Spanish protection had become Spanish domination, and now they saw an opportunity to regain the independence of their Republic: invoking the protection of the Virgin and the King of France they forced the Spaniards to abandon the city. And although the French had done nothing as yet to help them, the fact that the Sienese had risen under the banner of France, could not but please the French King Henry II inasmuch as it weakened the position of the Emperor in Italy and blocked the Pope as well as Cosimo de' Medici. So the interminable wars on this peninsula between the French and the Imperial-Spanish broke out again.

As secretary to the Cardinal of Tournon, I was privy of course to the role that prelate played in stirring up the Sienese; in fact I exalted his merits as liberator of that city in a booklet I wrote—a *Discourse regarding the Reorganization of the Republic of Siena*—based in part on certain ideas expressed in several of my earlier works on the *Repubblica Fiorentina* and my *History of the Venetian Republic*. Needless to say, I never discussed any of my political concerns with Michelangiolo Buonarroti especially these days when I was in and out of Roma in the wake of my new peregrinating French Cardinal, weaving his webs.

And while the Holy Father was preoccupied with the Sienese events came the bad news of the progress of the Turks in Hungary and hedonist Julius was laughing and feasting and carousing less and less, and soon all the hilarity was quite departed from Hilaritas Pontificis.

In the late autumn of 1553, while still in France on business, I received a copy of Condivi's *Life of Michelangiolo* published, at my recommendation, by Antonio Blado who had earlier printed my *Libro della Repubblica de' Viniziani*. Perusing that little book in the glittering palace of Fontainbleu was a strange experience: an echo of distant and disparate voices: Caro's witty elegance, Condivi's simplicities, and running through it all, Michelangiolo's own strong dignified voice narrating the truth, especially with regard to the tomb negotiations (in which I also played a role). Certainly the complicated stylistic passages relating to the Sistine ceiling must have been dictated directly by our Maestro, and polished by Annibale. And I wondered, chuckling, whether those sophisticated remarks about the enduring examples left by Michelangiolo should be followed by the best artists as Petrarch is followed by the best poets—I wondered, chuckling, whether Annibale had made up that list: Bembo, Sannazaro, Vittoria Colonna, Giovanni Guidiccioni and . . . Annibale Caro:

> E più d' onore ancora assai mi fenno
> ch' esser mi fecer della loro schiera,
> si ch' io fui sesto tra cotanto senno.

except that Annibale was only the fifth among such intelligences, nor would I put even the great Bembo on the level of Dante's *Signor' dell' altissimo canto* . . . Lords of Highest Song: Homer, Horace, Ovid, Lucan, Virgil . . . Or mayhaps the Maestro dictated that passage himself? Caro is twice mentioned in the little book, which was in sum a delight to its final sentence (which could have been written by no one but Ascandio Condivi himself 'And with this I make an end . . . *E con questo fo fine.*'

How I regretted I could not have been at Macel de' Corvi to celebrate the publication! But political events were reaching their climax.

In January of 1554, Cosimo de' Medici, the most unscrupulous political man in Italy, having signed a secret pact with the Emperor, took possession of the Fort of Camollia situated immediately outside the gate of Siena, declaring to the Sienese that his intention was simply to restore to them the liberty of which they had been deprived by the French! The Sienese of course were not taken in by such hypocritical benevolence but set about resolutely to defend their independence.

From October 1554 till the end of January of the following year Julius III sought in vain for a peaceful solution of the Sienese crisis. He died even before the death of the Republic of the Virgin. His old illness of gout and his senseless dietary habits brought him to a swift end in March 1555, and I was so enmeshed in the French business of my Cardinal that I could not even get to Roma in time for the Conclave.

VII

Messer Michelangiolo

During the five years of his Pontificacy, of course, I could not but compare this Julius III with the great Julius from whom he had taken his name. Surely they had nothing else in common. The Second Julius, notwithstanding his bellicosity, had been a great Maecenas, for it was during the reign of this Mars in pontifical garb that I had been contracted to make his ill-fated tomb,—which I never did, painting it instead on the vault of the Sistine. But if the Third Julius asked nothing of me perhaps because of my age, yet he asked nothing of younger artists either. Yet I think kindly of him because he defended me always against the scurrilities of the San Gallo sect.

Nor was this fearful and irresolute man capable of staunching the blood which every day poured forth from the Church wounded by the growing apostasy from the North. Like Leo (of whom he reminded me often) he occupied his time with his new villa and comedies and buffoons and card playing

Since del Monte had been educated by the humanists, immediately after his election everyone began to chatter about a new Age of Gold which was of course a reference to the Pontificate of Pope Leo except that the Medici Pope had started with the gold and ended with none, whilst this one started with none. And so the works of St. Peter's were paralyzed.

No sooner was Julius elected when that scoundrel Aretino sent him a sonnet blown out of all proportions and puffed with the winds of rhetoric like a galleon at full sail. Indeed three years later the Aretine came to Roma and was so amicably received by the Holy Father, that he deluded himself into believing that he would soon receive the red hat of a cardinal. Fortunately, this never happened, and fortunately too he made no effort to see me. For ever since that scurrilous letter, we had ceased to communicate. Sniffing the winds of change, Aretino these days was writing nothing but works of piety. No more plays about the whores of Roma. Instead, penitential and theological dissertations on genesis, the humanity of Christ and the Psalms—dedicated of course to the new Pope.

How I would have enjoyed witnessing his rancor in front of my Last Judgement!

Did he recognize himself as St. Bartolomeo?

And yet this Pontiff who could honor an Aretino also expressed his love for me in a phrase that soon was known all over Roma: "I would willingly add to Michelangiolo's years those which are still remaining to me."

And in fact he was always a loving protector of my person and of my art. Toward me he demonstrated a reverence and fidelity beyond even that of Paul III. Sometimes, to my embarrassment, he would insist that I sit by his side in the presence of many cardinals and great Lords; and so the reverence due him was also shed upon me. And he assigned me a high salary of 50 scudi a month notwithstanding my enemies never ceased to intrigue against me. My insistence that in the vast works of the fabbrica no one be permitted to exercise influence by way of promises, bribes, or gifts simply increased day by day the number of my adversaries. I would not approve construction materials that were not of the first quality and suitable, even if they should descend from Heaven.

And in all these conflicts the Holy Father backed me to the hilt.

Just as during the times of Paul III so now it was still the San Gallo sect who unleashed tempests against me. And given the easy-goingness and shilly-shallowness of Julius III, this time I was afraid my enemies might indeed achieve their aim. Alas! one weapon I myself provided them. I never could work with others. After a brief attempt at assistance I had painted the entire Sistine Vault alone and I suppose now I would, if I could, have built St. Peter's alone. At any rate, I shared my plans with no one.

Armed with this habitual secrecy of mine with regard to my plans for the fabbrica, the San Gallo sect managed to prejudice the members of the building council against me so that finally they sent a letter to the Pope intended to subvert the great confidence the Holy Father reposed in me. The chief complaint, other than the waste of moneys, was the fact that I kept secret my building plans. For, they lamented, they could not even report on the progress of the new works because everything was kept in the dark. No doubt. No doubt. And yet I could not otherwise.

They could only protest, as they had in the past, and were now doing again, (for the sake of their conscience) that they disapproved of the way I was conducting these operations, especially the demolitions which they considered excessive.

After which thenody the letter ended with an obsequious *Notwithstanding if your Holiness approves matters as they stand we have no cause to complain.*

Well, the result of this accusation was a meeting convoked by Pope Julius III of all the building committee and others engaged in the new fabbrica before which jury I was supposed to justify myself. Jury! It was more like the Inquisition! And I, who was sacrificing my old years and waning strength to build the supreme temple of Christianity, was now being put on the rack by a flock of cardinals who sat looking down at me as if I were a Lutheran or a Turk. The Pope began by saying that some of the Deputies were complaining about what they called the poor illumination of the apse.

"Who are these Deputies!" I burst out. "Let them speak for themselves!"

At which the Cardinal Marcello Cervini nodded: "We are the one."

"Monsignor," I said (addressing him in the singular). "Above those windows in the vault which are to be made of travertine, there will be three others."

"You never told us that!" exclaimed the Cardinal in a tone of hurt surprise.

"I'm not obliged, nor do I wish to be obliged to tell either your Lordship or anyone else what I should or want to do. Your job is to raise money and avoid thieving. As for the plans for the new St. Peter's you have to leave that responsibility entirely to me."

And I turned to the Pope and said. "Holy Father, you see what I am reaping for all my pains. If these hardships that I am enduring do not profit my soul I am wasting time and labor."

At which the Pope who loved me well, put both hands on my shoulders and with the sweetest of smiles, murmured: "You are laying up rewards both for your soul and for your body."

I suppose my fierce remarks might have cost me dearly when the selfsame Cardinal Cervini was elected Pope four years later. But unfortunately he only reigned twenty-two days and had no time to occupy himself with the old architect of St. Peter. However, when I learned of Cervini's election, I thought of fleeing Roma.

But though after this meeting my authority was unquestioned, yet the works languished for the next four years for want of funds. And learning of this from his agents in Roma, Duke Cosimo renewed his efforts to woo me back to Fiorenza. Giorgio Vasari, the Duke's agent, exercised all his eloquence in favor of such a move, stressing with warmth the cabals against me in Roma and the little comprehension I met with here. Giorgio, of course, was right, but yet with trembling hand—for my old hand had begun to tremble and that was ten years ago when I was seventy-nine and you can imagine how it trembles now!—I wrote a letter to Giorgio,

Messer Giorgio, dear friend.—You will surely say that I've become old and crazy wanting to write sonnets: but since many people are gossiping that I'm in my second childhood, I want to play my role. I see by your letter the love you bear me: and you certainly know how dearly I would like to have my feeble bones lie alongside those of my father, as you have besought me. But if I should depart from here now, it would result in the utter ruination of the fabbrica of Santo Pietro, to my great shame and even greater sin. But once all the plans have been established so that they cannot be changed, I hope to do as you suggest, although of course it isn't a sin to keep a few fools on tenterhooks waiting for my early departure

A dì 19 settembre 1554

Michelangiolo Buonarroti in Roma

With this letter I sent a sonnet beginning: *Giunto è già il corso della vita mia . . .* but only now in this cold rainy February of 1564 is the course of my life really coming to an end. This time I know. And that witness to my knowledge is this spectral Deposition.

Giorgio kept me informed not only of Ducal but also Buonarroti affairs in Fiorenza. Earlier that spring he had sent me a vivid account of the baptism of my nephew's first child, a boy whom he had named Buonarroto after his father. (surely Vasari's letter gave me more pleasure than my nephew's indecipherable and terse (thank God for that!) announcement. I replied:

> Messer Giorgio, dear friend—Your letter has given me the greatest pleasure, seeing you still remember the poor old man, and still more so for having attended the triumph about which you write and for having witnessed the beginning of another Buonarroto. I thank you with all my heart for this account. But all the same such pomp displeases me, because man should not laugh when the entire world weeps (I was referring to Duke Cosimo's imprisonment of Piero Strozzi who had fought with the French for Sienese liberty, and of the Duke's cruelty in that war); hence it seems to me Lionardo didn't display much judgement especially making such a celebration for someone being born with that rejoicing which should be reserved for the death of someone who has lived well. Nothing else occurs to me. Above all I thank you for the love you bear me, although I'm not worthy of it. Things here are so so. On I don't know what day of April 1554.

> Your Michelangiolo Buonarroti in Roma.

⁕

My days—more properly my nights—were spent with Nicodemus. During those nights, still but for the chipping of my chisel, lonely but for the thronging of my thoughts, I felt indeed that I was old Nicodemus, that secret follower of Jesus among the Jews, who came to the Lord at night and asked Him how can such things be?

How, indeed, can such things be?

How could it be that the more the works at San Pietro languished, the more His Holiness' pleasure villa flourished? Giorgio Vasari was making the first sketches based on the Pope's own fantastic schemes and I in turn curbed somewhat Vasari's fantasies whenever he came to enlist my counsel, which he did quite often, I must admit, hearkening with uncommon gravity corrections.

And when I wasn't counseling Vasari, I was counseling my nephew on the choosing of a proper wife so that the name of Buonarroti should not run into the sand and be lost forever.

More than half the years of del Monte's (and even the last year of Farnese's)

pontificacy were spent on this complicated search. Complicated because my
nephew wanted a wife who would provide him with adequate dowry, dignity,
delight, and devotion. As if such qualities were easily combined in a single
maiden. I counseled him to be more modest in his demands; I must say my nephew
was more difficult to please than I. But after all I did not have to sleep with the
lady. My art is mistress enough.

And the only art I truly had under my hands then was the Nicodemus group. O
it was a comfort to be sculpting again after so many years! to grasp the irons in my
hand, to liberate the image from within the stone (and from within my head) to
see the sparks flying in the dark studio as when a blacksmith shoes a horse, and
smell the marble dust and feel the crunch of it under my boots and know the wild
joys and torturous frustrations of creation. How much more Nicodemus' arms
around the Madonna were to me than the Pope's arms around my shoulders and
the love in his eyes. Or even than the basilica abuilding (though I set great store on
that as a kind of gigantic ex-voto.

When I carved I felt (forgive me!) like God himself (who might forgive me).

With the exception of the Brutus bust I had done no carving since I turned over
what was left of the Julius tomb to the heirs. The Moses and the partly finished
Rachel and Leah by my own hand and all the rest by alien hands, the roughed-out
Prigioni still up in Fiorenza, the two other Prigioni sent to Roberto Strozzi in
France. Otherwise, since I settled permanently in this City of Roma after
Clement's death, I was painting *al fresco*: five years on the Judgement and nine
years in the Pauline.

So now as I happily resumed the theme which had haunted me since my
youthful Pietà in the Chapel of the French King in San Pietro,—a subject revived
in my mind by the Deposition drawings I made for Vittoria Colonna—Nicodemus
became my closest companion: closer than His Holiness Julius III.

When I first began the Deposition, I was dictating my memoirs to young
Ascanio Condivi who had been introduced to me by that delightful burlone
messer Annibale Caro (whose niece he eventually married). Caro suggested (and
how perceptive he was!) that I correct the manuscript for errors. And since I had
been rankling about Vasari's errors especially with regard to the negotiations for
the Julius tomb (though I never told that to Giorgio), this seemed a golden
opportunity to rectify . . . Again, rectify! Rectify Giorgio's plans for the villa.
Rectify my nephew's plans for a wife. Correct the blunders of others! As if it's not
enough to correct one's own!

So though I first only made corrections in the manuscript Condivi had already
undertaken on his own, soon he had become simply my omanuensis, jotting down
what I said to him and then writing out for messer Caro to correct. Then we would
all go over it together.

Condivi, for all his simplicity, proved to be a charming writer, if a bit ungram-
matical and ingenuous; he was by no means the half-literate apprentice boy messer

Tomao took him to be (or wanted him to be?) I understood Tomao's coolness in this affair. As for the grammar, messer Caro unraveled some of the more tangled vines in that unkempt vineyard. But I begged him not to fundamentally alter Condivi's own style which pleased me for its honesty and the ring of its simplicity which made me think of contadini talk on the slopes of Fiesole and Settignano. They were true sentences, clear as a well-cast bell, solid judgements and rounded and impermeable as a shapely amphora so that not a drop of truth was lost.

I tried to be modest. I set straight the story of the tomb which almost became my own tomb.

If there are hosannas in the work, these are strictly Condivi and Caro. I could not insist they be removed. Not when I saw the hurt clouding Ascanio's clear blue eyes.

"O lascia stare!" I gave him on occasion a cartoon to color which he did with a lack of taste so total that it was almost an act of genius. He even managed to swell out the contour lines of my cartoon so that it resembled Aesop's frog who tried to blow himself up into an ox.

Dear Ascanio!

Of course all this time I breathed not a word to Giorgio Vasari of this correction to his *Vita* which had added a literary feather to his already well-feathered cap. I cautioned Ascanio and messer Caro not to say a word to anyone about our joint project, words get around, especially in this casino of Roma which is a sounding box of rumors of all sorts, and I didn't want to offend Giorgio Vasari under any circumstances.

We even planned—Ascanio and I—how to suspend operations with grace and ease should Vasari appear at Macel de' Corvi while we were working on the book. The manuscript pages swept under Condivi's cloak with the servant's announcement of Vasari at the door. Inky fingers explained (if need be) as blots of drawing. Caro's file-work on the syntax metamorphosed into the latest joke heard in the *stufa*—how Mona Tarquinia leaped over the horns she had placed on her husband's head, an Etruscan sport.

We waited till Vasari had returned to Fiorenza, before we published Condivi's little book at the press of Antonio Blado in July of 1553.

In his dedication Ascanio elevated me to the same rank as the reigning Pope Julius III! His Holiness he called the Prince of Christianity and me, the Prince of the art of drawing!

I am not responsible for these hosannas. They see—these Ascanio's and Vasari's and Ariosto's (who referred to me as *Michele più che mortale*) only the surface of my soul. I alone have plunged to darker depths. "Divine Angel"—Dio mio! I am "more than mortal" only in the sense that I am more vulnerable than most mortals and my secrets bear daylight no more than the secrets of any other man; I am no more a stranger to sin than messer Ariosto himself who hymns me as a sinless angel. All that I have in common with an angel is my name.

Not long after the publication of his little book Ascanio married messer Caro's niece and returned to his native town of Ripa Transone in the Marche. All the Marchigiani in my household—Urbino and his wife Cornelia, the cook and the clean-up boy—were sad to see their *paesano* go. Although Urbino expressed his regret with a sort of irritation, but Urbino was not feeling well those days and his wife Cornelia had already confided in me (she had swiftly become my loving and beloved daughter) that she was concerned about her husband's health.

I counseled her as my old father had always counseled me—Francesco should keep his head covered, especially during the rains, and eat garlic.

And pray more. What else can a man do?

My Nicodemus group was almost completed when Ascanio left us and I have never seen him since. His little book made a pleasant stir in Roma, and even in later years when Giorgio returned, he never made mention of it. You would think that his was the only life of Michelangiolo Buonarroti, and I saw no reason to mar our friendship (and his usefulness as a bearer of Ducal information and Florentine gossip) by making mention of it.

Ever since I had made for the Marchesa of Pescara a drawing of a nude Christ being taken from the Cross, the subject of the Deposition has never left my imagination! It seized me even to the point of suggesting to me the vision of my own tomb. And all those years I was working on the frescoes of the Pauline, for every new being I birthed on the wall, Death removed another of my friends or kin: Vittoria Colonna and Sebastiano del Piombo and Luigi del Riccio and his fifteen-year-old nephew, and my brother Gian Simone and Pope Paul—blow after blow for my every brushstroke on the wall and I am as familiar with Death as with my own hand, and twice I fell from the scaffolding into his arms and I thought (I hoped)—Now you will take me!—but he didn't. Instead he took Luigi who nursed me and Sebastiano who amused me and divine Vittoria who exalted me and whose death left me rudderless, bereft of my senses. Every year brought me more grief. After one of those deaths (I forget whose) I wrote a sonnet and sent it to messer Giovan Francesco Fattucci up in Fiorenza and said if you don't like it, throw it in the fire and just reflect that I am struggling with death and my mind is on other things than the making of sonnets.

So my entire being was informed with this theme of Death. And once I lay down the brushes on the Pauline, my greatest joy was riding or walking around the city with Tomao and my inseparable Urbino (who was supposed to be my servant but gave me orders as if he were the Master but I took no offense ever with one who acted like, and whom I loved as a dutiful son). Our peregrinations led us often to the ruins of antiquity. Tomao was now on the Committee for the Fasti of the Campidoglio and he had developed a reputation as a tasteful and knowledgeable collector. One day we all went to see the ancient columns at the monastery alongside St. Peter in Chains (where what was left of my Julius Tomb is enchained to the wall) and there I chose and obtained the capital of one of the eight great columns of Vespasiano's Temple of Peace. For weeks after Peter was finally crucified upsidedown *al fresco*, I had been sketching versions of a Nicodemus group and I also found on copies of letters and amidst the scatter of my papers some earlier essays on the same theme. All these images had been simmering for many years in the crucible, and now I had a piece of marble echoing with honor and antiquity—a good piece of stone, clean and smooth and without veins, somewhat yellowish in part (I guessed it to be Parian marble). So we had it carted to Macel de' Corvi and soon my irons were happily ringing on the piece with the angelus bells of nearby Santa Maria di Loreto, and often with the matin bells as well. Since the frescoes were completed and work on the Fabbrica at a standstill, I could devote most of my time now to the Nicodemus.

I had chosen Nicodemus because he spoke directly to the Lord.

Without intermediaries.

At night. In secret.

And for the first few years this group was my chief consolation and source of health. For carving stone keeps Death at a remove—that same Death who was ravishing all around me—so long as I work at the art for which I was born, stonecutting, so long I am alive. I explained this one day, between blows of the hammer, to a visiting French physician—a Monsieur Blaise de Vigenère who seemed almost frightened as I knocked off at a single blow chunks of marble three or four fingers thick. As these pieces catapulted from the block, he kept bouncing away, covering his eyes with his cape.

"Are you not fearful, M'sieu (so he addressed me—M'sieu) that you will cut away too much?"

"The compasses are in my eyes."

"But if you do, can you glue in a correction?"

"I detest such corrections. I always avoid them."

"You have much self-assurance, M'sieu."

"God-given, M'sieu. (I mimicked him to perfection). I am grateful for the gift."

He marvelled and went away and I continued to hammer happily away. I think with all my thoughts of death those days—once I had gotten that Nicodemus piece underway I was happier than I had been for many years. My nephew was finally married to a Ridolfi and I imagined he was hammering progeny of nights as I was hammering Nicodemus. It was a hard stone, full of emery sparking under my chisel irons but I like hard stones so long as they do not crack. I like the resistance of the marble, I find my concept in that resistance, the invisible Form hidden in that hardness goads me all the more in my quest. I know it is there wanting to be freed of the block and at the same time, concealing itself in obdurance, as if it would avoid and evade the very liberator who is arriving.

It is a quest which has sustained me all my long life, and it is difficult to explain

in simple words to a French physician. He did marvel at the powerful development
of my shoulder muscles and scapulae and biceps and the strength of my hands as
much as he marveled at my creations! I said I suffered from the stone and could not
urinate and he smiled—

"I should say, M'sieu, the stone suffers more from you than you from it. I find you
in remarkable health, considering your age. There is, I am told, a certain water
here in Italy which helps dissolve the kidney stone. You might—"

"I have. I have. It has helped during my worst attacks. What disturbs me most is
that when I cannot urinate I cannot work. But it's all in God's hands."

He was a pleasant man, withal, that French physician, one of a constant stream
of visitors, many foreigners amongst them, who came to Macel de' Corvi those
years I was working on the Nicodemus Deposition. Many of them were artists—
Taddeo Zucchero and Lorenzino da Bologna came, both ardent in their admiration. At that time Zucchero was decorating in fresco a chapel of the church of the
Consolation at the foot of the Capital and he made a painted copy of my
Deposition group. Lorenzino also did a painting from my group, adding three more
personages to my four.

Well, after I had been at it for almost three years—one of the few serene periods
of my life—there was a Pope who loved me and had reconfirmed my appointment
as architect of St. Peter, Cassandra was expecting her first child, I felt that despite
a cabal of enemies I was venerated in Roma—and my Nicodemus had almost
entirely emerged from my head into the stone. And out of it. Only the Magdalen
was scarcely blocked out. But the other three figures: the Madonna holding the
dead Christ in her lap (as she still holds Him in her lap in my first moonlit Pietà in
the Chapel of the French Kings), the Christ, and Nicodemus in a hood towering
over all of them, containing them all in the circle of his arms— this complicated
composition had emerged so well, I took such joy in carving again after almost
fifteen years of painting, that I could not wait for the hours—sometimes during the
day but more often during the night—when I could return to my colloquy with
this Nicodemus group. Not a silent colloquy, I often said to dead Vittoria, as my
irons rang with the bells of the neighboring campanile, my marmoreal prayers
echoing with the Angelus and Matin.

I had conceived a gigantic triangle greater from baseline to apex by half more
than the size of a normal man, and my Nicodemus in his hood was the apex of that
triangle. And the arms of Nicodemus linked with Mary's arm and the arm of
Christ and the arm of the Magdalen to inscribe a circle within my giant triangle.
So I had reversed the Doni tondo of my youth wherein the triangle of the Holy
Family is inscribed within a circle.

Circles and triangles. Divinity is in those forms as in the form of Man. Arcs of
circles, suggestions of triangles in every muscle, bone, ribcage, flanks, genitalia,
skull, fingers, toes, eyelids, ears, noses, mouth . . .

Our souls are expressed in liquid geometry.

My work was ringing singing winging. My nights became longer and longer. Then I was truly myself. Daylight was Urbino's loving nagging and Cornelia's sweet care and Tomao's companionship and the sweetness and devotion of new young disciples like Daniela da Volterra and Tiberio Calcagni who were grateful if I permitted them to sweep up marble dust, looking upon me, as they did, as some kind of divinity. Daylight were the world's obligations of advising a Pope or drawing up a dowry contract for the grocer's daughter in our neighborhood so that the poor girl might wed (meanwhile she moved into the household as another necessary servant). Daylight was hearing the latest Florentine gossip from Donato. Or presenting a design to the Town Council for enclosing the excavation at the foot of the Trajan column so that I and my neighbors might be spared the obnoxious emanations from the filth gathered in that pit. All these other quotidian affairs seemed to occur in a far-off realm, in the new lands called America, beyond the seas, where shadow figures moved in a muffled gray void. My reality were the hours I spent with Nicodemus.

And then I saw to my astonishment that the same thing was happening as had happened in the Pauline frescoes. My own portrait had emerged. *I* was Nicodemus! *I* was enclosing in my arms the dead Christ, the Madonna, the Magdalen. *I*, Man, was holding all sacred history within the circuit of my arms. And the opening of the hood—wherefrom peered my old face, my tremulous lips in the sparse beard, my gauzed blind-seeming eyes, gazing inward, my expression of sorrow and serenity, pity and peace beyond pity—was contained within the opening of the hood which shaped a mandorla; my face, human all-too-human, contained within the sacred form in which the Christ is contained in the works of the older masters!

I, Michelangiolo Buonarroti Simoni, Florentine sculptor, in the 79th year of my life, was the apex of the Sacred Triangle, the human in the mandorla, *I* was pitying the Christ who pitied us.

I trembled sometimes at the thought of it.

And when I saw that I myself was Nicodemus I thought—this piece will serve for my own tomb.

I also have come in the night and asked—How can such things be?

The day I signed the dowry for the grocer's daughter I saw that I was running into trouble. I had designed the piece so that the dead Christ's right thigh straddles His Mother's thigh. Variants of this theme had intrigued me all my life. I always felt the need to indicate the closeness of the Mother and the Son. And so the Christ Child I sent away to Flanders stands between his mother's thighs, and the Christ Child in the new Sacristy of the Medici straddles his mother's crossed legs. But I had never ventured this treatment with a dead Christ. I thought to have His limp body, removed from the Cross, and deposited in his Mother's lap in such a way that his right leg would straddle her left thigh.

But just at that point the marble block proved obdurate.

There was a fault in the marble and as I chipped at it, small and then larger flakes broke off the skin of the marble and ruined that tiny bit of the form.

So I worked more cautiously around the troublesome area, shaving it, and the fault began to reveal itself in the Madonna's thigh as well, like a spreading infection, and I became very wary, using finer and finer chisels, for fear of splitting what I had already achieved.

Now my colloquy was no longer a joy and Urbino was nagging at me, even more than was his wont—"You've been at the piece for more than three years now! Finish it! Finish it!"

He has always been very free with his tongue, this Marchegiano man-of-all-work, but now he seemed more querulous in his nagging, it was not so much the impatient spurring of love (to which I had been accustomed for almost thirty years), there was another altogether different tone in it, an angry heat which, together with his drawn face and coughing made me think that my Francesco Urbino was ill. Cornelia, in tears, begged me to relieve her husband of some of his duties; and so we engaged another countryman of his to take some of the burden off his shoulders; thus relieved, Urbino had more energy to devote to nagging me to complete my Nicodemus. Everyday he was at me—*When will it be done? Maestro, when will it be done?*—and I was back on the scaffolding of the Sistine and Papa Julius (the *other* Julius, the great Julius) was hammering—*When will it be done? When will it be done?*) My man-of-all-work *terribile* as a Pope!

"I plan it for my own tomb, Urbinino. There is no patron pressing . . ."

"Finish it, Maestro! It drags on."

I loved this faithful man so I suffered in silence the kick of his spurs.

I left the unsatisfactory leg and returned to the Christ. Every day I thinned out the lower of his torso portion to intensify the weight of his abandoned body. And that's when I ran into another fault in the marble— even graver than that in the leg—at the junction of the thigh and thorax and I knew that shaving off the slightest bit more would have cracked the piece entirely. The leg had already given me so much trouble and now this. I feared I would have to sacrifice entirely that wounded leg. I began by removing the knee cap and already I knew the work was doomed for I hate to glue together pieces that are missing.

Daniele thought the severed knee was so beautiful and he uttered so many *ohs* and *ahs* about it that finally I gave it to him and he carried it off with the triumphant expression of one who has unearthed a piece of Roman antiquity in his garden.

After the mutilation I lost all interest in the marble. If I worked on it occasionally it was only because of Urbino's sick nagging. That is, I worked without patience and without profit. And without patience one achieves nothing, especially in so obdurate a medium as stone. But I had really lost interest now, the detestable quality of that block multiplied my troubles.

Troubles breed troubles. They fly in swarms. Urbino now was more frequently in bed than out of it. Cornelia was constantly running from my studio to his bedside. I was worried about him and I was worried about the vicious turn of events in Fiorenza, resulting from Cosimo's ruthless Siena campaign. Now he was more securely in the saddle than ever; the violence of his victory had evicted the French forever from Tuscany and there was not the slightest hope of reestablishing a Florentine republic.

Plagued so, I tried, as always to lose myself in work. I returned to my Nicodemus. But every day new deficiencies were revealing themselves in the stone, especially in the torso of the Christ. That was a new ill-omen. I went back to working nights again. I felt I could not abandon this work which, just at the apex of success, had transformed itself into a battleground as if the pagan marble wished to revenge itself against being employed to depict the founder of Christianity. Below the skin it was full of flaws, obdurate flakes of emery; a rain of sparks flew from my chisel, more brilliant than the pale flickering of the candle set in my paper cap. Those sparks which come from some fire hidden within the marble are the very fires of my own soul and my ailing body is the very marble being smashed by the hand of God. So if I become all powder, dust, and ashes I would serve as the ground for a higher celestial imaging as marble dust mixed with plaster serves as the ground for fresco painting.

So, after the removal of the leg, I continued stubbornly but with ever more vexation to wrestle in the loin of the night with this Nicodemus group which I had thought would be a blessing and had proved instead a curse, when there came a knocking at my door.

It was the first hour after sunset and I knew who it was by the very rhythm of the knocking—a nervous ratatat like messer Giorgio Vassari's own tongue a-rattling and prattling. So I rose from my work and took a lantern in hand and it was he indeed, wrapped in a black cloak and hooded like my Nicodemus and dancing from foot to foot against the January cold. He had just returned to Roma at the Pope's behest: he was looking for a certain model of the Villa he had left with me and some drawings which I had corrected.

With my lantern I found the model he was seeking, and sent Urbino upstairs for the drawings and tried to shift the conversation into other channels since Vasari's eyes all the while were glancing at that leg of Christ which I still hoped to salvage. And because I didn't want Vasari to see it, I dropped the lantern and from the dark called Urbino to bring a light; meanwhile issuing forth from where we were, I said— "I am so old that Death is pulling me by the cape that I should go with him. And some day I myself will drop like this lantern and my light will be extinguished."

Giorgio's silence after this was most eloquent. He was completely at a loss for words, a most unusual situation for him. He took the drawings which Urbino had brought and bade me adieu and was gone. Gone from Roma too after a short while. He charges up and down the peninsula like a courser at Siena. He must have a hundred arms and legs for all the works he is undertaking.

And my poor Christ was already lacking a leg.

For soon after that unexpected visit I realized there was no hope of saving the piece except by an amputation. I had to remove the hopelessly damaged leg and make a hole in the thorax wherein to fit a replacement.

And then a few weeks after my eightieth birthday, Julius III died so that he never had a chance to embalm my corpse. He was a frivolous man and the scandals of his personal behavior had not helped the efforts of the Council to stamp out the Lutheran heresy, but he had always been my great protector.

When I learned that his successor was the Cardinal Cervini—the very man who had accused me before the Pope of failing to cooperate with the Deputies of the Fabbrica—and when this new Pope assumed his own name, Marcello, as his papal name, Marcellus II—I took it as a bad augury. The last Holy Father who had used his own name was the Fleming Adrian and he had certainly been no friend of the arts. I felt this new Pope would not conceal his hostility toward me especially in the work at St. Peter's, that he would most likely support the carping Nanni and relieve me of my post. I was already preparing to leave Roma and return to Fiorenza when came the unexpected news that Marcellus II had departed for a better life after only twenty-two days in the Papal See. There was talk of poison, there always is.

His successor was the Neapolitan Carafa who took the name of Paul IV. He ordered me to remain, and so I remained, notwithstanding there were already rumblings of the eruption to come.

It was not an auspicious year for me, that first year of the Pontificate of the Neapolitan. Almost immediately he deprived me of the revenues of the ferry crossing of the Po. The intrigues around the fabbrica of St. Peter's had grown ever more menacing. An architect protected by Paul IV, Pirro Ligorio was whistling nasty rumors about me all around the City, outdoing even Nanni di Baccio Biagio in his filth. But I was not surprised. All Roma is a Cloaca Massima. I have never felt clean in this Holy City and I was so indignant at what was being said about my senility and second childhood and incapacity that I thought seriously of returning to Fiorenza for Duke Cosimo was intensifying his efforts to have me return to my Patria to complete the church of San Lorenzo.

But yet I was reluctant. I had been forced to accept the office of architect of Saint Peter's and now that I was about to vault the cupola I could not abandon this task which I was carrying out not for money (for I accepted none) or glory (the glory of slander!) but for my soul's sake. So I wrote to Giorgio Vasari to thank the Duke but I would not return until I had completed Saint Peter's for otherwise it would have brought a great shame to all Christianity and great sin to my own soul. But soon there were new solicitations from the Duke by other emissaries; and I found myself wavering with every new flaw disclosed in the Nicodemus group on which I worked desultorily amidst all these storms. And there were new threats of war resulting from the eruptions of this Vesuvius of a Pope against the Spaniard whom he hated with a violence that served only to provoke the Emperor even more against Italy.

Now it was Autumn, the larches lost their manuscript-leaves and Urbino could not leave his bed. He knew he was dying but I refused to know it. I knew I was dying. I have always known that and I do not fear Death for why should we fear the same hand that fashioned us? That is, I do not fear Death for myself. I am a citizen of that realm even in the midst of the most lifeloving laughter.

But the death of those I love is unsupportable. Let the knocking at the door be for me, not for them! I cannot tolerate the pain. To be deprived of my friends is worse than being deprived of myself. And Francesco d'Amadore was more than a servant, more than a friend. He was my son.

So Urbino knew he was dying and he bade Cornelia to summon two of his countrymen down to aid me. There was a Lucia and an Antonio and Antonio is still with me but Lucia has gone and good riddance too. For the moment these two entered my service—and I paid them well—one full scudo per month, each of them—there burst forth a domestic *scampiglio* similar to the end of the world.

I escaped to my Nicodemus.

In November died my last brother, Gismondo, and now my cup of woe was trembling at the brim. For although I felt he had brought little honor to our noble house of Buonarroti, living in solitude as he did up at Settignano, having made himself into a peasant, cultivating the fields himself, following the oxen, stepping in the merda of those oxen like any contadino. And when he wasn't doing that he might as well have been a rock left in the fields for he came alive only when there was need to plunge his horny hand in my purse.

Yet he was my brother withal and toward the end he had come down occasionally from his hillside, was a Counselor of the Duke and served my interests too, I suppose.

So I wept for him and wrote to Lionardo that we must have patience, especially since Gismondo died with all the sacraments of the Church.

The next month my cup runneth over, Francesco d' Amadore, my belovèd Urbino, died of the plague which had kkept him bedridden for many months. He had served me faithfully for more than twenty-two years, and had been, for all his rioting and quarrelsomeness and nagging, a faithful and loving son—yes, I thought of him as a son, not as my servant or assistant and I loved him as he loved me, and as living he had taught me how to live, now, dying, he taught me how to die. O the weeping! the weeping! Cornelia was inconsolable; and her infant son Michelangiolo whom I had held at the font screamed as if he knew that his father had departed forever. Soon after the funeral Cornelia returned with her two children to live with her family and she has since written me letters which reveal the same filial devotion her husband had displayed.

In that cold rainy winter after Urbino's death, I tried to work again on the mutilated Nicodemus. Since he had always set such great store upon it, I thought to make Urbino's ghost happy, and in the night chipping away I thought to hear his voice crying: *Finish it! Maestro. It must be finished!*, the querulous insistance that had not even ceased all the months of his confinement to bed.

But there was no voice. Nothing but the steady rain, the blows of my hammer, the singing shower of sparks, the gonging of the neighboring campanile. Night after rainy night I struggled with it, but misfortune always dogged me, the stone seemed cursed. After some minor accidents a bit of the Madonna's elbow broke off. Perhaps it was cursed because I was working on it too desperately, not knowing when to leave well enough alone as Urbino had repeatedly urged me to do. And now when that piece of the Madonna's elbow broke off, I lost all patience and took a sharp-pointed pickaxe and smashed it; and I would have smashed it even more to smithereens had not Antonio, awakened by the blows (and I must have cried out too—*Urbino!* you see?! Now it is truly finished! Now your spirit can rest!), appeared in his nightdress, gaping like a gargoyle, and begged me to desist. So I desisted. And the young fool with tears in his eyes, begged me to give him the pieces, they were so beautiful, he would do something with them, he would glue—

"They are yours!" I said, "Now let me be."

He departed. I looked at the debris. I had committed a massacre. I was eighty-one years old and I had committed a massacre. Ah how that pagan marble had conquered! Several years ago, before all the trouble with the leg had started, the work had already been brought to such a state of perfection that many visitors thought it practically complete, how many had admired it! Competed to copy it! How often Urbino had warned me to leave it alone: let him complete the Magdalen, he would polish it here and there— as I might desire—with pumice— according to my orders—it's done, Maestro! Leave it alone! . . .

Instead, what remained now? A Christ deprived of both legs, his left arm smashed, even the blocked-out Magdalen gouged, the Madonna without an elbow.

This was the ancient capital out of which I had striven for six years to extract a Deposition for my tomb, an abandoned rock-pile.

Only the Nicodemus was unwounded. He was gazing down—*I* was gazing down—with the same, no, with more pity than before at the wreckage of another dream.

VIII

Magister Elia del Medigo

I came down to Roma originally in the service of Don Amatus Lusitanus, a great master of anatomy, thin as a shank bone himself. His beard was streaked mahogany and he had a curious habit of resting his left leg as he pondered a question, jiggling his right foot as he thought..

And how he did indeed think! One could *see* the question under examination floating in his greenish eyes, being turned over and prodded; I had the distinct impression that the problem was being *fried* there in deep hot oil, one could almost see it coiling and browning in the heat of this man's mind.

As his predilected fellow, I accompanied this Master of the Long Robe in all his peregrinations: first in Ferrara where he was house-physician to the House of Este; and then when he was summoned to Roma during their Holy Year, to the palaces of various great prelates and eventually to the Vatican where he joined a team of papal archiaters attending to the body of Pope Julius as he attended to souls. Not to the souls of Hebrew physicians, be it clear. We were there at best by a kind of sufferance. We were needed, not loved, as our loan bankers were needed, and when not needed, expelled. One learns to live on one's toes, my father says. One learns to walk like a man, on one's feet, my grandfather Andrea used to say. They are both doctors, both Masters of the Long Robe, but they don't always agree in their diagnoses or prescriptions.

My grandmother Ziporah sat silently during these wrangles, but my mother would sometimes engage in unpredictable deflections " . . . on one's toes," Father said, and my mother Ester would dance around the room on her toes, gracefully swinging her arms, fingers love-locked over her head, swaying like a willow to the adoration of her son and grandson and the patent disapproval of my father, Daniele. She had learned this dance from a cousin, ballet-master at the Gonzaga court at Modena. "On one's toes," my father repeated, "and ready to strike one's tents."

His words meant nothing to me then. But now under the Carafa! . . . My grandfather, thank God, has been spared that. But even he, with all his cynicism, remembered the past so clearly that it lay unrolled before him, a Torah scroll.

Don Amatus lived on his toes. On the very tips. What none of these prelates knew, I knew. Don Amatus was a New Christian, that is, a crypto-Jew: behind his Christian facade he continued to observe the Law; somewhere, soon, he would publicly cast off the mask he wore for most of his clientele but not for me. Nor indeed for several distinguished Hebrew households also numbered among his patients.

He was known as Amatus Lusitanus, that is to say Amatus the Portuguese, but he had a sufficiency of other names in his time, witness to his travels. When his parents had become New Christians to avoid expulsion from Portugal in 1493, he had latinized his Hebrew name Habib to Amatus and in his early years under the mask he was known as João Rodrigues. But New Christians were almost as suspect as the old Hebrews they had been. The name "Marrano" (Pig) was more commonly applied to them than "Christian"; and as Marrano they were not infrequently roasted in the burning pieties of the auto-da-fè.

When Don Habib-Rodriques-Amatus told me his story, I felt immediately a special kinship, for my grandmother Ziporah had fled to Fiorenza from Seville with her family the very year Habib became Amatus. I always took delight in the Spanish lilt and sibilance of my grandmother's Tuscan; and my grandfather who prided himself as a born Florentine never ceased to tease her for her "baby-talk Italian." But the teasing ceased abruptly the moment the name of my great uncle Bartolomeo de Cases was mentioned. For this uncle—my grandmother's brother—had been stoned and gashed and torn to death by a Florentine mob the very year the family had arrived and my grandfather had witnessed that horror. He tried to avoid this subject but it would come up in family talk whenever there was a resurgence of religious intolerance, stirred up by certain Franciscan preachers or during their Easter season.

"So then, after my graduation from Salamanca," said Jaõa Rodrigues (his name at the time), "I eventually wandered to Antwerp and then to Italy . . ."

We had met originally in front of the Basilica of San Marco gazing up at the flood mosaics in the atrium. There was this skinny jiggling man in the long red robe of a Doctor of Physic gazing up at the animals entering the ark and reciting their names to himself in a kind of comic litany. I thought he was mumbling Hebrew but when I introduced myself in that tongue he frowned and didn't understand. Or so it seemed. We fell into conversation. His eye was sharp and so was his tongue. He held an appointment at Ferrara in the medical school. I wasn't sure of what he was but somehow I found myself boasting of the tradition of medicine in my family. I was at that time still studying at Padova following in the footsteps of my father who in turn had followed in the footsteps of his father. " . . . and my great grandfather," said I proudly, "Elia after whom I am named, Elia from Crete, had even held an appointment at Padova . . ."

"How 'appointment'?" asked this mahogany-bearded man looking curiously at me with his green appraising eyes.

"O I mean he was Professor of Medicine. In fact, he was the first to hold such an appointment."

"How 'first' "?

"O I mean openly as Elias Cretensis Ebreus—Elia the Jew from Crete."

"Hallelú!" he said and he sounded like my mother.

So then I knew and there in the great Piazza walking under the glittering mosaics and fluttering banners of the Serenissima, I told this strange Master of the Long Robe how my great-grandfather had taught (aside from medicine) the true text of Aristotle (via Avverhoes) to the young Count of Concordia Pico della Mirandola who in turn had taken him down to Fiorenza where he participated in philosophical discussions with the Florentine Platonists of the great Lorenzo the Magnificent and there it was that my great-grandfather had given Hebrew lessons to Pico who was eager to read Cabala in the original (to prove the truth of Christianity) and that was why my grandfather Andrea had been born in Fiorenza . . . I said all this in a sort of long single outpouring of breath compounded of family pride and pride of patria. " . . . so you see, I come of a long line of physicians . . . Fiorentini . . . Spagnoli . . ."

Don Habib João Rodrigues Amatus Lusitanus smiled mockingly: "Fiorentini . . . Spagnoli . . . We are all sons of the One God."

Our friendship began that very day. I had floated down from Padova to Venezia along the Brenta by flatboat: a dream journey culminating in a dream city. And when I returned to Padova to learn that my Professor of Anatomy, a young Fleming named Vesalius, was leaving the University to publish his new book at Basle, I decided to transfer to the Studium at Ferrara and pursue my anatomical studies with Don Amatus. Our friendship, born under glittering Noah and the animals, was to continue even when I was finally laureate, a Master of the Long Robe myself, practicing in Ferrara. I was honored often to be called in for consultation by Don Habib (privately I never addressed him otherwise because I knew this gave him pleasure); I was honored, I say, to be called in for consultation by such an extraordinary physician although I deeply suspect the true reason for the summons was his desire to discuss philosophy with me. For like my great-grandfather Elia he had as true a passion for philosophy as for medicine. Notwithstanding the fame of his dissections, essentially he considered the body only as elegant (and unnecessary) evidence of the existence and power of the One God. In this he differed from my grandfather Andrea who felt that the Body (the body of humankind and the body of the world) was coterminous with God and certain jestings that he made along this line angered my father and sometimes my grandmother too.

Another reason for our corroboration was the great work on which Habib was engaged: what was to be eventually seven volumes of *Centuriae Curationem*, each volume containing one hundred medical histories in Latin which had come to his attention or in which he himself had effected a cure.

Aside from being in the service of this prestigious man, there was another reason why I followed him so willingly to Roma. For I had never been to Caput Mundi although my grandparents not infrequently recalled their years in Roma. My grandmother's family had fled (a second fleeing!) from Fiorenza to Roma after the brutal killing of my uncle Bartolomeo. And my grandfather had also transferred there for reasons never clear in my mind; there he had met again my grandmother; there in fact they had been married.

Now my grandfather had a curious interval in his youth about which he was reluctant to talk. He had once had, it seems, an outlandish ambition to become a painter. He had even been apprenticed for a while in Venice in the workshop of Giovanni Bellini, and in Roma in the workshop of the Pollaiuolo. A painter! A Hebrew painter! The idea is absurd. A Hebrew making images of the Imageless, the Beyond-all-Imaging. A Hebrew making idols who are Christian saints, painting fantasies of Joshua of Nazaret, painting stories of a bleeding host . . . My grandfather smashed the panels of his ambition and returned to medicine.

All this I learned at intervals by hintings, indirection, melancholy recollections. But there was one name recurrent and sunshiny in these beclouded reminiscences. My grandfather, Maestro Andrea of the Long Robe, had in his youth been a close friend of that supreme Master of the Arts, Michelangiolo Buonarroti of Fiorenza.

And so I came to Roma with a sort of map already in my mind. Instead of making the rounds of the seven basilicas as Christian pilgrims do, I make the rounds of the works of this great master who is reputed divine. I am really less interested in these works than I am in filling out my memories of my grandfather.

In Roma, Don Habib certainly did not have to conceal for professional reasons his never-relinquished faith. Even these days, when the fear of Lutheran heresy from the North and the threat of the Grand Turk from the East has made most Italian Catholic minds beleaguered fortresses, and intensified their distrust of all those outside their one true faith—and first of all, of course, we Jews whose rejection has been, so to speak, primordial, having rejected our Joshua as their Lord—even in these days of growing darkness, Jewish physicians continue to minister to Christian bodies: even the bodies of popes and cardinals and bishops as well as foreign kings and Italian princes.

This does not surprise me. Hebrews have always been accounted excellent physicians even in ancient times. There were other members of the team of papal archiaters who were Jews. This has been true for centuries: pontiff after pontiff, prince after prince, had Jews in their employ as personal medical attendants.

And yet Don Habib was still debating in his mind whether to cast off his mask.

The first few times I had accompanied him on his medical consultations of the cardinals under his care, I had been cautious and silent amidst all that panoply. When finally I saw the Pope himself, stripped naked at Habib's orders, and lying on a table, he seemed terribly vulnerable, if fat, and surely there was nothing of divinity in his person! Stripped of its vestments, the body of a Pope or of an Emperor is no different from that of any other man. Nakedness is the ultimate humanity. Or is it the divinity we all share? the Alpha and Omega? Master Habib's long bony fingers were probing the Pope's groin and His Holiness cried out at one point, at another he laughed because the point of the physicians long beard was tickling his most private parts. Now Habib was palpating and auscultating the

abundant flesh that almost disguised the fact that His Holiness possessed a rib-
cage; and now Habib had laid his head gently as a lover on the pontiff's heart and
was listening to his husky breathing. Now he was pulling down the corners of his
rheumy eyes and staring into them and shaking his head and recommending that
His Holiness display a bit more restraint at table, and Del Monte chuckled *Carpe
Diem*, surely it was unchristian for the Highest Prince of Christianity—the last of
the Apostles—to live as meanly as a fisherman in the Tiber. His fishing was for
souls; meanwhile his flesh had need of plentiful sustenance to be fit for that
arduous and never-ending task.

Don Amatus bowed gravely to the half-naked pontiff. At the same time, Habib
winked at me. Perhaps I imagined it. A metaphysical wink, unseen by a Pope's eye.
The Holy Father was now being re-vested by his grooms. In his nakedness I had
perceived no more divinity than is possessed by any other man. I knew that his
organs performed the same functions as mine, suffered the same decay.

I cannot understand the worship of Man as God although I well understand the
worship of God in Man.

I have found more of God in the functioning of the liver than in all the sacred
books, ours as well as theirs.

Of course Jesus was divine.

So am I.

So is every man.

Almost invariably after one of these Papal ministrations, Habib spoke again—
and frequently with mocking impatience—of his desire to cast aside his cloak of
Christianity and reveal himself as a Jew. But fear restrained him. He was certain
that upon such a revelation, his practice in rarified ecclesiastic circles, the honors
he enjoyed among the Princes of the Church, would abruptly be closed to him. In
vain I tried to convince him that such a revelation would most likely have no effect
whatever on his status, especially during the reign of HILARITAS PONTIFICIS.
My grandfather, of blessèd memory, used to scoff at all credal and rigid observances, amongst Jews as amongst Christians, and my grandmother would sometimes become angry at his scoffing. He used to say that in all his examinations he
had never found an organ of infallibility in any man, not even in Moses Maimonides, the great Rambam; and my grandmother cried: "You have never performed
a notomia on the great Rambam for he was dead long before your time!" (My
grandmother still posseses that ancient Sephardic pride, that capacity to take
flame at the slightest scintilla). And my grandfather Andrea would laugh, "I have
examined his writings, my bird. But even he—the greatest of our Rabbis—he who
wedded Aristotle to Torah as Aquinas wedded him to their reading of Scripture—
even Maimonides is prone to human error."

He was chucking her under the chin and my grandmother cried: "you said
examinations! examinations! . . ."

And my grandfather, smiling: "I speak *metaphorically*. I have probed the guts of more than one of our Rabbini—if not the great Ramban—and I find their causistry as befogging as the incense of the priests."

At that my grandmother would begin to cry about the fate of her brother Bartolomeo—and then grandfather was suddenly quiet.

But from him, I have inherited the vitality of doubt.

And making the holy rounds, with master Habib, in the midst of a Holy Year, I seemed to hear Grandfather's voice ever more and more frequenly. Andrea was a palpable presence, I heard his laughter frequently, and the joy he seemed to take in proving reliquaries bones, and miracles necessary or unnecessary myths. He had read much Maimonides and Aristotle and even scattered those seeds on my bony head. But they didn't take root. I am not my Grandfather. I am not as brave to strive as he did, laughing, between two fires. I long for sheltering. And when I came to Roma, I began almost at once to search for it among the ancient Jewish community of that ancient city.

The Urbs I was seeing now for the first time was not the Urbs my grandfther had visited before the Sack. Frequently after dinner, still around the table, my grandfather would tell us stories of that pre-Sack Roma, vivid as if we saw it. So when I came to Roma with Habib in 1550, the reality of the city I saw was familiar and unfamiliar. The art of painting which my grandfather had abjured had flowed into the art of painting with words. He was a marvelous story teller. I came to Roma with a Roma already in my head. It was the same and not the same.

The Sack of '27 had reduced the population in half, many of the great palaces had been damaged and the Landsknechts had left visible scars everywhere.

I wandered everywhere in Roma. I am a wanderer. I suppose it is the ancient tradition of our tribe. I found many Hebrews still living in the quarter near the Trastevere and Arena districts where they had several synagogues: one for the Spanish and Portuguese who—like Mother's family and Don Habib—had arrived after the Iberian expulsions, and one for the older Italian community (my grandmother on Father's side), and one for some Ashkenazim who had escaped down into Italy from the persecutions in Lutheran and Calvinist lands across the Alps.

I made these rounds. And I made the rounds of the works of my grandfather's friend.

One Saturday afternoon I went with Don Habib to see the famous statue of Moses by Michelangiolo Buonarroti, the Florentine, which stands in the church of St. Peter in Chains near the Esquiline Hill. Generally, Hebrews are reluctant to enter the churches of a faith which has visited so much suffering upon them. In Roma especially there are forced baptisms, and during Carnival old Jews, naked except for loin cloths, are set to racing down the Corso to the screams of delectation of the plebe, and Popes have more than once applied special taxes upon the Hebrew community whenever there is need for funds.

Although some of these practices have declined somehwat, they still obtained in the main, even under easygoing Julius III.

Yet every Saturday there was a stream of Jews who visited the Church of St. Peter in Chains to gaze upon the Moses.

Since I had no inhibitions on the matter to begin with—an attitude I have inherited from my father—I went along willingly.

In front of the door, I saw a Venetian I had known in Padova. I recognized him by the sprouts of red hair spilling out under the broadbrimmed hat like hay from a cart.

"Josef!"

"Elia!"

"How do you overcome your reluctance to enter a Christian Church?"

His gaze surveyed me and Don Habib swiftly and wisely like a torch searching a dark corridor.

"And you do not need to overcome this inhibition?" he replied with a soft smile.

So I smiled too. And even Habib sickly. In the warmth of that communal smile, we all removed our hats and entered the church. Out of the side of my eye I saw that Don Habib was dipping his fingers in the holy water font and crossing himself, but furtively as a passing bird. He was obviously concerned that some prelate in his care might have seen him enter, and was embarrassed to be still playing this charade in my presence. But as a Papal Archiater entering a Christian Church, he could hardly do otherwise.

The spectacle inside the church of so many members of the Jewish community of Roma gazing at that astonishing statue, struck me as a supreme irony. Moses, the iconoclast, himself an idol! But immediately I realized that the crowd of Hebrews were whispering in admiration, but not in veneration; Michelangiolo's Moses was to them a marvel of art, a great honor paid to The Lawgiver and his people. But it was not an object of worship. My irony vanished. I too found myself overwhelmed by that fierce marble frown, the knotted veins in the hand and arms, the titanic contained force of the gesture, a thunderstorm about to break, the astonishing beard flowing like all Time. In Moses I recognized immediately the David I had seen outside the Palace door in Fiorenza, the same David grown older, the Hero become the Judge.

Habib had lagged a bit behind to make his furtive sign of the Cross. When he caught up with us in front of the tomb, Josef was saying sententiously to the little cluster of Hebrew pilgrims gathered there. "Is it not a great honor for us Hebrews that the divine Michelangiolo should carve so nobly the figure of our lawgiver Moses?"

All this, I thought, was gondoliering down the wrong canal.

"And those horns? Is that also an honor?" whispered Don Habib in my ear: his voice conspiratorially sardonic, his expression puzzled.

"Oh those are not horns!" I said, "they are the emanations of light that issued from Moses' head when he descended from the Mount.

"Ah, but they seem like horns to me."

"The Christians often render them so. I have seen it often. Even in the center of the Jewish quarter of Siena. It's all the fault of their Saint Jerome who rendered *keren*—emanation—as *cornus*—horns. So hale, emanation, radiance became horns. But why are you surprised? Their entire church rests upon a pun . . ." And I went on and on, since I saw I had an audience of fellows, but in almost a whisper for it was for that audience alone. "Since their Jesus said to Peter "On this Rock I build my church' and Pietro means rock and so it is all semantics, a structure built on a play of words."

A young woman in the crowd was staring at me, staring, I could feel her gaze like a ray of sun shining through an oculus. She was a tallish maiden with a marvelous heap of honeyed hair and she had a way of listening to my dissertation as if she alone understood what I was saying, as if I were speaking just to her in all that crowd. Her gaze warmed me from the pit of my stomach upward; I became so conscious of that gaze and the slight smile playing about her lips and the honeyed heap of hair and the full bosom swelling in the cape, that my joking began to limp like a spavined horse.

But I did not lose so much of my self-control as not to dare to speak to her. I found an excuse to ditch Don Habib after we had proceeded less than an arrow's flight from the church. I rushed back and met the girl just as she was dancing down the long flight of steps. Dancing, that's how she walked. I felt she was always dancing. Her name was Miriamne. She belonged to that small group of Trasteverini Jews who claim descent from the captives Vaspasiano and Titus brought from Jerusalem to Roma after the destruction of the Second Temple in the year 70 of the Christian era. "When my ancestors came here," she would say with a surge of pride, "most Romans were not yet Christians."

"They are still not Christians."

A trickle of laughter. Soon I was living for that laughter. It sustained me, amidst many horrors. Together we explored the great city. Her family knew me as Maestro Elia of the Long Robe, and confided not only their most intimate ailments to me but also their most secret pre-occupations. They had lived in Roma always and divided the periods into those when they were obliged to wear a special sign and those when they were not. And they knew that we physicians were almost always exempted from such restrictions, that we could wear caps like any of the Christians even in those periods when other Jews were bound to wear red caps. And they welcomed me particularly because they knew I was privy, through Don Habib Rodriguez Amatus Lusitanus, of much that was bruited about in the Vatican.

With every change of Pope, the community was wary, wondering what the attitude of the new Pontiff would be in their regard. Under Paul III they had been quite as free as any other Romans, although special taxes were sometimes levied upon them; and the horror of the annual race of old half-naked Jews down the Corso was still a humiliating aspect of Carnevale. Mariamne's family remained locked in their homes during almost the entire Pasqual season, violence ran high then; the plebe were re-living the Passion. Some years, especially if there had been a series of recent preachments by one of those itinerant monks, wild rumors were circulated: the most outrageous being that we used Christian blood to make our ritual Easter bread—the matzoh. I am always tempted to say no one could believe such things, but believe them they did.

I had, I say, come down to Roma with a certain image in my head. Now exploring the city with Mariamne, accompanying Don Habib on his rounds, even to the palaces of prelates, even to the Vatican itself. I soon realized that the atmosphere had changed since my grandfather Andrea had last been here. After the Sack Roma was never the same, not even during this pontificacy of an easy-going hedonistic Pope like Julius III. He may, as I learned from Pasquino, have set up *Hilaritas* as his idol, pleasure as his principle, but there were too many cardinals whose outlook on the world was gloomier than his; a new order of ecclesiastical soldiers had been founded by a Spanish monk, Loyola, and the fear of Lutheran heresy was compounded by a fear of the Turk pressing from the East. A nice point of doctrine: is an infidel more to be damned than a heretic? We were infidels. Christianity itself was the greatest of all heresies! the heresy of worshipping a man as God.

The atmosphere had changed. The Council was meeting up at Trent, girding the Church's loins against the Protestant heretics, and by extension infidels as well, including non-believing infidels. The girding also involved some curious dancing on the heads of pins.

I assisted while Habib was cupping a most amusing witty patient, named Annibale Caro, secretary to some cardinal, and he, unaware there were two infidels, one open and one cloaked, within reach of his hearing, was recounting to a friend, a Fiorentino, I believe, named Gianotti or Gianetti, a report he had just received of the debate on the question of the Immaculate Conception of the Virgin.

For many months, it seems, a certain Cardinal Pacheco had been sustaining this cause with great zeal, backed by a considerable number of Fathers, including the Pope's own theologians. But the opposition of Dominicans was so strong that the Most Reverend Cardinal Pacheco finally offered a compromise. He would be satisfied if in the decree be included the words that the Immaculate Conception of the Mother of God was a pious opinion.

"But not even this compromise succeeded," chuckled messer Caro, "for the majority was determined that for the moment, no decision be taken on this matter—"

"—E allora?"

"—E allora . . ." Messer Caro's voice took on a mocking drum-roll. , "the synod finally declared simply that it was not its intention to include in its decree any reference whatsoever to the Blessèd and Immaculate Virgin and Mother of God Mary (*Non esse suae intentionis, comprehendere in hoc decreto, ubi de peccato originale agitur, beatam et immaculatum Virginem, Mariam, Dei genitricem*) being obliged, with reference to such a matter, to adhere to the prescriptions of Sixtus IV." The drum-roll ceased: the eyes twinkled. Messer Caro and his friend seemed enormously amused. Amused even beyond the irritations of the cupping. Master Habib, busy at his task, pretended deafnesss.

Miriamne's father was a Rabbi but in keeping with ancient tradition he would not use the Talmud as a spade to dig with. He earned his living as a printer and he possessed indeed that peculiar reverence for books and manuscripts typical of so many of our people. Peculiar especially in his case because Rabbi Vitale dello Strologo tended to look upon any words committed to print or carefully written by a scribe as somehow related to the Book of Books, all scripture was Holy Scripture and he could no more tear up and cast away printed or manuscript pages than cast away bread. It was sinful. He was, with all these eccentricities, a most sympathetic man, and soon, courting Miriamne, I spent more time with her family than with Don Habib. The dello Strologo—Miriamne's parents and numerous brothers and sisters—lived in that quarter near Palazzo Cenci, a quarter where there were so many Jews that the central piazza of the neighborhood was called Piazza dei Giudei. There was another concentration of Jews across the Tiber. They were not required to live in any particular area, but some of these families, and the dello Strologo were one, traced their ancestry back to the times of ancient Roma. Rabbi Vitale indeed talked about Julius Caesar and his friendship toward the Jews as if he were a contemporary. Perhaps that is what makes of us a peculiar people. We are the eternal contemporaries.

I introduced Don Habib into the dello Strologo household too. He was increasingly troubled these days. His hands trembled so at a blood-letting that I feared for the patient. His nerves were drawn ever tighter by the peg of contradiction. He was driven by an ever-more intense desire to cast off his cloak and openly assert himself a Hebrew. He had been on the point of doing this shortly after we arrived in Roma. This new Pontiff's easy-going ways seemed most propitious for the daring act which Habib had been excogitating for so many years. On the other hand, he feared (without reason) the consequences such an open assertion might have on his prestigious preferment as papal archiater. In vain, I was still trying to convince him that there would be no consequences whatever; had not my father Andrea served Giuseppe Gallo, papal archiater, who had never concealed his faith? And had he never heard of the Spanish doctor of physik, Jacob Mantino, body-physician to Doges and to Pope Paul III, lecturer in medicine at the

Sapienza—always and openly as a Jew? Had not Mantino—how my father laughed at this!—even been consulted by Clement VII regarding the biblical legality of hot Henry's first marriage? always and openly as a Jew.

Consequences? During a new Age of Gold? The Pope was building a pleasure villa. And laughing. What was there to worry about?

But Habib had Iberian sensibilities which I lacked. He had learned, immediately upon his arrival in the Holy City, that the Inquisition, long moribund in Roma, had been revived only eight years earlier, under the spur of the zealous Neapolitan Cardinal Caraffa. "O Dios! exclaimed Habib, "This Supreme Tribunal of the Holy Office is organized along the same lines as that set up in Spain sixty years ago."

"Ah," said I, "but the authority of this Holy Office extends over heretics, not unbelievers. We are unbelievers," I added, not without a very special private reference.

Habib looked at me with that long lugubrious gaze of his, so much like that of a very intelligent horse, an anomaly.

"The conversion of my family originated from the burning of unbelievers . . ."

"Well, Maestro, it will not happen here in Italia. Italia no es Espana."

He was silent, munching his preoccupations.

He loved to join me for an evening at Miriamne's home. In those warm halls, he had immediately dropped his cloak. It was a relief, like unlacing a tight jerkin. He could breathe now in his own atmosphere and we spent many congenial evenings there, Habib exchanging his gossip of the Pontifex Maximus with the Rabbi's gossip of Julius Caesar. I attended to their epoch-leaping with my ears but my eyes and my soul were consumed only with Mariamne's loveliness: her smile—dazzling sun emerging from cloud—, her honeyed hair, the rhythmic perk of her shoulders with the long confident stride. Her mother was busy usually fluttering wings over one or another of her many children. The dello Strologo's were rapidly becoming my family and I had already written to my old mother in Bologna of my intentions to take unto myself a wife.

One September, returning from this pleasant household, Habib and I found ourselves sucked into a great funnel of people pouring into the Campo dei Fiori. In the center of the square—usually mosaic-bright with carts of game and fruit and legumes and fish, the vendors screaming their invitations to buy, crying out their wares as if lanced with agony—we saw, as soon as we could find a space to breathe in the stream that had carried us here, a scaffold. Tall as a crucifixion over the mob—not vendors—that was screaming today, a monk was tied to a stake, the heap of faggots at his feet already lighted. My physician-eye saw at once that he had already blessèdly fainted before the brutal flames leaped up around him, a blazing cape furred with smoke.

"Jew! Jew! Jew!"

Habib and I exchanged glances. The cries were an indecent brew of brutality and righteousness, the ecstacy of killing in the name of piety.

Discreetly questioning, we learned that today's victim was a Franciscan friar named Cornelio da Montalcino who had embraced Judaism as a result of his studies. Silently, except for the groans of our exertion in extricating ourselves from the howing mob—*Burn! Jew! Burn! Burn!*—we left that Field of Flowers whose chief blossom now—a tall pillar of orange-lanced smoke, crackling with sparks, the smell of burning flesh— continued to grow into the epicurian indifferent azure sky.

And less than a month later, Miriamne and I witnessed another burning in that same Campo dei Fiori.

I remember the date exactly because it was on Rosh haShana, our New Year's day. That morning I had attended services which I did for Miriamne's sake: her father was the Rabbino of the Temple School: one of five small synagogues on the Piazza della Scuola near the Portico Octaviano. His was called the Temple synagogue because it served the Roman Jews, the oldest continuous Jewish community in the Urbs; sixteen centuries they have clung to this city notwithstanding the most outrageous efforts to annihilate them or convert them. The other schools were the Catalans, the Castilians, the Sicilians, and some newcomers: Askenazim from beyond the Alps, who speak a curious Hebrew and in all but few respects seem as barbarian as their recent hosts.

I always felt all these synagogues were situated here as a stubborn challenge to the nearest Church, Sant' Angelo in Pescheria, where every Saturday some Jews of the quarter were forced to attend Christian service. "Fishers of souls. Netted and hauled." Rabbino Vitale would say, his fine-cut lips scornful, his furry black eyebrows curving like squirrels in flight. The whole neighborhood smelled of fish. I liked their shining geometry, their piscatorial perfection, their rainbowy glistening on the marble market slabs. I remember that my grandmother Ziporah had lived here as a girl; I made inquiries as soon as I came to Roma. None of her family remained.

I met Miriamne in front of the Scuola and soon we were strolling along the ochre Tiber, hand in hand, saying the tremendous nothings lovers say. Never had the world seemed so beautiful, never had the Ponte Sixtus leaped so agilely from shore to shore, never was the enormous cube of the Farnese Palace so cubic, so overwhelming. Love has this effect upon the senses. It intensifies like a burning glass: the pale quotidian becomes the fiery eternal, the river was more rivery, the enormous space of the Piazza of the Duke seemed to reverberate with shouts and yet there were but few people in it.

And then we realized where the shouts were coming from. Was it a bullfight in the Campo dei Fiori?

So we went to see. There was another bonfire, another mob gathered around it and shouting obscenities. But they weren't burning a monk this time. They were burning books.

An insignificant heap of them set aflame in the center of the piazza was sufficient to set off these wild screams, these jubilant roars, with every tongue-leap of the flames another cry. The Roman mob needs but the slightest pretext; it has been roaring thus since the circuses, the gladiatorial games of ancient days in the Colosseum.

The color of the smoke and flames was different from that of burning flesh. Emerald and azure flashed gorgeous glintings in this fire; and the violet dusky smoke was coiled thick as Mariamne's hair. A Dominican bearing a cross was mounting a portable wooden pulpit. He delivered a sort of sermon, explaining to the mob who needed no explanations, (total ignorance would have sufficed to set off the same incendiary zeal) that this was an auto-da-fé of Hebrew books, haphazardly seized from synagogues and private homes, Talmuds and kindred works; all accused by recent Papal decree as blasphemous, insulting to Christianity and the Lord Jesus Christ.

It seems that Rabbino Vitale already knew in advance about the book-burning to come. Although luckily the requisitions had spared him, the homes of several of his congregation and friends had been sacked. He was bitter about the role played by several apostates—formerly Hebrews—in Roma in drumming up this event. He wondered if Don Habib might be able to exert some influence in the Vatican. Habib was curious whether one of the apostates whom Rabbi Vitale had named, a certain Joseph Sarphati, was related to Samuel Sarphati, the famous Doctor of Physik to Pope Julius II?

"Is it possible?" I asked.

"It is possible, it is possible," replied the Rabbi melancholically stroking his beard. With every stroke his squirrel eyebrows leaped.

Habib gave me a long-faced Portuguese look. Had I not cited Sarphati as my strongest argument regarding the feasibility of Hebrew Papal archiaters?

Vitale said there were two rival sets of apostates in Roma propagating on behalf of two rival Christian printers of Hebrew books, each accusing the other of producing works that were offensive to the Holy Catholic Faith. A number of these apostates had become converted and taken Holy Orders: I felt surges of disgust listening to Vitale's accounts of this malign coterie: those days I abjured entirely my love-quarrels with Miriamne over questions of faith.

When I had studied at Padova the most celebrated Professor on the faculty was a young anatomist from Brussels named Andreas Vesalius. He was a phenomenon. He had been appointed Professor of Surgery at but twenty-three years of age in 1537 a day after the faculty in solemn convocation had granted him the degree of Doctor of Medicine *cum ultima diminutione*, a backward way of expressing the highest achievement inasmuch as Vesalius was required to pay a fee of only 17 ½ ducats, diminished in accordance with the excellence of his examination. The next day, after performing an astonishing dissection, he was appointed Professor of Surgery.

I remember his dissections very well. He never employed an assistant, which is still very common practice, sitting in a niche with a wand a safe distance away, and reading from Galen while the assistant cuts open the cadaver and a dog licks up his guts, and we all saw what Galen said we would see. Vesalius instead did the actual cutting of the corpse himself, and he held the firm and unorthodox conviction that what could be observed by the skilled eye was more valid than the writings of Galen among the ancients, or Mundinus' emendations of that classic text.

In 1543, this wondrous man left Padova to oversee the printing of his great book, *De Humani Corporis Fabbrica,* up in Basel; he was succeeded by his favorite assistant, Realdo Colombo from Cremona.

When Habib and I came to Roma, and began to circulate in medical circles, the most famous anatomist in the city, we learned, was this very same Colombo, who had been called to teach at the Studium of Roma just a few years before our arrival. Soon Habib was consulting him on a number of cases. Even those days amidst the rising smoke of burning monks and Talmuds, he was pressing ahead on his series of medical histories, the *Centuriae Curatio Orationem.* The first volume was soon complete and Habib made a trip to Fiorenza, about a year after we arrived, to supervise the printing. He wanted these books to be used as clinical handbooks. In the field of anatomy he rested, as all of us did by this time, on Vesalius' brilliant work, which since its printing in 1543 was already circulating all over Europe. No one could, or even tried, to supercede that incredible study.

I saw the book for the first time in the clinical studio of the Magister Colombo. He was kind enough to permit me to glance through the pages. I was enthralled. I felt new manscapes of wonder had been revealed. For the next few months every time Habib visited his colleague, I came along merely for the opportunity of entering again that marvelous world of the Flemish Vesalius. The woodcuts alone, drawn by painters in the workshop of the Master Titian of Venice, were a lesson in the wondrous architecture of the human body. Musclemen disposed themselves— stripped of skin, and with tendons rolled back or muscles exposed—against amiable landscapes of the Veneto. Smiling skeletons leaned against Roman columns. Males and females displayed their intestines, coiling out of the abdominal sac like garlands and ribbons in a painting by Perugino against a background of smiling rivers and sailing ships. And as our first Parents knew no shame before their expulsion from the Garden of Eden, so Vesalius' Adam and Eve—universal and without sin—revealed their organs of generation from every point of view and even in open section, smiling the while at the infallible articulation of those parts. There was as much reverence, I thought, in this great book by Doctor Vesalius, as in the Pentateuch. I sought by every means to procure a copy in Roma without

success; and wrote to my father in Bologna and to friends at the Medical School at
Padova to see if they could find me a copy.

One sunny afternoon in September, we arrived at Magister Colombo's studio to
find him rather agitatedly on the point of departure. He suggested we come along.
Perhaps his patient would benefit more from three brains than from one. I must say
this Colombo was almost inordinately modest: whatever reputation he possessed
as an anatomist he ascribed to his studies under Vesalius, and now he frankly
admitted that he was profiting greatly from the pages of the *Centuriae* which my
master Don Habib had shown him. Colombo's total lack of vanity is a rarity among
his countrymen. He is always ready to listen to someone else, and with his buzzing
ways, his shiny black hair, the unpredictable staccato changes of direction in
movements and thought, he made me think of a bee plunging his proboscis into
flower after flower, sucking up their nectar to brew a honey of his own.

"Come along!" he said, almost as soon as we opened the door. In fact, he never
permitted us to remove our hats, but hustled us out with him. A ruddyfaced
hornyhanded fellow was waiting with two horses. He mounted one and indicated
the other to the doctor who was soon galloping after him; and we barely in time to
mount our own steeds and keep up with these two.

We rode down muddy streets—it had been raining the past few days— through
the Region of the Banche and down Ripetta and past the Pantheon and the
Antonine Column and soon near the Trajan Forum, tied our horses, and were
ushered by the ruddyfaced man, into a house more impressive for its size than for
the elegance of its fittings. It seemed indeed rather like a barn, the furniture was of
the simplest—rustic heavy tables, some sgabella chairs, a number of heavy chests
ranged along the walls. The ruddyfaced fellow roared some instructions to an
elderly lady who appeared—Hot water! Hot water! pads of wool. Presto! Via!—
and she disappeared into the kitchen as if blown there by the blast of his words. A
moment later as we passed through the adjacent room—a huge salotta—a very
pretty young woman appeared. Smiling, she stood right in the path of our guide
who managed to gallop even without a horse, millwheeling his powerful arms for
us to follow. "Sta calmo, Maestro," the girl said, "the Old One has passed it." Our
ruddyfaced guide steered right around this pretty maiden, and sailed into the
Master's bedroom, and there I saw for the first time the famous artist
Michelangiolo Buonarroti, of Fiorenza. He was sitting up in bed, a velvet brown
cap on his head, smiling with the smile of one who has just been relieved of one of
the most excruciating pains known to man. "Here you are, Dottore," he said, "a
veritable jewel," and extended his palm in which reposed a kidney stone about the
size and color of a small pea. "Stones!" the old man said, "all my life I have been
plagued by stones—great and small."

He blew a breath of relief and leaned back on the great white mound of pillows
the young lady was fluffing up behind him. He turned to her with a grateful smile,

and kissed her hand, and she in tender confusion: "O Maestro!"—and wiped his brow which was still shining with the sweat of the agony through which he had so recently passed.

He seemed very old. I had no idea how old he was. I knew he was older than my grandfather Andrea and my grandfather—blessèd be his memory— had died at the age of seventy, the year I entered my medical studies and that was eight years ago. Swiftly I figured this man must be at least in his early eighties. Rivulets of sweat had gathered again in the deeply grooved brow. Mona Cornelia (for such was her name) wiped his brow again. "Pain?" "No, no—just the talking about it . . . the memory of it . . . Would you believe it, Doctor, I was rolling on the floor, doubled up screaming like a woman in labor . . . And then . . . and then . . . right there at the foot of the bed, I could pass water at last, once this cursèd stone had passed, it came fiery-burning and then the burning was gone and I was pissing as abundantly and freely as in my youth. Ho fatto una bella pisciata, Dottore. Ah, pissing is a great thing, don't you agree, Doctor?"

Colombo nodded. "Indeed. Happily you did not need me. But so long as I am here . . ." He took the great man's pulse, bent his head to listen to his heart, auscultated his chest, lifting the white nightdress the old man wore. His torso, I saw with astonishment, was that of a young man, powerfully muscled, the rib-cage covered with flat firm layers of flesh, the scapulae developed, the biceps of the upper arms vigorous and hard, and the hands with their thick square-nailed fingers much larger than one would normally have expected of a man of his stature. The knuckles were prominent, protruding veins stood out clearly in the gray-brown fuzz on the back of his hands. And while he was speaking—his baritone voice low, almost a gruff whisper—these hands were never still, the fingers arching and articulating always in accompaniment to his words: a dance of fingers, a ballet of that executive instrument of his mind. His thumbs were unusually spatulate.

He smiled, his smile though restrained, was wonderfully illuminating, his small eyes, the color of mica, disappearing in a network of wrinkles. He wore a short clipped grizzly beard, forked below his chin, his clean-cut mouth clearly revealed in the stubble; his brows protruded a bit, he had small ears, and a curiously flat nose, as if the bridge had been broken. He made me think somehow of an ancient satyr. I would not have been surprised to find a tail under the coverlet. His hands were now resting on the counterpane. All the *servitù* had gathered around in a chorus of murmurous congratulation and sympathy. There was an elderly cook, still holding a wooden ladle in her hand, several gawking young men and girls, a rustic fellow named Antonio, and a somewhat older man with a very loud voice, called Urbino. They all seemed to have come from the same region for amongst themselves they spoke the same non-Roman dialect which I could not identify. But they reverted to buon Toscano when they addressed their old Master in the bed. Urbino it was clear was the chief factotum of this household and soon he had bullied them all out: the cook to prepare a lentil soup, the young man Antonio to see to the horses, and the other servants to attend to household affairs.

Mona Cornelia remained to nurse Maestro Michelangiolo. She held the old man's hand and acted toward him as if she were a devoted and loving daughter.

"I have heard," Michelangiolo said to Colombo (who had finally presented Don Habib and myself to the Master)" of a special water from a well near Fiuggi, that has the property of dissolving the stone. Do you know anything about this?"

"No, but I will make inquiries. Who told you about it?"

"The grocer down the street for whose . . ." He stopped midsentence and turned to me with knitted-brow inquiry: "What did you say your name was, young man?"

"Del Medigo. Elia del Medigo."

"Did you have kinfolk in Fiorenza? A Doctor of Physik, like yourself?"

"My grandfather was from Fiorenza."

"Andrea? . . . Not Andrea del Medigo?"

"He was my grandfather."

"O Dio! So many years . . . How betides your grandfather?"

"He is dead."

He was thoughtfully silent. Not grieving. Just thoughtfully silent. "So Andrea has already obtained that boon. I have lived so long with Death that I feel he is my brother . . ." He fell silent again, and we too all silent in respect for his. He didn't look unhappy thinking about Death, if it were truly Death he was thinking about. He was simply in another world, perhaps that World, that Otherness.

Then he broke out of it again and said. "Tell me about your grandfather. I remember him well from my youth. It's a curious thing. The older I grow the more clearly do I remember the days of my youth. But I cannot remember where I left my goatskin gloves last week. I cannot find them. Only distant—O distant distant distant as the moon—yesterdays. The body curves back to the earth. And so does the mind."

He touched my hand—gripped it, strong, dry. "Tell me about your grandfather."

So I began to speak, haltingly at first. The old man listened, his grizzled head cocked. Sometimes, he seemed to be falling asleep in the midst of my narrative, and then I stopped—and he woke up immediately and said "Yes? You were saying—?"

"I was saying that my grandfather praised you, and your works, Maestro, beyond those of any other man. And I have been hoping to see all your works here in Roma."

"What have you seen thus far?"

"Only the Deposition of the Fever in St. Peter's and the Moses in St. Peter's in Chains. I cannot adequately express my admiration, I am not skilled in—"

He waved off my stammering, and turned to Colombo who was saying:

"Remain abed, Maestro, at least another three days. I will seek to secure this magic water for you. Drink copiously of it. It will help you— any water will—to urinate. And you must void as much water as possible. Urinate! Urinate!"

"Ben volontieri," Michelangiolo smiled, "but often that is in the hands of God. And when I don't urinate I can't work."

"He certainly won't remain in bed," Urbino said brusquely. He had just returned and caught Colombo's last admonition. "You will have to tie him first. I know my master Michelangiolo better than any of you. He rides out in all weathers. Says it keeps him in good health. And then doesn't sleep of nights, hammering away at one work or another. Doesn't know when to stop, either . . ."

"O via, Francesco!" said Cornelia warningly.

"I'll stay in bed! I'll stay in bed!" the old man grumbled, obviously to quiet his scolding factotum. His grizzled head fell back on the pillow and he closed his tired eyes. Even open they seemed closed, or at any rate seemed to be veiled, as if they looked inward at some private landscapes of his soul rather than at anything in this world.

Colombo made a silent sign for us to depart.

That very night I wrote to my parents, but especially to my grandmother that I had had the good fortune of encountering the great artist Michelangiolo the Florentine. A month later arrived a letter from my parents with an abundant postscriptum added by my grandmother Ziporah.

Querido Elijah: (She still used the Ladino salutation of her youth in Spain).

This Michelangiolo of whom you speak, could it truly be the same Michelangiolo your grandfather and I knew here in Bologna so long ago? When next you see him, speak the name of Properzia dei Rossi and tell me if he blushes. He was madly in love with this maiden, a comical business, I thought, though your grandfather took this caprice of Michelangiolo's as solemnly as he took all his other goat-leaps. I never saw any of his work and I am not at all desirous of seeing any of these idols of the Christians. But your grandfather—Blessèd be his name—considered him a genius notwithstanding they were always quarreling about theological questions as if there is not only one God over all and his Torah all written down so there need be no discussion, but I think your grandfather would rather discuss than eat and I remember more than once I had to intervene to break up the talk of those two and get him to the table before all my efforts turned cold. He was a great man, your grandfather, but certain things he didn't understand and I trust you will be careful to cover your head always and not only in the rains or in the synagogue and avoid the swamps near the Tiber for I lived in those parts

and know where the plague arises even though you are a Doctor of Physik I
know certain things better than you and better than your father or mother
certainly and if you see messer Buonarroti again send him my greetings and
ask him if he remembers me your loving grandmother

—Ziporah

❊

I did meet Michelangiolo twice again. When I relayed my grandmother's
greeting, he nodded amiably enough but I don't believe he remembered her in the
slightest. He was particularly interested during this visit—again Colombo, Habib
and myself—in talking about anatomy. En route—we met near the house of the
Vestal Virgins, and walked this time—Colombo said he was hoping to secure a
cadaver for the Master, who in his old age, on the very brink of cadaverhood
himself, was eagerly studying with him the art of making a *notomia*. "He has
already done some dissection under my guidance, but of course, his knowledge of
the body is all surface, he knows the skin, and the bulge of the muscles, and the
bones that make a protrusion in the body's envelope. But true *notomia* is beyond
his present grasp. I must say though, he wields the scalpel more skillfully under my
directions of course, than most physicians. It must be his experience with brush or
chisel. His control is truly fantastic. His hand wields the knife with astonishing
precision. He cuts a swift straight line as if he were drawing."

"I have a grave robber at my service," Colombo added as we passed the white
coil of the Trajan Column, "so perhaps we can steal a good cadaver for messer
Michelangiolo's use. Naturalmente, it will have to be a Musselman or a Jew or
some other infidel to avoid problems with the Holy Office—" and Habib and I
made not the slightest sign, our faces as expressionless as that of the future cadaver
himself.

Urbino let us in. There was another visitor whom I had not seen heretofore,
another Marchigiano as it turned out, red-haired like Urbino, a countrified
squash-round ingenuous face, a modest young man listening with the air of a
conscientious student as the Master was pointing out to him some drawings in a
bound leather book lying open on a long oaken table.

"Ah, my friends!" Buonarroti said. He was in fine humor today, entirely cured
of his stone, his voice firm, his eyes brighter if still gauzed, but today as the
sunshine hit them I saw tiny gold flecks in the gray. He was wearing cordovan
boots and a floppy woolen hat and cloak though it was late spring. Standing he
proved somewhat shorter than I had deduced from seeing his broad shoulders and
robust torso in bed, and for all his years, his movements as he riffled the pages or
pointed to the drawings in it, were astonishingly swift and assured.

"Have you seen this, Doctor Colombo?" Colombo peered and shook his head.
"A new book of drawings dealing with human proportions by the German master

Albrecht Dürer of Nuremberg. I have just been going over these with messer Ascanio Condivi here, the author of my Life. The latest Life," he added hastily. "Came out two years ago."

None of us had even heard of Condivi's biography.

"Perbacco," Michelangiolo said. "Why should you be expected to? You are physicians, not artists."

"Mine is the only honest Life of messer Michelangiolo, the only *valid* Life," Ascanio Condivi said now with surprising lack of modesty. The statement emerged unexpectedly from his general air of self-effacement like a mountain emerging from a plain, a profile of surprise.

Michelangiolo elicited our judgements as physicians concerning Alberto Dürer's book on human proportions. We all stood around the table while Buonarroti slowly turned the big pages.

"Well," said Colombo thoughtfully after a few moment's survey, "these are not anatomical drawings at all. When next you come to my studio I will show you the book of Andreas Vesalius of Brussels. Now there is true anatomizing. The skin stripped, all the muscles exposed, the organs displayed to reveal their functioning."

"Oh, I am not concerned about that," said the old man. "It is not the artist's task to explain the functions or even the shapes of inner organs. But these"—and he swept a disdainful hand across a page showing the human skull from above and from the front with a graph of the mathematical proportions between brow and nose, nose and chin, and so on— "these serve neither you anatomists nor us artists." He flipped a few more pages and pointed to a series in which nudes, male and female, are presented from front and rear perspectives. Again there were horizontal lines cutting across the figures with numbers at the edges to indicate the mathematical proportions of head, thorax, length of limbs—.

"What messer Alberto does not seem to understand," said Michelangiolo scornfully, "is that the secret of the body resides in its movement. You realize," he added modestly, "I speak of that cognition which is necessary to the arts of painting and sculpture. Not of those minutiae which you anatomists observe."

Condivi nodded a vigorous acquiescence.

"Maestro Michelangiolo's figures show so much art and learning that they are inimitable by any other artist. I believe this is fixed and ordained by God."

Buonarroti laughed at this and went on.

"I have, you know, messer Realdo, always been interested in your art of anatomy. I used to frequent as many dissections as I could and even tried a few myself, both animal and human, until my stomach revolted: I couldn't eat or drink, so I've had to give that up—"

Habib laughed. "Making a notomia seems to have a contrary effect on medical students. Every dissection concludes in a banquet."

Michelangiolo had a far-off look on his face. He turned to me: "As a matter of fact, the first notomia I ever saw was performed by your grandfather's father Maestro Elia in the cortile of Santo Spirito. I was only a boy then. Oh, it was terrifying, sickening, the sight of that cadaver laid open, the guts spilling to the floor . . . I vomited. Later I found it beautiful. I would indeed like to write a treatise some day on the movements of the human body, its aspects, the bones: I have a theory all my own . . . But I need to know more. If you could get me a cadaver," he said to Colombo.

"But your stomach, Maestro."

"Well, this one last time."

"As soon as I can secure one, I will arrange to have it brought here."

"No, no, have it brought to the sacristy at Sant' Agata, near Ascanio's house. The sacristan there is a good friend. Here, it would create a scandal. Why that mere grinning skull there on the staircase frightens every new servant or trades-man who enters this house." He returned to the book, slowly leafing a few more pages, shaking his head. "I find this book of messer Dürer's very weak. He treats only of the proportions and diversities of the body for which one cannot establish fixed rules, making figures as regular as posts. And what matters more, he says nothing about human movements and gestures. In my art, the gestures of the body are the Alpha and Omega, the alphabet with which we say everything."

"Then, Maestro, in the arts of design, you do not consider landscape of fundamental importance?" Condivi asked, obviously eliciting for our benefit an answer which he already knew.

"Oh, trees and flowers and cloud-speckled skies and little bridges over canals, all that is pleasant enough; they may even bring tears to the eyes of pious old ladies. But properly designing the nude body is the art of arts. Everything else is commentary. Is not a man's foot more noble than his shoe?"

A few weeks later Colombo invited Michelangiolo to his home to see the great volume of Vesalius' *Fabbrica*. He chuckled as he told us the old man's response. "He thought some of the gestures were very good, even though the figures were disembowled. But he wanted to know why it was necessary for these skeletons and muscle-men and veiny-arterial spectres to be displayed against landscapes. '*I don't need landscape to deflect interest from my nudes—and they don't even make a show of their livers and their guts!*' A funny old man. I think we'll have a fine cadaver for him soon. Would you like to witness his skill with the knife?"

·✳·

The sacristy of Sant' Agata flickered with two candelabra set on both sides of the corpse. The candelabra lacked one stem, otherwise they could have been Menorahs.

The body of a young Moor lay nude on a marble slab. He was very beautiful. He seemed to be sleeping.

"An extraordinary cadaver! Extraordinary," Colombo said.

"A slave in the service of the Cardinal Caraffa. He died after a brief illness, at the peak of his vigor."

"Poisoning? Stabbing?"

"No. No. A natural death. Who would poison a slave? Mysterious. At any rate, as soon as I heard of it, I arranged with my man to bribe the Cardinal's man and so we brought the corpse right from the sickbed here. No grave-robbing, you see. Never reached the grave! And beautiful, too. Now then, messer Michelangiolo, as I have already indicated, for a full anterior dissection of the muscles, we begin here—"

Michelangiolo took the knife from the physician's hand. Colombo indicated where the first incision should be made: down the center of the rib cage anterior. The old man's hand moved unwaveringly straight as if he were following a plumb-line. Abruptly, Colombo gestured for him to stop, and then pulling with his bare fingers and cutting with a knife, began to strip away the skin, together with the fat and all the sinews, veins, and arteries existing on the surface.

"Why do you remove the deep fascia?" asked Habib.

"Because our purpose today," said Colombo, "is designed not only to reveal to us physicians the superficial arrangement of the muscles but for the special use of artists, like our venerable friend here—"

"O via! Via!"

"Now Messer," he nodded to Michelangiolo, "continue here, carefully removing the fat as I have done—" and Colombo began wiping on a rag the blood off his hands as the old man took over again. Michelangiolo's face was absolutely impassive, incredibly so, I thought, for a layman unaccustomed to the grizzly sight of dead bodies being opened and skinned as rabbits are skinned. A foul smell already pervaded the sacristy. Now and again I dipped a sponge in a bucket of water at our feet and wiped away the blood of the area being dissected. The blood does not spurt as in a living wound. The wounds of the newly dead merely trickle. The monk seated in the dark shadows of the door—Michelangiolo's friend who with head resolutely turned away was audibly telling his beads rather than attending to our demonstration—coughed and sniffed: the echoes coincided with a sudden guttering of the candles. Young Ascanio also seemed less than totally at ease, although he did put up a brave face. There were two lectures going on in tandem: Colombo's more technical nomenclature and description of the functioning of the various muscles as they were brought to light and messer Michelangiolo's comments upon the shapes of these muscles as the body engaged in various actions, and how these shapes—elongations, protruberances, flattenings—would be perceptible through the envelope of the skin and these must be known by the artist if he would create true forms to express his concepts. "For," said he, speaking primarily to the sole auditor of *his* lecture, Ascanio, who was taking notes and sketching as the Master spoke— "without dottrina the artist is merely a hand. But the hand alone—no matter how skilled—is not enough. La man dev' ubbidir all' intelletto. The hand must obey the intellect. An ignorant artist is not an artist at all. We must *know* in order that we need not merely imitate. More reflection without knowledge is a looking- glass."

He spoke all this without removing his concentration from the dissection, his voice velvety deep, almost murmurous. Condivi's quill scratched feverishly. I glanced at his drawings. They were very poor, I thought, although I am no judge of art. I speak only of verisimilitude. Swiftly, the body was being strippped of all its skin, messer Buonarroti pausing at regular intervals to permit Colombo (and Habib also after a while) to cut away the deeper fat and fleshy membranes. The head was left to the last, and I noted when finally Michelangiolo's hand with the scalpel hovered over the smooth warm brown brow, a momentary hesitation,—did I fancy a tremor?—before the knife struck. Now the facial muscles were being uncovered.

Once Michelangiolo's knife had begun to penetrate the throat— following Colombo's pantomimed shaping gestures—the blood was running so plentifully here that sponging it away, as I had been doing before, was insufficient and with my hands I scooped up water from the bucket and splashed it over the face. Alas, that beautiful dark face, that faint smiling adumbration of saintly peace, those shapely lips and white staring eyes, had already been replaced by a bloody stained mask which still maintained as in mockery an echo of the expression it had previously worn.

The marble pavement was slippery with bloody water. The sacristan coughed again. A rumble. Then a mumble. He was furiously praying.

"You will observe," said Don Habib to me softly, "there is no paniculus carnosus."

"Vesalius always denied it" said Colombo. "That notion was derived from Galen and too much dependence on animal dissections. Except for this platysma muscle—" he pointed— "such a paniculus is absent in man."

"Notice, Ascanio mio, this triangular sheath—this is what causes the upward drawing of the lips in laughter. So if you wish to depict laughter, that muscle must be revealed. A stroke will do it. Like this."

He seized the quill from Condivi's hand, and with incredible certitude, drew a laughing face. It came alive, the incongruity of seeing that face come alive and the dead mutilated Moor who no longer had any face at all! Instead he was a complex of platysma, buccinator, masseter, temporal and nasalis muscles and his wooly cap of hair was gone to reveal a bony skull.

Condivi stooped closer to see the facial muscle his Master had emphasized, then drew it carefully and wrote some annotations alongside.

By the time five of the candles had almost guttered the anterior of the body lay completely stripped of its skin. Colombo stooped, picked up the bucket and splashed the remaining water over the corpse. We were all doused a bit by the blood-pinked liquid.

"That is all the cutting for today," he said to Michelangiolo. "For your purposes, we do not want to dissect away any muscles except those which constitute the fleshy membrane. Tomorrow we will turn the cadaver over and strip the skin off the posterior surface. We can also dissect away then these transverse ligaments near the wrist. Best to do that posteriorly. But now let us consider the myology of this entire anterior notomia . . ."

And he began to lecture on the entire fasces of muscles from skull to toe, their functions, their attachments, their peculiarities. When his dissertation arrived at the region of the thorax he graciously insisted that my Master Don Habib take over as one who had made unique observations in that portion of the body. He resumed with the genitalia, hanging incongruously unstripped in a hairless bed of pink rolled lower muscles of the groin. While these two Masters spoke, I took notes but Condivi did not. But whenever Michelangiolo raised some question (invariably dealing with the effect of function upon appearances)—if the forearm were raised one third from the horizontal, how greatly would the bicep protrude? and so on—then Condivi did take notes.

By this time the smell of putrefaction had become indeed almost insupportable. Condivi looked as if he were about to vomit. We were speaking through cloths held against our faces. The almost-Menorahs were almost out.

"Tomorrow, then, Maestro, for the posterior." Colombo reminded Michelangiolo. His voice came muffled through the cloth. "I would not recommend waiting much longer than that."

The sacristan was already jingling his keys.

Silently we left the stripped Moor in the redolent darkness.

❉

I never saw messer Michelangiolo Buonarroti after that. I could not return for the second notomia since I had a full day of patients to attend to. It was the Season of the Feast of Tabernacles and Roma was rainy and shepherds in fur boots and goatskin coats came down from the mountains of the Abruzzi and played bagpipes and oboes in front of churches. There was much ringing of bells and presepios even in the streets. Habib couldn't attend Rabbino Vitale's festive dinner or the seventh day of Chanukah because His Holiness' gout was suddenly so painful that an extraordinary counsel of his team of archiaters had been summoned. The aggravation of the Pope's malady was undoubtedly a result of his intemperance at table. Judging by some of the menus Habib described, it is a wonder that the swelling occurred only in the Holy Father's feet.

So we arrived at the New Year of their Lord 1554 and Miriamne and I had pledged our troth—my parents wrote their approval but said they could not attend my marriage because of my grandmother Ziporah's illness—and I could not, at that moment anyway, ride up to Bologna. We postponed our marriage for the Spring.

I had been so impressed by my three meetings with the great artist Buonarroti— which stirred up in my memory all the tales told of him by my grandfather—that I began to engage in a private pilgrimage round of all his works in the city of Roma. Miriamne accompanied me on many of these visits, casting a special glow upon the art-works we saw.

Art is not my particular *mestiere* but I am not lacking in appreciation of beauty—Miramne was a beauty—and my curiosity had been truly piqued by my few encounters with this extraordinary old man. I knew his reputation, of course, who did not? Michelangiolo was as familiar in Roma as the current Pope and he had outlived six of them. In my youth in Bologna my grandfather took me to a church—I don't recall the name— where there were several statuettes, among them, I believe, a kneeling angel holding a candlestick. But this made little impression. Later on a visit to Fiorenza I saw his Giant David standing a pale guard in front of the Palazzo Vecchio. I remember I thought the anatomizing especially convincing: a perfect displacement of muscles according to the stance, and a superb rendering of the ribcage—that struck me especially because I was already a medical student. The nudity of the work also impressed me. This man, I thought, reveres the body. This is a monument to the divinity of the human.

I saw nothing else by Buonarroti in Fiorenza.

The only art I cared about then was the art of medicine. But now, I wanted to see everything of Michelangiolo's I could in Roma. Some works, I knew, must be in the possession of prelates or great houses which would be forever closed to me. But with Don Habib (I was always careful in Christian precincts to address him as Magister Amatus Lusitanus) in the Pope's medical entourage, I hoped to gain entry to the Sistine Chapel where I was told Buonarroti had frescoed the ceiling vault and altar wall; and I had no hesitation in entering those churches which contained his works, once I learned where they were. Thus I went back again with Miriamne to see the Moses a second time, and now I looked at it with new eyes, new interest, seeing in those sinewy vein-marked hands, the hands of Buonarroti himself wielding the scalpel. In Santa Maria sopra Minerva—Michelangiolo's own church—I saw his risen Christ, a life-sized marble figure totally naked at the altar; and considering the theological atmosphere of Roma these days, I wondered how long it would remain thus unclothed. This work indeed struck me as a but slightly idealized figure of a nude fisherman standing a mast, although instead of a mast it was a crucifix. The buttocks were too protruded and there were some anatomical inaccuracies in the kneecaps and feet. If this fisherman is a Christ, thought I, it is suitably installed in a church where Minerva is Mary.

In St. Peter's, in the chapel of the French King, the Master's dolefully elegant Madonna with the dead Jesus in her lap spoke to me not of the Christian Savior but of any mother's grief for her dead son. Again, as with the Florentine David, I

saw that Buonarroti identified humanity with divinity; if David was Man become God, this was God become Man.

"Ah, but that is blasphemy!" exclaimed Habib with whom I shared my observations. He whispered his condemnation. We were in St. Peter's.

"But don't you see that Deposition of God is another way of reading Ascension of Man?"

"Blasphemy!"

He, new Christian, more orthodox than I!

I gazed again at the group floating pale and beautiful as a full moon. Michelangiolo's tenderness, I thought—his pietà—toward him whom they call the Christ just taken off the Cross is a tenderness unconfined by cult.

But nothing thus far, except my recollections of David, satisfied the particular curiosity that had been stirred up in me by his comments on Dürer's book, and his interest in anatomy which Colombo was seeking to enrichen.

The true—and surprising to me—relationship became clear only when I finally gained entrance to the Sistine Vault accompanied there by Master Habib and a Papal Chamberlain. Habib (this day he was emphatically Don Amatus Lusitanus, I had almost slipped once or twice) had pulled superbly the harp strings of ecclesiastic influence, and here we were now being escorted after a visit to His Holiness' bed chamber (and he was deteriorating rapidly, his feet swollen grotesquely, his face purple-puffed) along long long corridors incredibly rich with marble pavements and frescoed vaults and treasures of every sort heaped up on every side; Lusitanus-Habib striding swiftly down these halls, his Saturnian expression replaced by the mask of complacency he usually wore in such settings.

Finally we reached a door, outside which stood a tall Swiss guard in orange and blue dress, a halberd gripped obliquely forward. We were admitted to the Sistine Chapel.

I was stunned.

The vault thundered with Michelangiolo. Floating in the barrel vault, and soaring on the altar wall were a swarm of huge figures, hundreds and hundreds of them in every possible position. On the altar wall almost all of them were entirely naked. On the flat of the barrel vault a series of naked beautiful young men in couples held garlands of oak leaves and framed a series of panels from our *Bereshith*—the First Book of Moses of our *Toràh*. But none of these had any relationship with the lessons of the skinned Moor.

"Curious, is it not?" Habib remarked, after we had pondered in longish silence those painted anatomies floating in melancholia on the vault or hurled in a turbine of despair above the altar around a thunderous judging Jesus, almost nude alongside the Madonna who seemed cringing in zigzag fear away from her son's unpraised arm: The soft floating graceful forms of the vault and the denunciatory swirl of the altar wall were clearly delineated in the bright sunrays slanting through the high series of windows— "Curious that Michelangiolo who, according to

Colombo, is so well versed in the human figure, should create these, how should I say?, *departures* from the real nude! These males are not true males, and these gigantic amazons—if they are women—are surely not females. Look there—" he pointed "—at that series on the ceiling: those languid young men. Beautiful indeed. But the expressions on these faces are too sweet for male faces. And their skeletons are too wide in the hips. And there is too much fat on the bones. *Departures*, did I say? These are androgynes! Look at that, I don't know what—"

"—a Sibyl, Messeri," said the Chamberlain with a polite almost imperceptible nod, "—the Delphic Sibyl. Prophetess of the coming of Our Lord."

"No doubt," whispered Habib. "But surely that is not a *female*: Look at that bulging bicep of the right arm. And the breasts are absurd: appended as if in afterthought to a male torso. I must ask Colombo to elucidate this mystey. Why should messer Michelangiolo trouble himself to make *notomia* and study the correct proportions of the body, and the placement of muscles and the effect various positions would have on the appearance of those muscles and tendons—why should he trouble himself to master all this, when it is quite obvious that he ignores everything he has learned once he gets a paintbrush in his hand!"

What Don Habib had said was true. And yet remembering the David of Fiorenza or the naked Christ in the Minerva or in St. Peter's, I realized that these departures from the anatomical norm were not the result of ignorance or of lessons forgotten. This was deliberate. Buonarroti's mastery was apparent. If he created these anatomically abnormal figures—these small-headed Herculean Apollos, these monstrous pendulous-breasted females with titanic thighs—it must be because he wished to do so, he was obviously imagining neither males nor females, but Michelangiolesques—mythological creatures who combined the qualities of both sexes: the sweetness and grace of the female, the power of the male.

But the question remained: why then was he so intent upon mastering the real nudes of the real world? I was struck by the contradiction between the Michelangiolo of the dissection and the Michelangiolo of the Sistine.

Only now, here in the rational light of Crete, have I reconciled these two; only now do I realize that Michelangiolo's art is related to his science as the ideal is related to the real. The real was that skinned Moor on the refectory table; the ideal were these androgynous forms floating on the vault.

We remained in the Sistine almost an hour. The light dimmed. The giant forms were swimming in grayness. I have carried that curious anatomy lesson in my head ever since. It becomes particularly vivid every time I see my Miriamne washing our baby Andrea in the terra cotta tub. Our Greek maid, her cheeks the color of the jar, holds the baby as he precariously stands; and Miriamne splashes his sweet-shaped little naked form, fruit of our love,—I look at him splashing, I see him grown to manhood, that marvelous vessel of divinity which is the body;—and always in the background floating in a turquoise sea, those distant cousins of the real which are Michelangelo's nudes.

·※·

For all this merriment and hedonism, Julius III had not relented very much when the Rabbis of Roma, including Miriamne's father, made counter-representations against the book-burning which had now spread by Inquisitional order, even to those principalities outside of Papal jurisdiction. From Bologna I had received several agitated letters from my father. A bonfire of Talmuds had taken place there too, swiftly on the heels of that in Roma. But Bologna of course and Ravenna were Papal domain. So was Ferrara. But Mantova, Firenze, even Venice!—the center of Hebrew printing and so the supplier of the most abundant fuel for these theological pyres. The Council of Ten there did not limit itself to burn only the Talmud—but all books relating even most peripherally to it— so that (my father wrote) ". . . Don Leon Modena saw in the Piazza of San Marco even Bibles—*their* Bible, mark you, in *part*—blazing on the same pyre. It is a madness, my son, and I dare not speak of it to your grandmother for she would immediately burst into tears, recalling the pyres she saw in Spain as a girl, and the brutal killing of her brother Bartolomeo by a fanatic mob in Fiorenza. Besides, she is in very poor health. The times are darkening, I feel the Apocalypse approaching here in Italy, and I pray God I shall be dead before it strikes in full fury. Selah! See to your holy patient and be wise.

"Oh, I did forget to tell you that since the University of Padova is of course under Venetian jurisdiction the *numeris clausis* of Hebrew students, not to mention professors, has now been stringently applied. Every Hebrew has been evicted, his books seized to feed the Inquisitional bonfire. Remember how it used to be when you and I were there, even during your grandfather's time? There were Jewish medical students not only from all over Italia, but even from Germany, and Poland, and some law students, and students of conveyances as well. And we wore, remember?, a black headdress like any other student, and were admitted to degrees though with a modified ceremonial.

"Well, all that is finished now. No students at all, no degrees, no professors. Perhaps it may be temporary. It has happened in the past.

"But I am pessimistic. This new series of ecclesiastical discriminatory regulations no longer results as it did in the past, from local and sporadic causes, such as the preaching of Franciscan or Dominican friars, a San Bernardino, a Fra Girolamo Savonarola. No, these emanated from the Council of Trent itself and from the Vatican. We are the victims of their war against the Protestants. We are being struck by the fire of both sides.

"Friends who have come down here from Geneva—where Brother John Calvin rules—tell me that if anything, conditions are even worse there for Jews than in Catholic Italy.

"At least, there is always something to be thankful for. Since there are no Jewish students, the political fraternities from now on will have to raise their own dues

and drum up their own sweets for their graduation celebrations instead of squeez-
ing them out of us who were not even members of their fraternities.

"I pray only that these new discriminations apply also to Hebrew corpses, for
which, of late, they have been disturbing funerals even more than heretofore.

"I would like to write more pleasant news. Your mother Ruth is well. Her
serenity is a perpetual rebuke to my agitation. Learn from her.

Your loving father, Daniele del Medigo."

"P.S. I fail to understand the interest you have displayed in recent letters
regarding the paintings and sculptures of Michelangiolo Buonarroti. What has all
that got to do with us? I know your grandfather had a certain sentimental
attachment to this man and his works but I certainly never shared it nor did your
mother nor I pass it on to you. As far as we are concerned the so-called art of
Christians is strictly for Christians. But my father Andrea—Blessèd be his
name!—apparently speaks more strongly to you from the beyond than I do here
from Bologna. As I did not agree with my father on this question, you do not agree
with yours!"

The Holy Father, as I say, did not relent very much after the protest of the
Rabbis of Roma, even though they had the support of at least one Cardinal. They
weren't completely unsuccessful, however, the Bull issued in May called for the
destruction only of the Talmud and such other works as contained blasphemies
against Christianity; all other Hebrew books could be possessed and studied once
they had been cleared by the censorship.

But all this proved but scatter-drops of the storm to come. In March 1555, Julius
died, to nobody's surprise. Certainly not to Don Habib or any of the other
archiaters. But we of the team of papal physicians (and I always felt part of that
team, although truly I assisted only one member of it) were apprehensive when
rumor spread that we—the doctors—had been most responsible for the Pope's
death. For in our effort to cure his gout, we had prescribed a most austere diet, and
this, it was said, was bound to kill any man so given to the pleasures of the table!
Pasquino was in a state of hysterical *hilaritas.*

The deceased was duly succeeded by a certain Cardinal Cervini who departed
from this vale so rapidly that Habib had still not received formal reply to his
inquiry whether he was to remain in the new Pope's service.

But the swift election of the Cardinal Gian Pietro Carafa as Cervini's successor
precipitated Don Habib to take the action he had long meditated and feared to
take. Like a soldier long fearful to leave shelter, reluctant to face fire, he rushed
headlong to the attack when the danger reached its height. For with the election
of the fanatical Neapolitan, we all knew,—every Jew in Roma knew—that a
Vesuvius of hatred would soon erupt.

It erupted in less than two months after Carafa had assumed the tiara. On July

12th, 1555, a date I shall never forget, every Jew in Roma, those of the five schools and those like myself of no school at all, had read to us (and translated into Italian) a Papal Bull whose title was derived from the ominous opening words:

CUM NIMIS ABSURDUM

Forasmuch as it is highly absurd and improper that the Jews, condemned by God to eternal slavery because of their guilt, should, on the pretext that they are cherished by Christian love and permitted to dwell in our midst, show such ingratitude to Christians as to insult them for their mercy and presume to mastery instead of the subjection that beseems them; and forasmuch as we have been informed that in Roma and elsewhere their shamelessness is such that they presume to dwell among Christians in the neighborhood of churches without distinction of dress, and even to rent houses in the more elegant streets and squares of the cities, villages and places in which they live, to purchase and possess real property, to hire Christian maidservants and wetnurses and other salaried attendants, and to perpetrate divers other misdeeds to the shame and contumely of the Christian name; and considering that the Roman Church tolerates the Jews in witness of the true Christian faith . . . we do therefore order the following measures, which are to be perpetually valid . . .

I stood beside my Miriamne, my arms around her shoulder, as these words were being read to us in Rabbino Vitale's salotta. For once the noisy children were still—even they understood, or at any rate understood the gravity of their elders. Don Habib was there too and I could read upon his face the coiling up of indignation, his customary lugubriousness was replaced by anger, by fury, albeit silent. Vitale's wife was softly weeping, now and again others in the company—for all the neighbors crowded into the household to hear this translation of the document— uttered ejaculations, curses, maledictions—in Italian, in Ladino, in Hebrew. The reader was Benedetto Manzolo, a great Latinist in the Community, secretary to the Cardinal d'Este and friend of all the Hebreizing cardinals of whom there were not a few. He read impassively, intoning these juridical horrors with traces of a priestly inflection as if he were reciting the seven plagues during a Christian mass.

Henceforth we were to live segregated from all other persons in a special street, or in a special quarter, cut off from the rest of the city—that is from Christians—and with only one walled entry and one egress.

Henceforth, we were to be allowed but a single synagogue in each city (we had five on the Piazza delle Scuole alone!). All the others were to be destroyed and no new ones tolerated henceforth.

Henceforth, we could possess no real estate which must be sold to Christians forthwith. ("*In nome di Dio e buon guadagno!*" I heard a sardonic Florentine voice—"In the name of God and good profits!")

Henceforth we were to wear a distinguishing badge to mark us off from others—a yellow hat for men, a yellow veil for women. " . . . for it is absurd and improper that the Jews who have fallen into eternal servitude by their own guilt should presume under the pretext that Christian charity has taken them up, to make so bold as to live intermingled with Christians, to wear no distinguishing mark . . . " (Otherwise how could one distinguish Christian from Jew? Did we not look like anyone else? Were we not indistinguishable from good Christians? Or bad Christians?) Will that apply, I wondered, to physicians as well? Hitherto we had been absolved of such badges of shame. I felt Miriamne's body quivering. I held her closer. We had been married only a month ago, on 20 June after my parents had given me their blessing by post for they could not leave my grandmother in her present state of health, and I had promised to bring my new wife there to present to them as soon as I could. But these new unholy regulations, I realized with anger, will apply to Bologna as ruthlessly as they apply here in the Holy City, for Bologna is in the Domain of the Church, and I must—my mind was racing as messer Manzolo continud to read the galling proscriptions in his slow priestly incantating voice, blow upon blow, manacle forged to manacle.

. . . Henceforth we are forbidden to have Christian wetnurses or servants of either sex in our employment (Signora dello Strologo's Christian maid Concetta was in the kitchen at this very moment preparing refreshments for this unusual congregation. She had been in their service for twenty years and but for her mistress' strictest injunctions, she would have been here listening too, since she felt herself part of the family and had been Miriamne's most loving nurse, if not wetnurse).

" . . . nor to work in public on Christian holidays nor to associate with Christians on familiar terms nor to be addressed by any title of respect such as *Signor*" ("Signor! Signor! My Lord!" I heard Habib mutter)

. . . Jewish physicians (Ah here it was!) were no longer allowed to attend on Christian patients (and Popes? Are they considered Christian patients?) Habib and I exchanged glances.

. . . the account-books of loan-banks were henceforth to be kept in the Italian language and writing (not in Hebrew as heretofore)

. . . Henceforth Hebrews are forbidden to deal in corn or any necessity of life.

. . . Henceforth the only activity by which Hebrews shall be permitted to earn their living is dealing in old clothes and second-hand goods (*sola arte strazzariae seu conciariae, ut vulgo dicitur* . . .) read messer Manzolo with a slight sniffing of his nostrils at the vulgarity of the Latin phrase . . .

Henceforth all personal or local privileges conflicting in any way with this measure is declared null and void. . . .

Null and void.

We sat to tea and little cakes illegally served by Concetta who regarded the solemn and silent conclave of friends and neighbors with puzzled consternation.

"Is something wrong, Signora?" she whispered to her mistress.

"Do not call me Signora. *Henceforth* it is forbidden."

"Forbidden! Since when is it forbidden? By whom?"

"The Holy Father."

"Per l'amor di Dio! What concern is it of his that you are my Signora?" She laughed. "Who cares about—"

"Be still, Concetta!"

Donna Ruth, with stricken eyes, surveyed her company. Amongst all of us, Amatus Lusitanus, the only Christian, was most visibly shaken by the new decrees.

For almost a month my Miriamne and I did not perform the act of love. That was not forbidden by the Papal Bull. But it was rendered impossible by our despair.

As the days and weeks and months of the Carafa pontificate grew more and more inquitous we began to consider ways of escape. After all, this has been the history of our tribe. Pharoah and Exodus. Pharoah and Exodus. So eager was the Holy Father to reactivate the long moribund Inquisition— which he had revived as Cardinal ten years ago—that he paid out of his own pocket the expenses for chains and whips and instruments of torture. He might fail to attend other Papal functions, but never did he fail to be present at the weekly confabulations of the Roman Holy Office. The Inquisition was being extended to all the Papal States. There was talk of soon moving all the Jews of Roma into the restrictive district mentioned in the Bull. Most of us lived now in Trastevere and along the riverbank up to the bridge of Hadrian. Now plans were being drawn up to move us all to a sharply secluded quarter embracing a few narrow streets immediately on the Tiber extending from the Quattro Capi bridge to just beyond the Pescheria. A few blocks along the river. A *Vicus Judaeorum.*

No! I would not live in a *Vicus Judaeorum!* My mind was racing where we might take refuge. Outside of Christendom, I thought, nowhere within Christendom could there ever be a permanent place for us. With every turn of the screw I found myself thinking more and more like my father, with whom I had never been too close, and less and less like my grandfather Andrea, the greatest influence in my childhood. Andrea had always retained the trust of his apprenticeship in Christian art bottegas, the period of his friendship with Buonarroti. But my father had never possessed such a warm feeling of fellowship for Christians: he was wary always, and that wariness had been a source of dissension between us: I always felt he was a narrow and suspicious man. Now all his suspicions were being more than justified. Though I never had shared his rigorous observances, his jot-and-tittle practice of the Law, now I found myself admiring his prescience. I wrote to my parents. The new decrees had already been applied to Bologna. What did my father think of our removing—all of us: I and my wife, perhaps all the dello Strologo—to the island of Candia whence had come our distinguished ancestor Elia del Medigo, Ebreo Cretensis. Candia was under the jurisdiction of Soleiman, the Grand Turk. Under the Turk we Hebrews surely had always fared better than under Christians.

My father refused. He had no intention of leaving Bologna. He was a stubborn man. Besides, my grandmother could not live through such a voyage. Nor would the dello Strologo family consider leaving the Urbs. "We are more Roman than the Romans," said Rabbino Vitale. "Certainly more Roman than this Pontiff," he added scornfully. He was often meeting these days with other leaders of the Community. They had in the past been able to mitigate or even cause the cancellation of iniquitous restrictive legislation by the payment of special taxes initiated by themselves, that is, bribes and ransom. But preliminary soundings in this direction had already been indignantly repulsed. This new Holy Father was a man of principle. He would not yield to the bribes of the impious Jews.

Preparations continued for the removal to the restrictive walled quarter. Every week new families were being evicted from their homes and moved into the filthy streets near the Quattro Capi bridge. The plan was that by the following summer the mass transfer should have been completed. The low situation of those houses along the riverbank exposed the new occupants to malaria, pestilence, all the plagues of Egypt. Now all my ministrations as a Doctor of Physik were limited to those fallen ill in their new quarters. They coughed, turned yellow, the sweat and spots of plague appeared on the innocent faces of babes and the old men and women gave up the ghost and I wore a mask with a disinfected cloth pressed against my nose and ran from house to house, and every day there was as much fury in me as pity.

That was when Habib disappeared. He had been avoiding as much as possible his obligations as Papal archiater; besides, this Carafa, old as he was and consumed with a kind of continuous fury against the Spaniards and issuing furious threats against the Emperor so we knew there would be war and Roma would suffer a new Sack—for all these fulminations and the outrageous crimes of his nephews and the activities of his Holy Office— Carafa seemed made of iron, he attended to everything, and seemed to have little need of medical care.

Thus Habib's disappearance was not even noted by his colleagues. Then in June I received a letter from him. It came from Ancona:

"Querido Elia: I have transferred here where there is a sizeable community of Portuguese and Spanish Hebrews who long ago cast off their pseudo-
Christian cloaks and have been living freely and openly in the faith of our
fathers. Yes, *our* fathers; I too have openly proclaimed my allegiance. I
breathe great breaths of this sea air; the Adriatic is liquid sapphire; I walk

with a new step; you would scarcely recognize me. I am no longer João Rodrigues or Amatus Lusitanus; no, now I am openly Don Habib—(even though the new Papal Bull forbids the use of 'Don' as a title of salutation among us Hebrews). No matter, I shall employ it anyway. I am openly Don Habib to the world as I was Don Habib to you and our co-religionists in Roma. I can no longer tolerate living two lives, one false and one true, one my own and one mimed. I feel as if a great weight has been lifted from me.

"Thus far, the new decrees have been applied only sporadically to this Community. Of course I practice my profession only among Hebrews. But that is not because of the new decrees for there are many Christian Lords here who would happily ignore such regulations in order to have the service of a Hebrew physician. No, the decision is entirely my own. I want to see what the ultimate effect of the Bull will be. The Community is not of a single mind. There are many who believe that conditions set off by this violently anti-Spanish Pope will inevitably become more and more *Spanish!*—by which they mean burnings in the piazzas of Ancona—*acts of faith*— and not merely book-burnings either. These people talk only of departing for secular States like Fiorenza or Milano. Some have already gone.

"Others think the whole Carafean madness will blow over. After all the Pontiff is 80 years old; and if he continues his animadversions against the Emperor, Roma will again know the horrors of an Imperial invasion, and then the old Neapolitan will have greater worries on his mind than a handful of infidel Jews.

"We shall see.

"I personally am in a constant state of rejoicing! Does that strike you as odd? I have resumed work on my *Centuriae* and will soon have another volume ready for publication. Do you ever see Doctor Colombo, or does he avoid you for fear of the Carafa Bull? And that artist Buonarroti? Is he still alive?

Why don't you and Donna Miriamne come visit me in Ancona? Or better, consider settling in this salubrious place. I say salubrious not solely with reference to the physical setting (which is beautiful) but also to the moral climate.

Shalom,

Habib"

O the illusions of man! I have learned over the years to treat some maladies of the body but the illusions of the mind— even so fine-honed a mind as that of Don Habib—seem beyond all cure. In all the bodies I have opened I have never discovered an organ of discretion, the font of illusion, the liver, gall, lungs, heart-beat of our perpetual flux and reflux of mentality. And yet the spirit is there— somewhere there in that theatre of guts and feces and urine—the highest spirit is

there, somewhere. Perhaps everywhere. I have never been able to localize the seat
of our soul. Many believe it is in the liver, others in the heart, some in the brain.

I don't know. I have never seen it. One cannot bleed it. Cut a man and deprive
him of some of his organs—and if he remains alive, he still continues to think.

And think foolishly.

Don Habib thought foolishly. Bravely but foolishly.

Now five years safe in Candia, on this sun-bathed isle which the Greeks call
Crete, here where Aphrodite was born and where the sea is liquid sapphire, and
the waves break amethyst spume on long curling white sandy beaches, here now
listening to my Miriamne singing in the grape arbor and Andreino babbling his
first words (in Greek!), I sit on the flat roof of our little white-washed house and
stare at the sea, the sea, the ever- renewing sea, sea of time, sea of flesh pulsing like
the miracle of the body, blood of the world, as the wind is our breath, as these
gauzed lavender knife-edged mountains are our skeleton, as this soil is our flesh.

World and Man.

Cosmos and Microcosmos.

I dip my pen in the sapphire ink of the Mediterranean.

I am writing a history of the consequences of *Cum Nimis Absurdum.* I am setting
down all I myself observed and I am collating this against letters and documents I
managed to gather while Miriamne and I were still in Gehenna which used to be
called Italia. Additionally I have letters and documents sent to me since by
friends: some from Hebrews already enclosed behind the high Wall, some from
Christians in high places.

I seek to indite a nightmare. A form of therapy. Setting it down in my shapely
Italian hand (I write in my own native tongue and I am proud of my calligraphy), I
feel I might exorcise this incubus galloping within my skull, hoofs of that
apocalypse even on the sunniest days.

Habib thought he had found *the* salubrius place, *the* moral refuge. In Ancona
among his Portuguese friends, like himself recent Christians and more recent
Jews, he could speak his own language, practice his own faith.

But Miriamne and I did not accept his invitation to join him. We stayed in
Roma for more than a year after the promulgation of that infamous Bull. Soon
appeared papal bailiffs and notaries escorted by papal troops bearing halberds and
shields; every week more Hebrew families were hounded by the love of Christ to
sell their homes at absurd prices: and move forthwith into that unsalubrious
plague-ridden narrow low quarter running along the river from the theatre of
Marcellus and the bridge of Quattro Capi up to the hill of the Palazzo of the Cenci,
and in width between the Tiber and the ruins of the Portico of Octavia.

In August I received a letter from my father saying that *Cum Nimis* had already
been applied to Bologna, and the restricted area there was known as the Inferno!
"The enforced sale of real estate of Hebrews in the Ecclesiastical State has realized

for our people a half-million scudi, only—" added my father, a new curl to his script "—a fifth of its real value."

I seek to write without metaphors. The facts. The facts. Anger creates a flow of bile and beclouds the mind. I seek absolute clarity. Our Greek maid is chattering with Miriamne. How swiftly my wife has learned this tongue! Supple as Italian but spinier, some whip-cracking sounds, hiss of sibilants, sea breaking on the beach. I am less successful in the mastery of it. But my patients—Hellenic Jews of Heraclion and Greek mountaineers with curved moustaches and dark women with eyes like black olives, with black hair pulled tight back over the ears, and graven cheeks the color of plowed fields—they understand me, the language of my fingers.

The yellow caps appeared. Grim faces under yellow caps. I refused to wear it. For days, while Papal guards patrolled the neighborhood I refused to issue from our new quarters—a dismal cat-crawling alley almost abutting the ruins of the Teatro Marcellus. They were building a wall around the entire *vicus Judaeorum.* "13 Sept scuta 100 silvestro de Peruzzis architecto pro fabrica muri pro claudendo Judaeos . . ." (from my documents). On 9 Octob. the same architect Peruzzi received another hundred scudi for building a wall to enclose the Jews. On 14 Novemb. (I write in the style of the document) another hundred scudi for the same purpose.

These are the facts.

More yellow caps over long beards. Some beardless young men dressed in yellow from head to foot, thinking thus to be less conspicuous. Or perhaps it was a form of challenge. A committee offered the Pope 40,000 scudi to rescind the Bull, but in vain. Vitale dello Strologo was not part of this committee. He was ill of despair.

Now the Holy Father ordered obligatory sermons. The preachers were two learnèd Hebrews who were no longer Hebrews since the Bull had sent a soul- shaft of illumination to their minds and now they were the Dominican monks Sisto da Siena and Giuseppo Moro (I write only the facts). Pope Paul IV had ordered these obligatory sermons to the Jews for the purpose of converting them to the only true faith, the Holy Roman Apostolic Church. And many of them saw the light, as had Fra Sisto and Fra Giuseppe.

These are the facts.

And since a not insignificant number of Jews passed over to Christianity, Paul IV in March 1556 renewed the proscription of his predecessor, the life-loving hilarious Julius III, which imposed upon the community a contribution for the house of the catechumens of Roma.

In the winter came a fierce cry from Habib. " . . . The obscene quarantine has been imposed upon us too. At first in the interests of commerce. The Holy Father had made specific concessions to our community here in Ancona. But now the Holy Office charges us with taking advantage of these concessions to practice usury and seize undue control of Christian goods and committing violence against

Christian men and mixing our blood with Christian girls. And most rigid charges are leveled against the 'Marranos'—yes, against us, the Portuguese new Christians who became even newer Jews. The Papal Commissioners cry that our initial conversion was only on the surface (the only truth in all their charges). The Inquisition is already proceeding severely against us apostates. Many of the Portuguese here have already fled to Ferrara and Pesaro. The Duke of Urbino hopes to deflect commerce to Pesaro by means of these exiles, and also because the Hebrews in the Levant have already imposed a boycott on the port of Ancona since the application of the new restrictive legislation.

"But I will never see the result of this counter-attack.

"They sent a Neapolitan here to Ancona but we managed to 'corrupt' him and he fled.

"But now—but now—my quill trembles—now there is a new Commissioner and twenty-four new Christians—some *still* Christian!—have already been burnt at the stake in an *auto-da-Fé* and forty-two others including myself have had our death penalty commuted to slavery in the papal galleys. (I am smuggling this letter out via an Albanian sailor at dockside. Pray God it reaches you). A considerable heap of ducats played its role in this commutation of sentence. There was also, we learned, a letter from the Sultan Soleiman to the Pope, pointing out that there were some Turkish subjects amongst the prisoners, and threatening reprisals against the Christians in Turkey.

"The Pope is putting pressure on the Duke of Ferrara to burn Talmuds—and Talmudists.

"*Barach atah* . . . Blessed be Adonai! I completed my final volumes of the *Centuriae* before all this madness started.

"I no longer practice medicine. I pull a Christian oar. I understand the Pope is provoking a war against the Holy Roman Emperor. I suppose he considers them all Jews!—even Charles, the most Catholic King of Spain!

"Pray for me.
Habib"

Habib's fate decided mine. We would not remain in this Gehenna called Italia. Under Paul IV this land where my family has dwelt for four generations, and Miriamne's family for fifteen hundred years—had become a gigantic *vicus judaeorum*. Unable to convince Miriamne's family to join us, we stole out of Roma by night, and by stages, riding frequently by night, reached Bologna, and remained there a week. Conditions were as bad as in Roma. My family, too, like my wife's, would not consider flight. They had been forced to move into the 'Inferno'— located, to isolate them, leagues away from Piazza Maggiore.

My grandmother was dying. She smiled wanly at my kiss: a spark of light in the eyes that soon expired. She could no longer speak. When my father was at home, he spent most of his time at Grandmother Ziporah's bedside. We had our conversations there:

"Candia? Why Candia?"

"It's under Turkish jurisdiction. Hebrews are treated well there. And since great-grandfather came from there, I am curious to—"

"I am not curious. I am not curious about anything."

My father was in a state of continuous anger; he spent much time in the single synagogue still allowed to the Community. He wasn't even aware during an entire week of agitated talk, that I, who had quarreled with him in my youth, now had drawn closer to some of his ideas. To his ideas, not to him. He did not permit that.

My mother was more silent than I had ever known her. She didn't even seem interested in her son's wife although Miriamne confided in her that she was already pregnant when we undertook this exhausting journey. Vainly vainly Miriamne sought, with weary winning smiles, to enlist my mother's advice. My mother was not unsympathetic; she was simply dulled, remote.

After a week, Miriamne and I made our way to Ravenna. There, finally, we gained passage on a Venetian caravel in exchange for a cash payment plus my services as a physician for the Captain who was suffering from *Morbus Gallicus*.

So we reached this isle. And here my son was born and already he speaks Greek better than I shall ever speak it.

I have not heard from Habib for five years.

Perhaps some day a papal galley will stop at Heraclion. And I will be waiting at the dock. Will I recognize him? Will a papal galley ever stop here?

I think of Italia as a remoteness beyond the horizon. I have not made a notomia since I came here. I find myself attempting a notomia of the world's Body. I wish to anatomize the Cosmos. I want to embark upon the Ocean in the Blood, a greater journey.

Miriamne says I have become strange and I smile and kiss her and say I am no stranger than I have always been.

I am more sun-burned. I have already begun to lose my hair.

Elia del Medigo, ebreo, italico-cretensis, Doctor of Metaphysic.

IX

The Old Man on the
Slaughterhouse of the Crows

So here I am now on the lip of my ninetieth year puttering about my studio on the Street of the Slaughterhouse of the Crows and that marble arm there floating in marmorial space should be knocked off. But not yet. Not yet. Now it reminds me of another Pietà and that of yet another and back and back and back until I am quite reassumed within the block.

In old age time becomes space. It crystallizes into a block. Everything that I have felt and done, all the events of my long life—a century less a decade!—all the yesterdays (the day-before yesterdays and the lunar-distant yesterdays) and the tomorrows become yesterdays, all the *and then* and *and then*: my boyhood, my youth, my manhood, my middle years, my old age—with every year, every hour, Time's flow has slackened, slowed, thickened, ceased.

I am at Death's vestibule.

And it is odder than any vestibule to the Laurentian Library. There is no inside, no outside; no up or down; no here or there. All perspectives have converged into a point and the point is immense as nothingness, there is no Time and all time. Time has ceased to flow. Time is a block of marble into which I can cut in any direction and from any direction and uncover veins and arteries and muscles of my life that were always there. My life is in the block. My life *is* the block. I no longer care about an orderly release. Flowingness has frozen into being. I have lost a sense of chronology. The only date is Now. A crystallized Now. My life has become my own medium. I am carving myself out of myself—Michelangiolo Buonarroti Simone di Fiorenza, *statuario, statua.*

My Nicodemus lay in ruins. Blocks of that bungling, Christ wounded, one leg, one arm, Mary wounded, her elbow shattered, wounded white white (and yet I fancied blood) on the floor. And Antonio weeping, hauling the pieces away, absurd in his nightdress. There they are still, lying under the staircase, under the skull, a perpetual reproof.

I was no longer riding to St. Peter's for the joy of the long ride across the city and the need to control the machinations of that crew. At most I rode a bit around the Trajan Forum, or with Tiberio Calcagni and Tomao and chirpy Daniele walked on balmy evenings to the river and gazed at its yellow flowingness. Here Julius Caesar had been swept away and Augustus after him and every Pope from Peter to the last unlamented Carafa.

But I first.

The Nicodemus is in ruins. St. Peter's abuilding almost of itself. My unemployed hands twitched with boredom. Every time I saw that heap of wounded marble, I felt I must attempt a new Deposition, out of Pietà for myself, a work for my own consolation, my own meditation, a Church in which the only parishoner was myself and I myself the only priest.

In my studio I had another Deposition which I had earlier been working on and set aside when I became involved in that ill-fated Nicodemus group. This earlier work which I was extracting from a huge Roman column originally consisted of three figures: a dead Christ (already quite finished) just taken down from the Cross and supported in a limp vertical position by a Madonna in back of Him, and a Magdalen on His right.

Why could I not use this sketch as the basis for my new work? A palimpsest. Monks write new texts over old ones.

But as I was questing for no more than the shadow of a dream I decided to cut down down—down to the core of the rock, down to pure Essence, the Concetto itself. Not three figures but two and extract these two out of one. This reductive mathematics pleased me. Say more and more with less and less. I decided to eliminate the Magdalon. Then I destroyed the Madonna as well and proceeded to extract both figures from the single Christ that remained. A new Mother born of her Son!

But my preliminary chippings on this spectral Pietà (which floats before me now in a sort of mist) were too soon drowned in the sound of cannonades. Oh those were dreadful years! The death of my last brother Gismondo. The death of Urbino. The death of my protector, His Holiness Julius III. And soon there was that firebrand of a new Pontiff. Paul IV, setting off conflagrations and blaming others for having started them. He was an ill-constructed cannon, this Neapolitan Carafa, exploding at the breech. For he lacked the means to extinguish the conflagrations he had started. Irked by his threats and abjurations, the Spaniards marched troops commanded by the Duke of Alba to the very gates of Roma. Oh that was no time for carving Depositions!

Everyone in Roma thought only of flight. Monks were digging trenches and building fortifications. Work on St. Peter's was entirely suspended and everyone in Roma feared a new Sack. In September I too fled to Spoleto and returned to Roma only when I was recalled by special messenger at the end of October.

The threat had passed. I returned from Spoleto with the forest in my soul. My soul trembled with those dry leaves—I was a dry leaf—I was bark and ancient roots and loam and moisty shade. I had discovered among those eremites of Monteluco tranquility I had never known. Perhaps I should become a monk? Withdraw entirely from this cloaca of Roma. But I had first to resolve on the Dome of St. Peter's. Messer Tomao was pressing me to prepare a wooden model of the Cupola. He put it elegantly: ". . . So that if you should be removed—which God forbid— from the Works by a celestial Hand, (but that was the very Hand he was abjuring!) at least those who remain can follow your wishes to the letter."

"Via Tomao! Here I am still present in the flesh—if deteriorated—and who follows my wishes? Do you expect the Superintendent and the Committee of the

Fabbrica to be more obedient to a spectral than to a living Michelangiolo?, albeit he is no doubt already babbling in his second childhood."

"Maestro. No man is honored more. Prepare the drawings for the model . . ."

The works had reached the drum. Several mules had slipped off the spiral dirt path and plunged with their load of bricks to the holy pavement. Men too. An abominable world. Why should I not refute this illusion of art and live in a monastery as the Emperor Charles was said to be now doing since his abdication in favor of his son Philip II? Was I not the Emperor Charles of Art? Why could I not abdicate?

But first I had to prepare a proper Pietà for my tomb. This was for me, not for any Pope. For me. Making it I would be alone with my Christ, His Mother, as I had been with the ill-fated Nicodemus group.

And now began a new series of solicitations from Duke Cosimo and once again I felt a surge of that nostalgia per il Cupolone that only we Fiorentini know. That sense of nostalgia for the great brickredorange Brunelleschi dome curving against a star-speckled sky, nostalgia for the upraised fisted strength of our Palace of the Priors and the fortress-dwellings of our Medici and Rucellai and Pitti, nostalgia for the Arno snaking through the valley so Florentine-Tuscan deceptive: a summer brook, a timid gurgle trickling over pebbles in hot July; a violent overflowing, a flood of fury in rainy November. I missed the bridges—Ponte Vecchio and alle Grazie with their covered shops—, the gauzed violet hills of Fiesole and Settignano, the brown labyrinth of echoing narrow streets in the Santa Croce quarter where I grew up, the round iron ringholders set into great rustico stones, the rainbowed banners swinging from ringholder to ringholder on festive days, the torches set in them when the Signoria "gave the lights" to some honored citizen, as in my youth for messer Amerigo Vespucci when his letters of discovery of the New World were received at Palazzo Signoria. I missed Florentine curses and Florentine cadences, I missed the austerity of our cooking and the austerity of our art, Brunelleschi's mathematic Pazzi Chapel and Mona Margherita's measured and restrained beans and porchetta, Giotto's San Francesco frescoes in my church of Santa Croce and Masaccio's marvelous sculptures painted on the walls of the Brancacci Chapel where Torrigiani had flattened my nose rendering it *stiacciato* in low relief (a century ago!—almost a century ago and the broken bridge still tingles on foggy days!)

Ahi, Mona Margherita was long dead now too—so were they all—all the artists and friends and relatives of my entire life—all gathered into the *omnium gatherum*. Only recently a young Jew had come here with my physician friend Colombo and reminded me of his grandfather, another friend of my youth, also dead, a certain Andrea . . .

Also dead.

Also dead.

Also dead.

Tocsin of a bell. Midnight. I should really remove that arm. It is perfectly inharmonious with my new intention. It is, as my theologic friend the English Cardinal Pole (also dead. Also dead) used to say: *Falsus in uno, falsus in omnibus.* Ahi! that much I can understand.

A language I should have learned in my old age. As Cato learned Greek, according to messer Donato. I haven't seen messer Donato often these past years. Always in and out of Roma on some diplomatic mission or other for the Cardinal Alessandro Farnese. France, and frequently to his belovèd Venice.

I thought to concentrate, you see, on my new Deposition, and on the model for the Cupola. So I wrote to Giorgio Vasari to thank the Duke for me but I would not—I could not—return to my homeland until I had completed Saint Peter's. Otherwise it would have been a great shame to all Christianity and a great sin to my own soul.

Soon after writing that letter in response to the Duke's tempting offers, that Florentine letter, there came to visit me one day messer Francesco Bandini with his son Pier Antonio, father of no less than thirteen children.

Now these Bandinis, like Donato Giannotti and my late friend the banker Luigi (also dead) and all of us in the circle of Cardinal Ridolfi (also dead) are exiles because we are held in suspect by the Medici although of late many of us, including Bandini, were beginning to strike an accommodation with Duke Cosimo. The Bandinis were an old Florentine family who had recently grown rich in commerce and in banking, and now they took great delight in works of art. They consulted often with my Tomao who has one of the great art collections of the Urbs and has gained a considerable reputation as a connoisseur of taste and financial disponability.

Ahimè! When I think of the foolish letters I wrote Tomao when first we met, almost thirty years ago, in which I hailed him as *Light of our Century* and other such idiotic terms of endearment and foresaw for him a great career as architect— no worse! acclaimed him for the magnificent works he had already achieved . . . only in my head! only in those hot tropics of my passion, there alone did grow Tomao's great achievements! But he remains a loyal loving friend and if he has turned out to be neither architect nor painter nor sculptor (and fortunately he no longer perpetrates those clumsy inept drawings from the figure) he does discern the good works of others. He does appreciate the drawings I made for him a quarter century ago, albeit he has given some away (mine and others) as diplomatic gifts. And as Conservator of the Urbs, he is of use to me on the works of the Campidoglio. I used to enjoy visiting Tomao's Palazzo on the Piazza dei Cavalieri—his exquisite wife, his talented sons, his great collection of antiquities— mostly Greek and Roman copies and some modern commissioned sculptures and paintings (nothing of mine!) that is the talk of Roma and has now been described in detail in messer Aldobrandi's *Mirabilis Romae.*

Well, Bandini had been consulting often with messer Tomao concerning the acquisition of good pieces. He had recently bought on Monte Cavallo a vineyard from Francesco Colonna. Now, what they call a vineyard here in Roma is more likely to yield buried statues than grapes. And so it was with Bandini's acquisition. Included in his purchase price (1450 scudi di giulii 10 per scudo, according to Tomao) were all the statues, *anticaglie*, marble busts, bits of porphory columns of stone from Brescia, blocks of African marble and other antiquities which had accumulated in the garden. And now the Bandinis dreamt only of counting among their treasures a work by my hand.

They had been after me for years. Politely of course. And now and again an added grain of sugar was dropped by Tomao, practically their agent. It was amusing. I imagine what messer Bandini had in mind was a garden like messer Gallo's where the Bacchus of my youth still reels drunken (and lacking his right hand and libation cup) amidst Egyptian sphinxes and Roman sarcophagi. I imagine messer Gallo's grandsons believe my work is truly a work of ancient Greece. Their grandfather who had commissioned it, said it was better! So was his judgement.

But I didn't care to do a commissioned work for messer Bandini, much as I found the man *simpatico*—notwithstanding his new-rich merchant ways. I even liked his terrifyingly fertile son. I had long ago explained to my nephew (who had advised me of certain offers in Fiorenze) that he should tell the priest no longer to address me as Michelangiolo scultore, because I'm known here only as messer Buonarroti and if a Florentine citizen wants an altar piece painted, let him find a painter. I was never a painter or sculptor like those who keep shops. I have always looked out carefully for the honor of my father and brothers, and if I've served three Popes (at the time I wrote Leonardo. Seven now!), I've been forced to do so . . .

So my sense of honor prevented me from yielding to messer Francesco Bandini's request, but he patiently awaited a good occasion. Meanwhile the banker had introduced into my house a young Florentine sculptor, Tiberio Calcagni, very eager to learn my art, gentle, and discreet, and so much was he to my fancy that I often invented excuses to converse with this young man. He had the unusual grace of accepting and valuing the gifts of my experience without losing an olive pit of his own hard dignity. He was not at all like Condivi (who wrote loving letters to me on occasion from Ripa)—that is, Tiberio did not efface himself in the blaze of my fame and achievements. He learned from me, yes, and on the face of things, seemed merely to be following my instructions even to the finest minutiae executed with the finest irons and bits. But if you look at those works of mine which he repaired, his own unmistakable personality is there, his chisel-writing is not mine, he is a faithful disciple but all Tiberio and not a miniature Michelangiolo.

Daniele Ricciarelli of Volterra—another assistant these last years—also possesses a similar dignity, regard of self,—although his flavor is sweeter than that of Tiberio. But they are both Toscani, and I suppose it is this Tuscan sour-sweetness, this hard vein in the milkiest marble, this ultimate faithfulness to oneself, this refusal—perhaps inability—to melt entirely into another, even a greater Other—that I love.

I must admit I have been lucky in these two young men who have been my faithful assistants these late years.

Even poor Daniele, painting britches now in the Chapel, by order of the Pope! And I must console him, and clasp him round the shoulders and pooh-pooh his cursing and lamentations and quite unnecessary apologies. "Don't worry, Daniele. For every private part you cover, you make the figure more nude. Concealment is frequently a more hypocritical mode of revealment!"

At any rate, one day at the beginning of the year after my return from Spoleto—a wintry brutal day, flakes of snow whiter than the Trajan column whistling through the epicycle of the market like the ghosts of slaughtered Caesars, Tiberio and I had a long conversation in the room where the pieces of the destroyed Pietà were lying.

"Why did you do it, Maestro?"

"Do what?"

"Spoil so marvelous an effort?"

He made me smile, that naive young man, asking such a question. What did he know of the furies that seized me when obdurate marble refused to obey my will? So, in a moment of abandon, I, usually so taciturn about such matters, recounted all the miseries that had come to me from that damned marble, and how, were it not for Antonio's intervention I would not merely have spoiled it but reduced it to powder.

In a flash the young Florentine intuited that the sweet combination dreamt of by his patron had now offered itself. He told the story to messer Francesco Bandini who worked out a scheme whereby Tiberio promised Antonio 200 golden scudi for the fragments of the Nicodemus Deposition. For I had given the piece to my servant Antonio when he burst into my studio in his nightdress, terrified at the blows that had awakened him, and begged me not to reduce the crippled group to marble dust. I in a fury with the iron hammer raised and that poor boy on his knees—praying to *me*: "No, Maestro, no! Give it to me! Do not smash it entirely! Give it to me!" Praying and shivering and crying in his nightdress. "Give it to me!"

I gave it to him. I gave my crippled dream to a servant boy.

Of course Bandini would lay out this sizeable sum. Then messer Bandini came to me and begged my permission to have Tiberio repair and complete the work. "Thus," said he, "all your labors would not have been spent in vain."

And thus, thought I, you will have your work by Michelangiolo Buonarroti.

I assented. Why not? I was too old and weary to carve an entirely new piece for Bandini. "Oh, take it away", I said. Perhaps this twenty-five year old Tiberio might perform a respectable job of salvage.

At first Antonio grumbled at what he was being offered for my massacre.

Perhaps he felt called upon to grumble to demonstrate to me that he valued even shattered Michelangiolo more than 200 golden scudi. But 200 golden scudi was more money than he had ever seen in his life. It was even more than the veneration with which he held possession of the fragments I had given him.

So my Deposition was deposed again. He from the Cross and I from Macel dei Corvi. They came with a cart and carried the chunks away, together with the models in wax and clay from which to complete it, carting them all off to the vineyard on Monte Cavallo.

And I watched them go without regret. If only the other broken pieces of my life could be carted off and set to rights so easily!

I came often to Bandini's vineyard on Monte Cavallo to see what Tiberio was doing. Besides, in that same neighborhood also dwelt my melancholy and loyal other disciple, Daniele da Volterra. I say 'disciple' for want of a better word. Certainly these young men are not my apprentices. I have never kept a bottega.

So several afternoons a week I rode to Monte Cavallo to see what that young Tiberio was up to—he was only twenty-five and this was his first important work. And as I watched him chipping away at my Nicodemus group (for after the major broken pieces had been put together again, the real work of refitting new pieces and completing the blocked-out Magdalen and smoothing away the wounds I had inflicted) as I watched him chipping away at my work, I felt strangely remote from it all; remote and yet intimate, as if I were seeing myself being operated on in a dream and felt great pain and no pain at all.

And he was so humble in his sour-sweet Tuscan way, humble within the limits of his amore proprio and dignity; he would not dare tap a hair's breath off my work did I not give him permission. "Is this all right, Maestro? I mean to shave just a tiny bit here, Maestro. Are you in agreement? How should I adjust this elbow, Maestro?" (for the Madonna's shattered elbow gave him great trouble).

So, without touching my hand to a chisel, I recarved the piece, so to speak, through him: his hand obeyed my intellect.

It doesn't really matter, I tried to tell myself. One doesn't do sculpture with the hands anyway but with the mind. And withal my eighty- four years my mind has not aged though my hand shook and here was a fresh young pair of hands offered me as a gift, offered so graciously, so humbly.

So I guided Calcagni's hand and often the Bandinis were there aaccompanied by gawking members of their tribe and my melancholy Daniele who was already much at home with the Bandinis. So I saw and followed every effort of Calcagni and soon realized that my notion of total obedience of another's hand is simply not possible. Nolente Volente each artist's hand is obedient only to his own mind. And his deficiencies of concept—no matter how skilled of hand—cannot be remedied by the concepts of others.

I realized that whatever was merely glued together of my work remained *my* work, no matter how shattered or unfinished it might be. But wherever this boy set

about to finishing or polishing what I had done or undone, it ceased to be me—
even though he thought (and I too had thought) he was merely executing my
wishes. The hand and brain of an artist are inseparable. Even my destruction was
me. More me than Calcagni's repair. The Magdalen, especially, is entirely
Tiberio's, with too hard a finish although I tried to teach him my cross-hatching
technique that lends a fleshlike vibration, an organic pulse to the surface. But
Tiberio simply could not do it. I kept my dissatisfactions to myself as if locked
within the strongbox in my bedroom. We decided at first to fit a new left leg of
Christ (of which Daniele still proudly owned the kneecap) into the square peghole
I had already made after the miserable demise of the original leg. But I realized
soon that Calcagni could not do it. And I would not do it.

So there sits my Nicodemus now in Bandini's house with a Magdalen all out of
scale and with a surface of parallel grooving that lends it so hard a finish instead of
the pulse I always seek to achieve; and with a one-legged Christ and a repaired
Madonna.

But all the heads (except the Magdalen's and the composition, notwithstanding its wounds and repairs, are entirely mine.

I, Nicodemus.

✳

Thus at last freed of the Nicodemus, I turned again to my skeletal Christ and his
shadowy Mother.

Freed not only of the Nicodemus I am being freed of everything. Although
nominally I am still in charge of St. Peter's, in actual fact I am like that cupola for
which I have had prepared a wooden model. I am simply a wooden model and I
have no assurance—none—that my successors in the Fabbrica will follow my
intentions.

I prepared that model at the urgent request of my friends—especially Tomao
and Donato Giannotti and Francesco Bandini, and the Cardinal Carpi— and I
became indeed suspicious and irritable at their too-often repeated admonitions
that if I did not leave specific instructions for the cupola— that if, so to speak, I
kept the cupola in my head as I have kept other plans for St. Peter's—the results
could not but deviate from my intentions, and deviate far indeed. No doubt they
spoke truth, but in their importunities, I heard the voices of the then Cardinal
Cervini and the Deputies of the Fabbrica and Urbino nagging from the grave, as
well as an unconcealed reminder of my imminent demise. And although I am
quite prepared to die, I do not like my friends to remind me of it. I can do that very
well myself.

But finally, I prepared a little clay model of the cupola, and then a larger
wooden one, and this was given to Antonio Franzese for the construction of a huge

wooden model. I had written to Fiorenza for exact measurements of Brunelleschi's cupolone and lanterna, for I knew—as every Florentine knows—I could not better that, but I could at least raise it loftier to the heavens.

There was another model, too, I had to prepare: this was for the staircase I had once conceived of for the Vestibule of the Laurentian Library in Fiorenza. First Giorgio Vasari had asked me about it and I tried to recall my original conception but it was all very vague. Then four years later Bartolomeo Ammannati who was continuing the work I had abandoned it seemed a century ago renewed the request and I replied that I had made a little clay model of the Library staircase and was sending it up to him in a box. I gave my opinion that it be made of fine walnut instead of stone— more in keeping with the desks, ceiling and door—and I signed that letter "I'm all yours, old, blind and deaf, and my hands and mind are out of tune."

So I prepared the model and sent it up to Fiorenza with a muleteer who I am certain was a thief. All these matters somehow now seemed to be enacted in a dream. For many years now the world around me—the streets the shouts the change of Popes the faces of my friends—all seem to be receding, I seem to see it all as if I held a gauze in front of my eyes, the contours blurred, the colors faded. I am not speaking of my physical vision although that is not as keen as it used to be. I speak of the eyes of the soul. Events come to me as if from a great distance. Even events that happened yesterday. Everything is rising up to my mind out of great depths. Even the slightest things. All transience seems silly and profound.

Now Duke Medici, having failed with Giorgio Vasari, thought to employ Benedetto Varchi to tempt me back to Fiorenza. I had only met the famous humanist a few times, when he came down to Roma soon after those lectures on my poems before the newly-created Accademia of Fiorenza. One of those lectures dealt with love in the Platonic sense, and he had praised my friendship with Tommaso de' Cavalieri (whose name he named in a flowerbed of compliments) as the loftiest example of such love. Naturally, Tomao and I were curious to see this man, who proved to be as charming as he was erudite, and as agile as a squirrel in the thick foliage of learning.

Something however—

"But, of course," laughed Donato, in Roma between missions. Donato had known the man since the days of the last Florentine republic, whose history Varchi was now writing. "From youth on not only had he studied Greek but he also took pleasure in the Greek way. Indeed one of the Pazzis tried to have him assassinated because he had corrupted his son. He has written not a few pederastic poems both in the Latin and in the Vulgate."

"Alas! I cannot read the Latin!"

"And you needn't read the Vulgate."

Tomao seemed a bit crestfallen by these quips of Donato. He had been immensely flattered by Varchi's references to him in his lecture but now he wondered whether the praise was entirely disinterested.

"O my dear fellow I haven't the slightest doubt that Benedetto Varchi set down everything with the utmost seriousness. Besides, his tastes are indeed ecumenical. In addition to being a sodomite, messer Benedetto Varchi, that paludian and be-toga'd writer, is also attracted to budding maidens. Just a few years ago he seduced a twelve-year-old girl, daughter of a contadina in Camerata (his home town) and although Varchi tried to pass it off on a priest who had confessed the girl, eventually he confessed to it himself and went to prison."

I laughed but Tomao didn't.

I found it amusing, to say the least, that this libidinous literatus should have been nominated by Duke Cosimo to the Florentine Academy only a few days after his prison sentence; and that it was this most carnal character who gave public lessons on ethereal platonism, and a year later read a long and (some say, boring; others brilliant) lecture on several of my sonnets.

My nephew wrote me an illiterate account of that most literary occasion.

Later I read Varchi's lectures, and (at Tomao's repeated urgings) wrote him a letter of gratitude for what he had said about my poems. These writings of his, I must admit, take deep soundings into my soul, but I wish he expressed himself with fewer feathers.

There is a whole tribe now in our Italia—and as the century has passed its median and Spanish power is entrenched all over this peninsula, and courtiers buzz like bees around the courts of Duke Cosimo in Fiorenza, and the Gonzaga at Mantova, and the della Rovere at Urbino; not to mention the greatest court of all: the Vatican here in Roma; buzz like bees I say and their speeches and their writings are too honeyed for my Tuscan stomach, and they buzz around me too and I have found only one efficacious way to brush them off—and that is to out-honey their honey. I have written letters of gratitude so beswathed in feathers and scrapings, so rich with bowings and ribbons and rhetoric, that anyone who knows my true nature must know that these statements are as incongruous to me as if a Tuscan contadino were to beribbon his rough woolen cap and put bells on his dirty boots.

Usually my effusions are veiled irony. What I truly feel is concealed in smoke. There is frequently no other way. That master-swinger of incense and poison-pots, Pietro Aretino, has just died of an apoplexy, 'tis said, laughing at some filthy joke. Giovio's epitaph. *Non lo conosco.*

But if there is no one with his evil genius, there is today a wider diffusion of hypocrisy. We live in a century of lies and we must learn to negotiate by indirection, arrive at true North by sailing round Africa.

To great souls—and some Popes—I speak bluntly as my mallet. I speak things. And to the others, words.

·✳·

The four years of the Carafa were not good times for my art. When indeed were there good times for my art? Nothwithstanding that he shared this new Pontiff's anti-Spanish animus, messer Donato was sardonic about all these rumors and alarums. Since Paul IV was baiting Spaniards and burning sodomites and convert-ing prostitutes and locking Jews behind a wall, all Roma seemed an armed camp.

"But," said Donato, "'those who puff up such smoke should be possessed of adequate weapons, and this Pope's chief weapon is his explosive temper. Monks digging fortifications are not much help against Imperial cannonballs. The Carafa, for all his Catholic zeal, does not hesitate to employ Lutheran landsknechts to defend the Vatican, and is negotiating with the Grand Turk as well. Paul's hatred of the Spaniard—or the Hapsburg since Spanish is but a small part of the Emperor's make-up—is no doubt ecumenical. But as viable policy—?"

And for some mysterious reason this Neapolitan, an old man of seventy- nine when he was elected—only two years younger than myself— immediately dis-played his indifference if not animosity toward my person. With his election I was deprived of my revenues of the office of Civil Notary of the Romagna, which had replaced my former income from the ferry across the Po. Now I had nothing since I received nothing for my work on the Fabric of Saint Peter. I imagine the Holy Father simply gave my benefice in the Romagna to some member of his family. It didn't take long for all Roma to realize that nepotism was this Pope's besetting sin, even more so than in the case of the previous Paul, who besides had many compensating merits. But this new Paul was beset by many furies. He besought reform like a Mussulman—with a sword. The sword of Paul. I feared for my friend the English Cardinal Pole for it was well known that Carafa suspected him of heresy for his connection with the Spirituali (I would have feared for myself too had the Carafa but been aware of the existence of the builder of his Temple!). Fortunately Pole was in England, as Papal legate to the new Queen Mary who had returned that kingdom to the Faith.

Despite the Pope's years, he was not by any means a senile old man. He was indeed all fire and smoke, a cannon, a tall skinny man who exploded readily and his words came out like shot and he seemed not to touch the ground when he walked. He was very learned and his piety was not mine and he drank vile black wine and displayed little interest in the arts. Rumor had it that so feared and hated was he that at his election Ignatius Loyola trembled at it for he knew this new Pontiff's violent anti-Spanish animus, and Charles V suffered an attack of jaun-dice. Indeed within a year, Loyola was dead and Charles abdicated the Spanish throne in favor of his son Philip II.

Almost immediately after his election, the Holy Office began to examine the case of the Cardinals Morone and Pole who would surely have been imprisoned (as

Morone subsequently was) in the Castel Sant' Angelo had he not luckily died in England before his projected return to Italia.

Inevitably Paul's provocations resulted in the invasion of the States of the Church by a Spanish army from Naples led by the Duke of Alba, and soon the light cavalry of the Catalans was riding up to the city gates, and everyone feared a new Sack, and thought only of flight. I was not fearful myself; I had known war intimately during the siege of Fiorenza in 1529-30. I had been Governor of Fortifications then and I knew the sound of cannonballs smashing into the Bishops palace at San Miniato where I had my headquarters, or thudding into the mattresses I had ordered hung from the campanile. I knew war and I knew the building of fortifications too.

During Paul's time (the greater Paul, the third) I had been consulted on the fortifications of this very Borgo which this lesser Paul was now manning against the Spaniards with monks in armour and nuns digging trenches. What fools we all are! How I had shouted in anger at that meeting of military architects when San Gallo declared that sculpture and painting were my art, not fortifications. "I may not know very much about sculpture and painting but certainly I know more about fortifications than San Gallo or any of his clique!" So Paul (the greater Paul) smiled his crooked weasel smile and bade me still my ire and they followed many of my plans in the building of those fortifications.

But this new Pontiff did not consult me at all in the preparations of defense against the Spaniards. Surely he must have known that as a Fiorentino in exile I had no greater love for the Catalans than he did. They were the tyrants who sustained the Medici tyranny over my city. And he might also have known of my experience as a military engineer. Yet he never asked my advice.

So it was not fear of the Spaniards that betook me to Spoleto. I had long contemplated a pilgrimage to Loreto and since the works at St. Peter's were shut down now because of all the agitation, I thought it a good time to go. En route to Loreto, I fell terribly a-weary and remained at Spoleto to rest. But I could go no further anyway for a messenger was sent after me recalling me to Roma. But those forty days in the mountains of Spoleto with the hermits of Monteluco were so great a joy that I felt that only a part of me had returned to Roma. My spirit remained in the woods.

But my obligations to St. Peter's came first and Paul IV notwithstanding he had taken away my benefice did re-confirm me in all my employments and offices. Perhaps my good friend the Cardinal de' Carpi, now chief of the Deputies of the Fabbrica was the secret hand behind all this. Certainly I am most grateful to Carpi who also wrote to the Duke of Fiorenza on my behalf explaining why I could not abandon Roma now that the works had reached the drum of the planned cupola. Carpi also was one of those who most urgently pressed me to prepare a wooden model of the Cupola. "For you must realize," said he, "'that all the Briefs of several

Popes denouncing future departures from your plans are, after their deaths, useless as the parchment on which they are written. Therefore you must prepare a model of such a size and so detailed that there can be no pretense for further transformation." And so besought by Carpi and Tomao and all my friends I made many drawings as well as a small clay model which was then constructed in the large in wood by Giovanni Franzese, a good carpenter, and its height was almost three times that of a middle-sized man and the drum was ten braccia in diameter. And as I had foreseen this took a year in the making.

And all the while that was being constructed the fabbrica of my own body was being deconstructed; I suffered a mass attack of all the woes of the very old (and to think that was seven years ago and I am still here!) dolor in the side and in the back so that I couldn't climb the stairs, which put me in a passion; and I had to forego the daily rides on my horse which have always been my pleasure late every afternoon before sunset; and I had fearful pains of gout in my feet, and stones in my kidney and could not urinate. So although I dreamt often now of returning to Fiorenza to die and be buried next to my father, and to this effect wrote to my nephew Lionardo, yet for fear of losing the grace of God I could not abandon the fabric of St. Peter, neither for all these personal woes or the agitation of the Pope's aborted war against the Spaniards, or the ever more enticing offers the Duke was now making to tempt me back to my *patria.*

For the Duke, thinking no doubt that the Spanish war might convince me to return, wrote to me in the name of his Chamberlain Lionardo Marinozzi, a frank letter declaring that if the closing down of the Fabbrica caused me grief there could be a compensating joy in seeing me back again in my "sweetest homeland" among my "beloved relatives and the entire city . . . now is the time that you can console our Prince, help your house and honor Fiorenza with your presence . . ." etc. etc.

And indeed soon after the Chamberlain himself appeared in person to renew the Duke's supplications. And I was sorely tempted to give up St. Peter's because money was lacking just when we were reaching the most difficult parts of the structure. And yet I feared most the shame and sin that would result after ten years labor solely for the love of God. I told the Chamberlain (and I wrote Vasari to so inform the Duke) how touched I was by his Lordship's kindness and excused myself from writing to him directly because writing is a great fatigue for it is not my art and I wander and I am losing my memory and my brains. Instead I asked the Cardinal de Carpi to write to Duke Cosimo and explain more gracefully (for that is the art of prelates and penmen) why I had to remain in Roma.   And the Cardinal did so and I am still in Roma. To my astonishment. Every morning I awake with astonishment.

·❊·

Because of my inability to visit the works frequently, errors had been made in the vaulting of the Fabbrica. This was the first time vaulting was being attempted in travertine. Had I been present I would have caught the serious blunders which had been committed by the master Mason in charge, preparing all the centerings of one curvature only. Much had to be torn down, to my shame, and we were in the midst of rebuilding, when in September 1557 there occurred the worst flood of the Tiber in all the years of my memory.

The crest-line of flood waters are recorded on the facade of Santa Maria Sopra Minerva, my church here in the Holy City, the church where my triumphant Christ stands (somewhat wounded in the knee). Only a few days before the flood, I had idly read again the plaque which declares that:

> In the year of our Lord one thousand five hundred and thirty, the seventh of the Pontificate of Pope Clement VIII, on the eighth day of October, the flood reached this line and the whole city would have perished if the Blessed Virgin had not made the waters recede.

My eyes always automatically graze over such commemorative tablets every time I ascend the steps for Mass. Fortunately, I was not in the area this time. For the flood waters reached beyond that mark: fourteen braccia of muddy Tiber at the adjacent Pantheon pouring into the structure so that poor Raffaello lay in his tomb like a drowned sailor. And the waters went even higher in the Via di Ripetta near the Tiber, and almost as high in the Piazza Navona so that they could have staged a maritime battle there as they did of old in the Circus Agonalis, that very spot. Hundreds of houses were washed away, and many people drowned in the city and many cattle in the countryside and of course afterward there was the inevitable famine and pestilence. Fortunately, there was no flooding in Macel de' Corvi. The only flood there, was the rain of filth tossed into the excavation around the Column and never properly surrounded by a wall as I have recommended.

But much of Roma was mud and lamentations. I am ashamed to say I derived a certain satisfaction from this flood. Nanni's bridge, which had trembled under Vasari's and my horses' hoofs seven years before, was entirely swept away. I had predicted as much. And the Lord had proved me right. The Lord had given me retribution for the fact that this bridge, which I had originally been ordered to repair in preparation for the coming Jubilee, had been taken away from me because of the usual impatience of the prelates at what they took to be my excessive caution in strengthening the foundations. So they complained to Paul (the greater Paul) and they took away my commission and put Nanni di Baccio Bigio in my place.

Why then was I ashamed of my satisfaction?

Perhaps I felt guilty of the sin of pride, the greatest of sins. Would the Lord have sent a flood merely to prove me right?

At any rate, Nanni's bridge was swept away, but he wasn't. His importunities and maneuvers at the Fabbrica continued.

The waters receded after three days and I couldn't urinate and here was my nephew Lionardo in Roma with his wife Cassandra to add their pleas to the Duke's that I return to my patria. Lionardo looked more Spanish than ever with his ridiculous solemnity. His beard was blackblack and black was his doublet in the Catalan style and coalblack were his brooding eyes. His solemn manner promised profundities but only platitudes issued forth. Yet his commonplaces were garnished in a new cleverness, a man-of-the-world sophistication I hadn't known hitherto. He displayed not the slightest interest in my art; not even when Tomao came to the studio, and warmly recalling their earlier meetings in Fiorenza, proceeded to sing my praises, and offered to accompany my nephew on a Cavalieri-guided tour of *marabilis Romae* that would have been in fact *mirabilis Michelangeli.*

But Lionardo begged off. Courteously, I must admit.

Mona Cassandra, whom I had never seen, proved to be a gracious if somewhat stiff lady with gray eyes and a keen mouth, very patrician in her ways as befits a Ridolfi, one of the great noble families of our Fiorenza, and I was pleased withal by her courtesies. She still mourned the death of her first-born baby Buonarroto, and I tried to console her pointing out that the Lord giveth and the Lord taketh away, and furthermore we Buonarroti seem not to be very lucky in male children. Francesca, Lionardo's sister, had also lost several. I remembered (but did not tell Mona Cassandra) the excessive fuss and ceremony attendant on the baptism of this child four years ago. Certainly I always take great joy in the birth of another male Buonarroti. But when Giorgio Vasari had written to me about the honorable procession of beautiful women who had accompanied this infant to the baptism, I had replied that such pomp displeased me inasmuch as man should not laugh when all the world wept (this was at the time of Cosimo's cruel war against the Sienese), therefore it seemed to me (I wrote Vasari) that Lionardo should not make so much ceremonial for one who is born, but rather reserve such joyful celebrations for the death of one who has lived well.

And all too soon this tiny Buonarroto was gone before he had even had the oppportunity to live well. and when the following year Lionardo was awaiting the birth of another child, he wanted, if it were a male child, to give it my name and I wrote that I would be content if he and Cassandra were content. But the child (who did prove to be a boy) was named Lodovico instead, after my father. And so, to this date no Buonarroti bears my name and I shall surely not live to hold another Michelangiolo Buonarroti at the font. But it doesn't matter. My works bear my name even if none of them (save the Madonna of the Fever) is signed and my works are my true children as my art has been my only wife. And these are children who may bring me grief in the begetting, but once begotten they may be forgotten, if they fail to bring pride and joy to their begetter.

My nephew and Mona Cassandra remained but a short while. I had to employ a broadaxe rather than a rapier to ward off the surprisingly skillful way in which he pleaded Duke Cosimo's cause. His diplomatic manner made me certain that he was here not unofficially, so to speak, but was indeed an agent of the Duke. Tomao surmised that my nephew was performing certain embassies to several Medicean supporters in the Vatican; perhaps he had even delivered messages to the Pope. Carafa those days was not ill-disposed toward the Medici, notwithstanding Cosimo's reliance upon Spanish aid. The Duke had even taken unto himself a Spanish wife, comely Eleanora of Toledo. But the Holy Father's initial zeal against all things Spanish had exploded against himself like a cannon at the breech. He had unwillingly relinquished his anti-Catalan crusade as abruptly as he had started it. Carafa was now threatened by enemies closer to home. These enemies indeed were his own nephews, whom he had created Cardinals, an honor to which they were totally unfitted: and now their scandalous personal behavior was especially grievous to this rigid Chietino who had publicly declared that he would light the faggots under his own father should he be guilty of heresy.

Everyone was waiting to see whether Carafa would light the faggots under his own nephews. And soon he did.

If there is not yet a member of my family bearing my name, there is a bambino Michelangiolo now up in Castel Durante in the Marche whom I had held at the font—the warmth of that little body through the swaddling cloths!—and felt indeed he was my grandson inasmuch as I had loved his father Urbino as if he were my son. Urbino's death had left me more dead than alive. He had been with me, faithful and loving, for more than twenty-five years and I did not know how to manage without him. Alive, he taught me how to live, and dying he taught me how to die. Ahimè! I was left in that middle state—neither dead nor alive—in which the echoes of his bustling noisy counsel were of no avail.

Fortunately Cornelia remained a while. Her love for me was as filial as had been her husband's, but of course she could not assume his heavy tasks. When after several months she departed with the baby Michelangiolo and her other child, I felt indeed bereft.

Not long after Cornelia's departure I received a desperate letter, recounting a complicated intrigue. I had painted two portraits of Cornelia's *putti* and given them to her and Urbino as a gift. Well, it seems the Most Illustrious and Most Reverend Cardinal Turnone had heard of them and he began to put great pressure on Cornelia to see them; members of her family and other agents turned the screws tighter and finally the poor girl acceded. The Cardinal came to the house and saw the portraits and was so pleased that he began to think at once of obtaining them for money. "But I had no intention of ever consenting to that, even though I was being ever more urged to do so by many people. Rather I became more stubborn, and as the offers on his part increased so much more obstinately did I remove from my thoughts any notion of satisfying him, always putting forth as my excuse that I kept these in memory of you to whom my children and I are so obligated, and that the portraits were never to leave the house even for the shortest time." Well, seeing how resolved and determined the poor girl was, the Cardinal withdrew and ceased to molest her.

But in October the Duke of Urbino (Lord of Castel Durante) learned that Cornelia owned two portraits by my hand, and he gave orders to a priest of his household to see to it that these portraits were brought to Urbino because he wished to see them. The priest sent agents representing both himself and the Duke and again the sad comedy began. Cornelia must send the pictures to Urbino. No, she would not. Her opposition—poor maiden in the face of all this authority—was expressed in most courteous terms and so for a while she deflected the attack. But now again the Duke dispatched his emissary for the province of Massa and with him another of his courtiers ". . . together with a most friendly letter begging me to send him the pictures along with someone I trusted." Here Cornelia's letter wrung my heart: "Not knowing how I should comport myself in these negotiations I decided to ask advice of several of my kinfolk who said to me— 'Cornelia, with the Lord Duke you should not behave as stubbornly as you had with the Cardinal Turnone, because his Excellence is the Patron of the pictures and everything else you own; and if he likes them, you have to give them to him no matter what. Hence, we advise you to send them together with a letter declaring that his Excellence is the Patron of your pictures, your possessions, your children and everything, and that he can dispose of them as if they were his.' And so I did as I was advised to do."

I could just see Cornelia, whose loveliness was enriched by her dignity, receiving in tears this counsel of obsequiousness from her family. I, who have spoken more rudely to Holy Fathers than to my own father, could sympathize with her case.

So, Cornelia sent a kinsman to the Duke together with the portraits. The Duke declared they were extremely beautiful, that the kinsman was not to depart without his leave. After four days he summoned him, ". . and told him that he was accepting my pictures . . ." (he, the Duke, was *accepting* my pictures! He was disposing of what had been born of my hand and spirit. Even my gifts are at the disposal of these Lords, I thought, and I became angry not only for Cornelia but for myself). ". . . he was accepting my pictures together with my good spirit (il buon animo mio) saying that he had obliged me to make the free offer that I had made . . ." (Oh, this indeed required the most subtle theological spinning to determine the relative weights of free will and predestination!) ". . . and that the pictures were so beautiful that there was no price that he could pay for them, it would have to reach thousands of scudi: but that he desired that the *putti* should, for his love enjoy one hundred scudi; the which my kinsman repeatedly refused, declaring that the children desired nothing other than to remain in his Excellence's good graces . . ."

Ultimately Cornelia was obliged to accept the one hundred scudi together with other favors to her family, freeing them of certain obligations and expenses and lawsuits; now she was uneasy that my gift had been so disposed of, and she wanted my approval and that I should write her to "quiet my soul, which, ever since I have sent the pictures, is still upset and will remain so until I receive your letter, because I know certainly that you will give your approval of what I have done. And since Francesco—whom God grant peace—had made mention in his will of these portraits; I would like your messer Marcello Venusti to make me two copies from those same drawings, cost what it will. You could pay him out of the interest in the moneys Francesco has on deposit in the Monte della Fede . . ." I was to let her know if Marcello agreed.

There followed a suggestion how this transaction might be carried out, however it pleased me. "Be in good health and should you need anything whatever that I can do, let me know: that I should not be found wanting to serve you with all my power, and I beg you to remember me and my children as always. My father, my mother and the *putti* send you a thousand greetings and I the same.

from Casteldurante the 13 of December 1557.

Your most loving daughter,

Cornelia Colonelli de Amatorij"

Of course I quieted her soul with my approval. What else could I do? She was my daughter. But as for copying those portraits, I had destroyed the sketches and how could I guarantee Venusti would get permission from the Duke to copy them?

The March before the portrait letter, Cornelia had written about sending the baby Michelangiolo to me. I replied that that was not a good idea: the baby was of too tender an age for such a journey and I have no women in my household to take care of him. Besides, I was thinking seriously then of accepting the Duke's offer of returning to Fiorenza so that I might die there; and if she wanted to send me Michelangiolo when I was back in my own patria I would raise him in Fiorenza with more love than for my nephew Lionardo's children and I would teach him that art which I knew his father wanted him to learn.

Such fantasies in my old brain!

The following December another letter arrived. Cornelia's second letter dealt with a gift more grave than that of portraits—the gift of herself.

It began:

Most Magnificent, best of fathers:

The loving kindness which Your Signory has always demonstrated to my children and to me has been such that it was greater by a longbow shot than that of my father, my mother, and any other of my kinsmen. Since, I know this in truth, I have always loved, obeyed and revered you as a father and as my most beloved patron, and I am always disposed to obey you, serve you, and follow your wishes; nor would I think of doing anything without first ascertaining your desires and obtaining your advice.

If Your signory may remember, recently I wrote telling you of my father's and mother's great desire that I remarry. And that among other suitors, they found especially to their liking a young man from Santagnolo in Vado, brother of the Abbot of that place. He pleased my father and mother more than all the others—always against my picture of things—and since I am always being admonished and advised to obey their wishes, I made up my mind as is proper for a most obedient daughter, to accede and do that which they ordered me to do; and so I consented to take as husband that one who so pleased them, no matter how contrary were my feelings.

And thus by my ill fate I've gotten stuck as is said, in a load of hay; and I've broken my neck to please my father; who has committed a greater error than any man has ever done, allowing himself to be convinced by people who have but little love towards him, my sisters, my nephews, and myself, to do that which he should never have thought of doing, let alone think of, letting himself be persuaded by the Abbot and the father of that one to whom I was supposed to become bride and wife.

Immediately after the dowry contracts were celebrated (which was done publicly, present all my sisters' husbands, and other relatives and close friends) my father, secretly, without my knowledge, and against all reason, only to gratify the Abbot, turned over to me all his possessions, thus depriving without any cause whatever, all his other daughers and grandchildren; and by this act, so lacking in honesty and so unreasonable, I was so afflicted and disturbed that now I find myself completely out of my wits; considering that my father should not have deprived his legitimate daughters, weighed down with sixteen children between males and females, and give to me, who already had received a much greater dowry than any other of my sisters, since I received a thousand florins for my dowry and my sisters only two hundred for each of them.

Having then made over this donation to me, Your Signory can well imagine how much harm this inflicted on my poor sisters who are also daughters of my father, as legitimate and natural as I am.

But God to whom fraud and deceit are displeasing did not wish that such iniquity be committed. Before my fiancé arrived, the matter of this 'donation' was revealed to my sisters and to myself, the which boundlessly displeasing me, and to let the world know that I was entirely innnocent of such traps and deceits, I tried by the best means I could, to undo this evil deed hoping to gain the consent of the groom's father and the Abbot; wishing to give back and reassign to my sisters everything that my father had given me, contenting myself, with my original dowry, and wishing, as is proper, that my sisters should have as much dowry as I have had.

But my fiancé's father and the Abbot lacking in that charity which Christians should have, didn't want to hear about it; rather they made, and they're still making, more fuss about things, possessions, than about my flesh; and I, with a more generous soul, have made, and I am still making firm proposals to take more account of my sisters and their husbands and children than of how much *roba* my father gave me; since I'm most certain that, acting otherwise, I will be perpetually in enmity with my sisters, their husbands and their children.

Whence I resolved with ready spirit to go again to my fiancé's father to whom with the utmost difficulty and effort I said what seemed reasonable to me, begging him to rest content with my first dowry, and not to be the cause of creating perpetual enmity between myself and my sisters, their husbands and children. From him I received no satisfaction whatever. Hence I sent my mother to the Abbot making the same proposal to him that I had made to my fiancé's father, and supplicating him in the same way. And he, similarly unreasonable, said that he would not agree to a retrocession and redonation; rather, turning to my mother, he claimed that if I was malcontent and dissatisfied with the gift and wasn't pleased with the way things were going, I should settle my own affairs and they would settle theirs.

Whence, since none of those people wanted to agree to my reasonable proposal, and furthermore since I'd heard some very evil and bad information about my fiancé, that he is full of the French Disease, very young and not very intelligent and certainly not very virtuous either and lacks many other qualities in his person, and possesses little, almost nothing; I've made it known publicly that I don't care to be his wife and I let his father know that he should mind his own business and I'll mind mine.

As a result, I now find myself very unhappy and so much the more so when I see my father displaying so little love toward his other daughters, and standing firm on his first idea that I take that one as a husband, uncaring of the laments and cries and upset that would cause his daughters, sons-in-law and grandchildren. And I cannot suffer all this nor will I ever be able to tolerate that so grave a harm and explicit wrong be done to them who are all very poor.

So that, Magnifico and most honored like a father, I find myself in all these travails and woes, as you understand, and I don't know how to get out of it thanks to my stubborn father who, even though he had been begged by many diverse good men nevertheless he refuses to admit that he acted wrong, and he will not repent of the wrong that he committed against his daughters. And if Your Signory does not help me with some loving letter, I am really really desperate. I don't know any order that would require that such a marriage take place, whether on account of the villany that was employed as well as the bad character of the intended groom; and also because these disagreements and turmoil have taken place between us, I am absolutely certain that I will never have an hour of peace. So that I'm determined that I don't want the marriage to take place. And in order that I might follow this sensible road, I beg you as much as I can that you help me and advise me that I might turn my father away from his hardness the which I am so far holding out against with equal stubbornness. But perhaps Your Signory might persuade him to drop this matter since he holds you in the greatest reverence and is most observant toward you. I rest in hope that Your Signory might give me some advice and persuade my father that he should not cause me such unhappiness, together with such grave harm to his other daughters, and let himself be considered by everyone as a cruel pitiless and one-sided man.

And if amidst all this, I can do something for you, command me as if I were your daughter for I am always ready to serve you and pardon me if I don't write more often because my head is filled with all these troubles that I don't know if I'm in this world. Michelangiolo sends his best wishes together with Francesco to Your Signory, you who are my father and my mother. I kiss your hand. Your Signory might deign to send my good wishes to Luisa and everybody.

> from Castel Durante, the 4th of October of 1558
>
> As a loving daughter,
>
> Cornelia Amatori da Collonello."

So I had become Cornelia's father in lieu of her own flesh-and-blood father. And her mother too! I wrote the best advice I could to her and to her father, seeking not to anger him by displacement, so to speak, for I can understand the clutch of family ties. Did I not feel that tie all my life toward my own father and toward my brothers?

At any rate, my intervention must have helped. For the following year Cornelia did in fact remarry with my blessing, but not to the young man with the French Disease. Her husband, Giulio Brunelli, was a well-to-do young man, a doctor of Law from Gubbio, and Podestà in Castel Durante. I was happy for Cornelia.

Somewhere along these same years—I can't remember whether it was before or after Carafa's death—another young woman crept into my heart and warmed these old bones. Metaphysically of course. I am no David.

Sofonisba Anguissola was a young woman from Cremona who had been sent down to Roma to perfect her art. She was that rarity—a female painter—and when this twenty-eight-year old girl, modest but not timid, her round pale face warmed by a ready smile, was introduced to me and I examined some of her drawings, I felt she was as talented as she was attractive. She frequented my studio quite often for the three years she remained in Roma, and not a few of the young men—Tiberio and Daniele—had their heads quite turned by her. Sofonisba's father wrote often to me concerning his daughter's progress in the art of painting and he expressed his profound gratitude that I had given his daughter Sofonisba a drawing which she might color in oil, as I had often done for Sebastiano and Daniele and so many others. And she painted it—a Pietà—most competently too. Observing the interwoven web that appeared between her knit brows when we spoke about the art of painting, my mind took flight back to my youth in Bologna where another young woman artist Properzia dei Rossi had held me in thrall. But Properzia was a sculptor and with her slender almost breastless figure and quick movements looked almost like one of my garzone though she was no boy. Oh, she had held me in thrall all the time I was working on the bronze Julius. And there were moments then when I doubted that my art was sufficient mistress, fearful as I was to lose myself in another. I was tempted oh I was tempted. But after I left Bologna I never saw her again. I am told she did some fine work for the facade of the Cathedral of San Petronio. When I knew Properzia she was running into difficulty with the overseers of San Petronio for the idea of a woman sculptor was as odd as the idea of a woman warrior. Yet she persisted and I recall a beautiful plaque of Joseph fleeing from Potiphar's wife and surely that was not intended for me but for another with whom she was enamoured.

No one considered it odd that Sofonisba should be a painter. Very unusual, yes, but not odd. She was dedicated and ambitious, her violet eyes thoughtful and attentive. Of me she besought judgements moral and aesthetic; of the young men—especially Daniele—in my studio, she asked only technical questions as if she were an apprentice in a bottega. She knew as much about the preparation of a panel or the laying of coats of gesso or the grinding of colors and the proper use of mastics as did any of them. She was especially interested in techniques of painting al fresco, although I could not see how she could ever hope to attain a commission in an art so physically difficult. Indeed, the likelihood was that she would gain commissions only in private circles. Whatever her purpose, she was a capable painter and a delightful girl. Her mere appearance brought a silly smile to Daniele's face, usually so melancholy. And I smiled too: her radiance summoned forth mine from its lurking Saturnian hiding place. She had a round full-moon face, lips like gulls in flight, wheat-colored hair and violet eyes. Her breasts promised to leap out of the bodice, and she spoke with the cantilena of Cremona.

Daniele's smile became sillier every day and he was walking sideways: he was tossing in the ocean of those eyes and that bosom. I was in the eighty-fourth year of my sojourn in this vale and so I could absorb the radiations of this deliciously-fleshed girl with no loss of equilibrium. I did in truth admire her art—quite apart from the warmth she brought into my life, and at a time when there was need for warmth: for the last year of the Carafa was even more bitter than his first.

One day when she showed me a charcoal drawing of a very young child laughing, I said I would like to see her do a child crying since that was much more difficult. A few days later she returned, and laughing (as it were by contrast) showed me the portrait of her little brother, crying.

It was so carefully studied that I asked her: "Did you make the boy cry in order to study it from life?"

"No," said Sofonisba. "I simply wanted to catch him in the act. He cries frequently. Too frequently. Usually this is annoying. But now I found it eminently satisfying."

It was in fact a fine drawing, very studied, a network of apt and revealing lines, a fluid freedom. She had to do it quickly, she unnecessarily explained.

"Yes, working from life, one must. At the same time one should learn to be free of the model. You will be free of it, Sofonisba. As I have long been. And yet the strangest rumors go around of my attachment to the real, my dependence on the model. It has come to my ears that I once stabbed a model to observe the sufferings of a crucified Christ."

"O Maestro, what a hideous notion!"

She clasped her hands together, her lower lip began to quiver and I was afraid that soon she would be crying like the weeping child of her drawing.

Tomao was present at this conversation and he was immensely impressed by Sofonisba's art. Subsequently he acquired that drawing for his collection, and two years ago, he sent it—together with one of my drawings of a Cleopatra—as a gift to the Grand Duke Cosimo (now he is a Grand Duke!).

Ahimè, Sofonisba did not remain long in Roma. Invited by the king of Spain, she is now Lady-in-Waiting to the Queen and, I have been advised, is making fabulous portraits for those Sovereigns, and is married, I imagine, to a Catalan.

It is indeed a Spanish century.

X

Tomao

The Old Man was never too happy about this Neapolitan Pope. He was, in truth, never too happy about any of them and yet circumstance has forced him to work in the service of the Papacy ever since he established permanent residence here in Roma thirty years ago. He admired Paul III for his qualities of a Maecenas but resented having been forced to make a patch-work solution of the Julius Tomb and set to frescoing the Last Judgement and the Pauline Chapel. He was embarrassed by Julius III's effusions of love (for him and for his monkey-keeper) but angered that funds destined for the new St. Peter's should have been deflected to the even newer Villa Giulia. The Cervini who had been the spokesman against him in the meeting of the Deputies of the Fabbrica didn't even have time to warm the Fisherman's throne, departing to a better life in twenty-two days. As for Pope Carafa, Paul IV, Michele resented the loss of his benefice on the crossing on the Po, and the suspension of all real work on the Basilica resulting from Vesuvius' continuous eruptions, mostly fire and smoke, but little lava against the House of Hapsburg, an endless provocation of tumults and alarums. And Michele feared this Holiness' crusade against the Spirituali among whom he counted himself. He was also dubious about the motives underlying the investigation of Cardinal Pole's orthodoxy by the Holy Office, fortunately concluded by Pole's death in England.

Certainly no one can say my Michelangiolo is anti-Christian. He is not even anti-clerical for he numbers many cardinals, prelates, and even the *popolo minuto* of the lesser clergy—monks and parish priests—among his most admired and loyal friends. No, he is simply anti-curial. He reserves his sharpest barbs for the corrupt curia of the Church at Roma: the discrepancy between the lives of the administrators of the Vatican and the teachings of Jesus Christ.

It is a discrepancy he finds ever less acceptable with the years. I think when first I met him he was more tolerant of curial misbehavior but now he feels the heresy of Lutheranism inevitably grows in that rank pit. Yet he is no Lutheran despite all the foolish gossip (and not only about Lutheranism) to that effect. Nor is my Michelangiolo's anti-curialism motivated by the philistine considerations of the Florentine merchants and bankers he frequents. No, his barbs are biblical, so much so as to evolve at times into a theological anticlericalism. He used to strike up biblical conversations with the crowd of Hebrews gaping at his Moses in San Pietro in Vincola. They gaped even more when they learned that the maker of the Moses was speaking to them! It was as if the incredibly bearded fierce Lawgiver himself were speaking. And Michele quoting from Isaiah or the Book of Job. He knows the Old Testament as well as Dante.

He continues to read his Bible in Italian even though the Council of Trent has placed that Nicolò Malermi edition on the Index of Forbidden Books. He is a great biblical exegete himself, and neither needs nor wants exegesis by Scholastics. "Besides, they're written in Latin." Several times I have heard him characterize the Roman curia as a 'bottega' or shop. And unlike the many artists and writers who had accepted (or striven for) clerical office—Sebastiano Luciani, Bramante, Rosso Fiorentino (in the guise of a canonico of Notre Dame in Paris), Ariosto (as a parish priest!)—Michelangiolo refused even to consider any such clerical office. When Francesco Primaticcio, the Bolognese painter to the King of France, once visited Michele with a commission to secure some work of Michelangiolo's for the King, we were surprised to learn that he had taken eccesiastical orders, becoming Abbot of S. Marino des Trois. "These pseudo-priests with a paint brush in their hands! The priestliness serves to get them commissions!"

He liked to say: "I prefer to preserve the hygiene of my conscience, hai capito, Tomao mio?"

But since he is at the same time an artist and sincerely religious— Christo-centric, religious in the sense of leaping over the very Church he is building to identify his own sufferings with those of Christ on the Cross—he often finds that the most seemingly innocent conversation with ecclesiastics will place him in a drama: how can he as artist reconcile his ideals expressed in fantasy and freedom within the logical net of dogmatic formulations?

How can he accept the Pope as vice-God surrounded by ecclesiastic courtesans?

Oh, Michele mio! You are extremely respectful of Papal office but not servile. Over the almost thirty years of our friendship I have rarely heard you say: *Our Lord* or the *Holiness of our Lord* or even *Holy Father*. Usually you simply refer to the Pope as Pope Paul or Pope Julius (distinguishing only in our private conversations between the 'greater' and the 'lesser'). I have never once heard you use the expression *Vicar of Christ*. Sometimes you say *His Holiness* but in such contexts as "His Holiness annoys me . . ."

When you were painting the Crucifixion of Saint Peter in the Pauline I asked whether such a subject had been assigned to you.

"No. I chose it myself."

"But isn't it more common to tandem the Conversion of Saul with the Granting of the Keys to St. Peter? Isn't that a symbol of authority?"

"Exactly."

"How, exactly?"

"You see, in this room (as well as in the Sistine) the new Popes are elected." I must have looked puzzled. You smiled.

"I prefer they be elected not under the sign of authority. The message here is different . . ."

And you refused to say further. But it was clear that your message was chastise-ment, a warning of martyrdom.

He is very Dantean, my Michelangiolo!

So he grumbles and makes sardonic remarks and returns to his lonely after-midnight colloquy with that skeletal Deposition which is rapidly disappearing the more he works at it. I think he is only truly happy then. Although I have never been privileged to be with him at those sessions I can sense the waves of happiness still radiant in his old drawn face when I arrive early some mornings to bring him some sweetmeats my wife Lavinia has prepared. He is surrounded by love: mine, my wife's, Daniele's, Tiberio's, that moon-faced girl painter Sofonisba who has recently gone to Spain. Talented, I must admit, draws better than I ever did. Fortunately I acquired several of her drawings before she left. Even that scamp Antonio conniving to wring more than two hundred scudi for the battered Nicodemus—even Antonio is devoted to the Old One and leaps at his most tremulous demand. And messer Bandini and messer Caro and the Cardinal de Carpi—oh the list of those who love him is far greater than he himself realizes, and sometimes—genus irritabilis—he misinterprets acts of love as he did with me briefly on one occasion and with poor messer Luigi too. Luckily they made it up before Luigi died.

I think we must notify his nephew. He is still on his feet (though no longer on his horse), he is still working on that skeletal Christ but it is a race: who will disappear first?

Yesterday afternoon, Daniele greeted me with: "Can you imagine, messer Tommaso? The Maestro has been working all day on the Deposition. He stopped only for a crust of bread and some wine. Been on his feet seven hours. See if you can persuade him to rest."

I went into the studio to find the Old One talking to the Christ. He was talking to Him, I say, between chopping out more of His substance. And humming a raucous parody of the music he had heard a few nights ago.

"—don't you think, Maestro?—"

"—Yes. Yes. Just a bit here. Amazing, you know, Tomao. I think I am beginning to learn how absence is as full of significance as presence . . ."

And chipping and circling the piece (from the side it was a longbow drawn) he was humming in that atrocious gruff singing voice of his (his speaking voice is baritone-melodic) his memories of the house concert my son Emilio had recently arranged with several of his friends: Palestrina, master of the Chapel of Santa Maria Maggiore, some beardless and ball-less Flemings with penetratingly white voices, the tinkle of lutes and the sweet poignant interweave of those voices and the Old One nodding and sleeping a little, suffused with joy at the concord of those sweet sounds. We all seek to shield him from the world's care. He is already very far away.

I think the very old withdraw from life even before life is withdrawn from them. It is a sort of antichamber to the Unknown.

Why do I say, Unknown? We all know that a place is already reserved for Michelangiolo in Paradise, very near the Lord.

Very near.

✳

XI

Michelangiolo

At the end of September six years ago Pope Paul IV and myself met for six days at San Silvestro Al Quirinale. Twenty years earlier, happy with love and poetry, I had come to this very place, bidden by the Lady Vittoria Colonna.

And this Pope, who hated even the memory of Vittoria, proposed among many absurd projects, that I destroy the garden where the Marchesa and myself had discussed art and theology.

The garden was already unrecognizable. A claustral wall had been erected by the friars to whom Paul IV had given the monastery. And how was I supposed to react to a proposal to build a triple staircase which would lead from San Silvestro to the Piazza San Marco?

It would have destroyed my house in Macel de' Corvi!

I refused to express my opinion. That ferocious old man prodded me and I refused to say anything meaningful. I can be master of circumlocutions too; I can play these games of feint and sideslipping although playing games with the Carafa is not easy. Oh, I missed del Monte's consoling arm around my shoulders (even his promise of embalming), or the Farnese's question-marked figure and ferret eyes, proposing and disposing (but these were the proposals of one who loved me, after all, though he did set me to painting for twelve years).

I was very cautious with Pope Carafa. I knew he was especially touchy these days because of the great scandal of his nephews. At the end of January 1559 in consistory before all the College of Cardinals, this bellicose pope, this man whose self-righteousness had fastened hoops of iron around all of Italia as a cooper fastens them around a barrel—this Pope had the courage, fanned by fanatism, to openly declare "the crimes of his nephews."

Annibale Caro was present as secretary to the Cardinal Farnese; the spectacle so moved him that he narrated it with no trace of his usual facetiousness. "As soon as the Holy Father appeared, we know from his appearance that something extraordinary had occurred. With passionate gestures he outlined in a long discourse scandalous matters which the Pope did not even dream existed. He was in a state of febrile excitation fulminating against their moral conduct, calling upon God as witness that he had suspected nothing about the evil lives of his relatives because from the beginning of his pontificacy he had had a veil in front of his eyes and had always been fooled; now however he wished to put his own house in good order."

Within twelve days all three nephews were to leave Roma, stripped of all their offices (although the Cardinal was left with his dignity as a Prince of the Church but this was only in name): in fact all three of them lost all their offices, benefices, and perquisites; and even before the twelve days had elapsed Carlo Carafa went into exile at Civita Lavinia, his brothers to Gallese and Montebello. Similarly there were sent out of Roma all their families, wives and children, even their mother old and in fact innocent. No defense was conceded to those accused of the gravest crimes; who never again saw their uncle.

"And at the end of the sitting which lasted two and a half hours," said messer Caro, unusually solemn, "the Pope said to the Cardinal Rannuccio Farnese that his father would not have been so ignominiously slain if Paul III had set a similar example of rigor toward his nephews. I must say I found this a singular example of the Holy Father's complacency and self-righteousness even in the midst of his penitence and woe."

And now that he had rid himself of these pernicious nephews, rotting away in the melancholy Campagna, the old uncle went back to his belovèd weekly meetings of the Holy Office (right near my own church of Santa Maria Sopra Minerva and there it was that I, seated alongside the naked Christ I had made for messer Vari and wondering how much longer in this epoch of shame my Christ would remain as naked and as pure as I had made him, when the Tuscan ambassador asked me for my opinion.

"About what, Eccellenza?"

"The Holy Father's new building plans for the triple Staircase?"

"I must consider them further."

I expected liberation by death. That has been my prevailing mood for many years now. Whatever problem arises—and they arise in myriads—I expect to be liberated from it by Death.

·❊·

The downfall of his nephews seemed to fill the old Pope with new vitality. In fact, "the year of 1559," said he, "should be considered the first of my Pontificacy."

He was eighty-two years old, two years younger than I.

Now he set about tightening all the reins of power. (I learned of all the new decrees through Caro and Giannotti, both in the service of Cardinals.) All complains had to come directly to him. He prepared a special book of his nephews' misdeeds. The Borgia apartment was kept locked. He intended to rebless the place with holy water because malevolent spirits had dwelt there!

But that was Roma after Paul's dramatic act against his nephews. If he had been rigorous before now he was trebly so. Fasting was more familiar than feasting and there was more lamentation than laughter. Poor messer Annibale! his lips were locked in public. He joked only behind closed doors. My doors were frequently closed. I didn't venture often into the Borgo. I am no friend to corruption, God knows, but furibond righteousness is best admired from afar. I had absented myself from my Fiorenza during the rule of Fra Girolamo and I would have absented myself now if I could. I thought of accepting the Duke's invitation. Edicts were being issued against Jews, whores, usurers, and comedians. Carnival masks were forbidden for hadn't the Pope's nephews fooled him long enough with their masks? The Bishop of Polignono was sentenced to life for concubinage, one third of each year his only sustenance was to be bread and water alone. A French count who had been arrested on a charge of political treachery wound up before the Inquisition because he had had a Jewess as a lover. Theology was creeping into everyone's bed. Women were not allowed to set foot in the Vatican. Scandalous images were banned: for instance, any life-sized crucifix with only four wounds. Rapists pimps sodomites whosoever uttered blasphemies, and whosoever failed to observe fasts— all of these were handed over to the Inquisition. And although the old Pope skipped many of his consistories and audiences, he never failed to attend the Thursday meeting of the Inquisition. This Holy Office he set above all other offices in Roma.

It is no wonder that I expected every day to hear that the Pope had given orders to carry out his old threat of purging my Judgement of its 'indecencies', or more likely, whitewashing the entire wall.

But then on the 18th of August 1559 he was dead of idropisia.

I suppose I should have felt a certain sense of gratification inasmuch as one of the moribund Pope's last wishes was that work on the Fabbrica of St. Peter be carried on.

His other wish was that the work of the Inquisition be carried on.

Before the Holy Father had actually died, he was already considered dead. The Roman mob could not wait. Nor were they satisfied with the traditional release of prisoners held in the communal prison. Off they ran hooting to the Palace of the Inquisition on the Ripetta, setting free the prisoners, maltreating the officials, burning the legal books of accusations and confiscations, and finally setting fire to the building.

The Romans hated the Carafa Pontiff because of the sufferings they had undergone during the war against the Spaniards and the misgovernment of the despised nephews.

The Eternal City was in turmoil, armed bands running here and there, the roar of the infuriated citizenry, the hacking off of armorial shields and bearings of the Carafa from public buildings, the lootings and burnings.

I scarcely stirred from my studio.

Even had not the precarious state of my health kept me home, I would not have ventured into the streets. To the mobs I would have been a creature of the late detested Pope and they would have visited their wrath on me. That I have never been a creature of any Pope though I have worked for seven various Vicars of Christ in my long lifetime, that I have never been a creature of any man—how could one explain that to the infuriated plebe? I have been fed and clothed by Popes, I have moved in Vatican circles as in my own house, I have been listed among the familiars of every Pontiff since Paul III, I have been awarded benefices and honors from the hands of the successor of St. Peter . . . how could I convince anyone, let alone the simple man of the streets, that I was not a creature of His Holiness, whatever Holiness there happens to be?

So while the slaughter roared redly in the streets of Roma, I kept within the walls of my studio on the Street of the Slaughterhouse of the Crows. I laughed with the skull on my staircase. I jested with messer Tomao. I reorganized sheafs and sheafs of my drawings and threw many of them into the fire. Some were unsatisfactory. Others unspeakable. For my eyes alone. I had made them to relieve a pressure in my soul and in my groin. But now I was long past concern for my groin. All my hopes—and all my fears—are centered upon Death. That double Death. There is what I fear. I try not to fear. For fear itself is sin. Fear bespeaks lack of faith and surely I do not lack faith. But the double Death? The Death after Death?

The day following Carafa's death, messer Tomao was up at the Campidoglio in his capacity as Conservatore entrusted with the realization of my project. "Suddenly a mob irrupted into the capital hill, roaring up the steps like a pack of wolves. In fact the wolf in the adjacent cage was howling that he could not join his two-legged fellows. They had rushed there the day before, as soon as news of the Pope's death was made known, and mutilated the marble statue of Paul IV erected there. When I arrived there were already chunks in the statue, an arm had been hacked off, Now they jeered and howled to complete the demolition, spitting at it and dancing round and round like bacchantes. Suddenly a Hebrew climbed up and set his yellow cap upon Paul's head to the delighted acclamation of the mob. Then they attached a rope around its neck and pulled it down and hammered at it with staves and shovels and pikes and finally kicked and slid and rolled it down the long flight of stairs to the bottom where it was attached to a cart and dragged through the streets and finally cast into the Tiber."

Poor Tomao! He seemed shocked. He had served on the committee which estimated the cost and evaluated the artistic merits of that very statue whose destruction he had just witnessed! Tomao's relationship to the Carafa was not unlike my relationship to the Medici: he may not have loved them but they honored him and favored him. The Cardinal Carlo Carafa, now exiled by his uncle, was the protector of the Confraternity of the Most Holy Crucifix of San Marcello where Cavalieri was a very active member of the building committee. So now he was sweating yes and no toward a ruling family, a not uncommon state with which I was familiar.

His story of the destruction of Paul's statue brought back memories of another destruction of a statue. Nor had I myself witnessed that one. But that Hebrew physician Andrea del Medigo had written to me from Bologna—when was it? O Time is such a jumble to me now: the day before yesterday and the decades before yesterday all jumbled together in my head. Yes, it was when I—mere man—was creating God creating the Sun and Moon, having arrived at the Beginning which was my end of the flat of the vault in the Sistine. Just then arrived that long letter from Maestro Andrea of the Long Robe describing the tearing down and destruction of my bronze Julius II on the facade of San Petronio. And the mob in Bologna had behaved like this mob Tomao saw: they lowered my Julius off the niche, and chopped off his head and hacked at the prone Pope with battle axes and danced around it by fires all night. And later it was melted down to make a cannon called La Giulia and the head set upon the breech. The same blood-lanced jeering, the same chopping off of heads, the same bacchanal around the prone body of the statue, knocked in more than one sense off its pedestal.

These are my countrymen.

So now by decree of the Roman People all ornamental escutcheons and armorial bearings and inscriptions "of the tyrannical house of Carafa" were ordered to be hacked off the palaces. I didn't venture out of my studio much during those riotous days. Tomao, however, wandered all over the City as my emissary and brought me back reports that Pasquino, as I could well imagine, was simply in a froth. Tomao copied an epitaph:

> Carafa, in odio al diavolo e al cielo, è qui sepolto
> Col putrido cadavere; lo spirto Erebo ha accolto.
> Odiò la pace in terra, la prece ci contese,
> ruino la chiesa e il popolo, uomini e cielo offese;
> infido amico, supplice ver l'oste a lui nefasta.
> Di più vuoi tu saperne? Fu papa e tanto basta.

> Here lies Carafa, by devil and by heaven hated.
> Here's his putrid cadaver, by Erebus taken.
> He hated peace on earth, denied prayer,
> ruined Church and People, mankind and heaven offended,
> a treacherous friend imploring an ill-omened Host.
> What more do you want to know? He was Pope. That tells you all.

Indeed for fear of excesses by the populace, the corpse was deposited in the deepest vault possible under San Pietro and a perpetual guard assigned there. And now when I think back upon the tumultuous career of this Pope, it seems to me he was a genuine Meridionale—one of those folk in whom thoughts immediately become words; there is no sluice gate of caution such as you see in the eyes and lips of Florentines. Whatever impulse seized that man, instantly poured forth in a froth of words, a storm of expressions and gestures, his furry eyebrows flying like swallows, his hands and arms windmilling. And soon enough—too soon—these burst into actions. All this flowed from that Vesuvius of a Pope like the hot breath of melting lava. Precipitous beyond bearing, that Neapolitan. Expressions poured from his mouth that were not to be believed. His choleric temperament inclined him ever to push things to extremes.

For several weeks the savage expression of popular ire reached its culmination. I didn't venture beyond the Trajan Column, taking my afternoon ride in company with Antonio around the vicinity of the Forum. The fragments of the statue of the fastidious Cato lay at the bottom of the Tiber, his escutcheons destroyed, the devastated prisons of the Inquisition were empty. The Colonna who had been declared rebels, reappeared in the city and were greeted with joy by the Roman people. The Cardinal Morone was liberated from prison. The Duke of Paliano, Giovanni Carafa, confessed that he had killed with his own hand with twenty-seven blows of a stiletto a would-be lover of his wife. Not long after, the unhappy wife followed her pretended seducer to death: she was strangled by her own brother and by another relative, notwithstanding her pregnancy. In this family tragedy the Roman people saw the further judgement of God against the Carafa.

So until the new Pope was chosen the Eternal City was in a turmoil, armed bands running here and there, a perpetual guard dispatched to the Campidoglio which had become the favorite spot of those who wished to make incendiary orations against the defunct Pope's family.

I don't remember when there was so much rejoicing at the death of a Pope. Not even when the Flemish Adrian, enemy of art and all things Italian, blessedly relinquished the Fisherman's Throne after less than two years of foreign occupation of it. But now with the death of Carafa there was an air of savage carnival. His statue on the Campidoglio had been interpreted by the indignant Romans as an act of supreme vanity, a Vicar of Christ setting himself up on the same hill with Marcus Aurellius!

·⁕·

The new Pope's pontificate began propitiously. The very morning of his election I awoke to find my ancient member erect as Trajan's Column!

O the tricks of the flesh! Even when the flesh hangs in tatters over a tottering skeleton! Here I was eighty-four years old and that part of us which obeys its own commands was hot and red and yearning as if I were a boy. I should have been thinking exclusively of Death and most of the time I did. But even in the midst of such thinking I was aware of the green singing of the laurels, the crisp incised hemicycle of the ancient stones of the Mercato Traiano, the elegant swift signatures of swallows, the curve of Antonio's calf.

My erection, unlike Trajan's didn't last but a few moments, but they were moments of pride (unmerited) and more than that, astonishment. The flesh has its own life, you see, I have always guarded against it. I do not trust Otherness, I do not trust Others. The chisel, the brush, the pilot wheel, must always be in my hand. I can still see the hurt consternation of that Florentine brigade when I locked the door of the Sistine against them and chopped out what they had done, and set about painting the entire ceiling by myself. I can still see the forge-red explosive expressions of the Building Committee as they complained to Pope Julius III about my 'secrecy'. It is no use. I cannot work with others. I cannot entrust my soul to anyone. I distrust the flesh because he steers by his own rudder. I trust no one except myself.

And Il Signore.

So Paul was gone to be succeeded five years ago, by Pius, fourth of that name, and of the House of the Lombard Medici and he is still the Holy Father as I carve here in the dark night of this year, dating from our Salvation 1564 and I am on the brink of my ninetieth year and the Christ and his Mother diminished every day I set my chisel to them and soon I shall be carving but a sliver of the marble column I started with ten years before as I myself am but a sliver of the flesh that entered this world nine decades ago in a hilltown outside of my Fiorenza and soon I shall be pure spirit sooner than this statue shall be pure idea.

The Cardinal Gian Angelo de' Medici was elected Pope after a conclave of three and a half months. These Milanese Medici are in no way related to our Medici. Not by blood, that is. But since his election had been sponsored by the Duke of Fiorenza, Cosimo de' Medici, and crowned with success by reason of the adroit maneuvering of Cosimo during the conclave, one might say that this Milanese Medici was a Florentine Medici by adoption.

So it is not surprising that I was wary.

The new Pope who took the name of Pius IV was as cold as Carafa had been hot, alien from all extremes as the Neapolitan had been nothing but extremes. Winter followed summer. There was no autumn.

But soon, to my delight, Pope Pius revealed that he wished to be taken for a genuine Medici, that is, in his zeal to carry on all the artistic projects which had been in suspension during the pontificate of his predecessor, as a result of the war with Spain, financial penury, inquisitional emphasis on ecclesiastical reform.

For not only did Pius reconfirm me in my long-standing post as architect of the Basilica but he also restored part of that income which Carafa had taken away from me. And, more important, this cold and canny man proved as loyal to me against my enemies as the Papa Hilaritas; and if he did not put his arm around my ancient creaking shoulders, he did parry and thrust against that cabal, headed by Nanni, who never rested in their maneuvers to have me removed from the Fabbrica. And so well had they maneuvered at the beginning of Pius' Pontificate that even so true a friend as Cardinal Carpi, of the Building Committee, began to believe that I was too old and feeble-minded to carry on my duties.

When this came to my ears, I wrote a long letter to the Cardinal, expressing my surprise that even he should have lent faith to this poisonous gossip. "Messer Francesco Bandini" I wrote, "told me yesterday that Your Most Illustrious and

Most Reverent Lordship told him that the Fabbrica of St. Peter's couldn't be going worse than it is going. Now that truly grieves me because you have not been advised of the truth, and that is that I—as indeed I must—desire more than any other man that the works should proceed well. And I believe, if I am not being fooled that I can truthfully assure you that to the degree that work is now going on, it could not possibly go better. But since perhaps my own interest and my old age might easily deceive me, and thus against my own intention, cause harm and damage to the aforesaid Fabbrica; I intend as soon as I can to send in my resignation to the Holiness of our Lord; indeed, to save time, I wish to beg of Your Most Illustrious and Most Reverend Lordship, as I hereby do, that you be pleased to free me from this burden, on which at the orders of various Popes, as you know, I have worked willingly and gratis for already seventeen years. In which time one can plainly see how much has been accomplished in the said Fabbrica. I repeat, therefore, my supplication to give me leave, that for once cannot but afford me the greatest happiness. And with all reverence, I humbly kiss the hand of your Most Illustrious and Most Reverend Lordship . . ."

But Pius IV had no intention whatever of permitting me to resign. Instead he gave me a gift of two hundred golden scudi; and amidst all his other ambitious construction projects, preferred my plans over all others for the Baths of Diocletian. I provided copious sketches for his plans to restore the gates of Roma which he desired both for reasons of fortifications and aesthetics. Between the ancient Porta Nomentana and Porta Salaria, we (that is, His Holiness and I) envisaged a new Gate to be named Porta Pia, after the Pope. I chose as my foreman of the works Pier Luigi Gaetta, who had also served me in the Fabbrica. This was a year or so before Pier Luigi found himself in prison because of that matter of six ducats out of circulation.

I was present at the ceremony of the laying of the cornerstone of the Gate. And during the digging of the foundation I was still riding then every day from my house halfway across Roma to the Porta Pia site or to the Fabbrica of St. Peter's. Only three years ago! But now I can no longer ride and that is a premonition. I am being tapped by a bony finger. I spend days sitting by the hearth staring into the fire. It's a cold February. The wind howls round Santa Maria di Loreto and sets the bells tinkling. There are all sorts of unecclesiastical hours being rung. I wrap my cloak tighter. The flames design living tongues, beautiful and hot.

That very same year when the cornerstone of the new Gate was laid by the Pope himself, I was asked to submit plans for the transformation of the Baths of Diocletian into a Christian church.

Now the odd thing was that this Pope, for all the coldness in his manner and the unemotional canniness of his jurisdiction of the Church, kept a brilliant court and scandalized even the Romans with his dissolute private life.

And so now, fittingly enough, and as a kind of spiritual reprisal, this Holy Father who had turned St. Peter's into a Roman bath, now wanted me to transform a Roman bath into a Christian church. There is a divine balance in nature; a moral equilibrium sets all things aright.

Diocletian had been the most terrible persecutor of the Christians, thousands of whom had worked in forced labor on these very Terme. Thus the Pope thought by this architectural metamorphosis to proclaim the Nazarene victor over the pagan Emperor. My project envisaged the transformation of the *tepidarium* of the ancient baths into the grandiose nave of the new Church which was to be called St. Mary of the Angels after a chapel by that name already existing in the ruins. The ruins house a number of other activities none of which can be called angelic. Transforming a *tepidarium* into a Christian church seemed not inappropriate. The hotter the external show the more tepid is inner faith. And I delighted in the eight colossal red sienite ancient columns which still stood in the *tepidarium*.

So I agreed to do this as I had agreed to design the new Gate. I also drew up a design for the Capella Sforza in Santa Maria Maggiore. My opinions have come to be regarded as oracles. O if only all these petitioners—from Queen Caterina de' Medici of France who wants me to design an equestrian monument for her late husband Henry II, to every Princeling in Italy who wants a salt cellar by my hand—if only they knew how doubtful was this 'oracle', how the public face is to the private as a steel visor is to the vulnerable and pitiable flesh.

Of course I will never see the completion of any of these projects. For all Pius' inciting me to new bursts of activity in the Campidoglio, in the new gates of Roma, in St. Peter's, I shall not live to see what is effectuated in St. Peter's, I shall not live to see what is effectuated in my name. The Dome I have conceived shall float only in the sky of my imagination. We run that risk, we artists whose imaginings are too huge for one lifetime; I dread to think of the monstrosities, distortions, and abortions that shall be shown to the world under the name of Michelangiolo Buonarroti.

·✻·

Notwithstanding all these signs of manifest favor of the Pope, hostilities toward my person did not cease. And as always, the prime mover against me was Nanni Bigio who used every means possible to have himself replace me as architect of St. Peter's; he even went so far as to write to Duke Cosimo, thinking in his madness that the Duke would use his influence in the curia in Nanni's favor. The Duke had the good grace to reply that he would never lend his aid to such purpose so long as I was alive for that would be an offence against my merits and against the love he bore me. All this I learned from my nephew Lionardo, and from Tiberio Calcagni who was in constant touch with Lionardo. But I was not surprised. For all my ancient emnity against the Medici has long subsided and we are now on the best of terms. My only enmity now—or indifference—is with the fables of this world from which, every day I am preparing to depart, and several times these past few years I was sure the moment had come. When I cannot sit my horse or mule, when I cannot stand up on my tottering legs, when there is a rush of blood to my head and darkness before my eyes. Yet astonishingly the departure somehow is still postponed.

As for the Duke, my confidence in his friendship had finally been confirmed on the occasion of a state visit to Roma which he made together with his beautiful Spanish wife Eleanora of Toledo, a year after Pius' election. He had come of course to make a state visit to the Holy Father of his choice, to pay obeisance to a Pope who would never have achieved the Fisherman's Throne without Cosimo's support in the conclave. This game of diplomacy is as full of windings as a summer snake. With what joy I take refuge from these false bowings and measured words that weigh up to what they are not and must frequently be read backward as in a mirror: all these interests covered by waving plumes, all these daggers in the sheaths of smiles! I take happy refuge, I say, from all this in my art: those long hours of silent, if agonized, colloquy with forms: the choice and shaping of them, the endless search to make them conform with some concetto in my mind of which I am never certain. But if I cannot precisely define it, I know when my statue or my painting has not achieved it. I know it by a prickle in the hairs of my neck, an angry rising of the hackles. I am an old dog ready to fight any monster of my imagining.

Cosimo's visit occurred just about the time when the wooden model of the cupola was being completed. The young Duke arrived—he was still young in my eyes although he had already reigned over our Fiorenza for twenty-three years— and to my surprise, he and his Duchess made a formal visit to see me, immediately after they had kissed the hand of Cosimo's Pope.

In that noble company swarming into my poor dwelling on the Street of the Slaughtered Crows, was of course my old friend, Giorgio Vasari, trumpeter of the Duke's name, and his ambassador extraordinary in the world of the arts. Giorgio has been writing steadily to me for many years, and I must say his letters are always a delight, no matter what may be my reservations about his art.

Giorgio had visited me earlier this same year when he acompanied the Duke's son Giovanni who came to take his red cap as a Cardinal; the Duke also wanted my counsel on the whirlwind of Vasarian projects up in Fiorenza: he showed me wooden models and drawings of new rooms in the Ducal Palace and I persuaded him to lift the roof of the grand *scala* of the Palace of the Priors thirteen braccia to permit more light.

So here he was again, his face redder above a bushier beard, the mill-race of words frothier than ever, ushering into my presence the Duke whom I had never seen, master of my patria, and foe of all my Florentine friends in Roma. But now at last the exiles realized what I had realized long ago: the Duke was solidly in the saddle and all hopes of unseating him were futile. This hard-faced man in his middle forties with his beard cropped almost like mine, but more bristling and military, this Medici whose hard bullet-gray eyes and sword-blade lips (so obviously the son of the mercenary soldier Giovanni della Bande Nere), elegant in ceremonial armor (I wondered whether that mad Cellini had designed those handsome grotesque gold arabesques on the breastplates)—Cosimo was now graciously bowing to *me* and I feared for a moment he was about to kiss my hand as if I myself were a Pope! The Duchess was lovely in her darkgreen velvet gown and puffed sleeves. She was gracious and seemed younger than her years. It was hard to believe that she had a son already created Cardinal—although Cardinals have not infrequently achieved that eminence with almost startling precocity. Had not this very Duke's distant relative Pope Leo X been made Cardinal at sixteen?

I must say the Duke was most gracious. He spoke to me man to man as if there were no difference in our rank; he discussed (with frequent interventions from Vasari his artist-in-residence) the various projects of architecture and painting and sculpture he already had underway in Fiorenza (Giorgio and a team were painting a Last Judgement inside the Cupola; Giorgio and a team were filling the Palazzo of the Signory with allegories meterological and mythical all glorifying the House of Medici; Giorgio and a team were covering the ceiling of the Sala del Cinquecento with further gilded trumpetings to the Medici; Giorgio and a team were designing or redesigning a new structure of Offices next to the Palazzo of the Signory) and could I—would I?—be kind enough to serve as Giorgio's consultant in all these matters? Might they send me models for my incomparable advice?

And so on.

There were no explicit reminders of the Duke's standing invitation that I come home to Fiorenza, to be honored there with all the honors due me, and buried next to my father in my native soil. Nothing was said but it was in the air; it was in the Florentine cadences and the Florentine faces and I almost said it myself for I am swollen with a great homesickness and have been longing to return and yet I cannot abandon St. Peter's to my enemies.

For soon after the departure of the Duke the situation reached a crisis. Because of the precarious state of my health, I could not visit the works very often, and I depended more and more on the superintendent I had chosen; another Marchigiano with whom I seemed fated to be involved. This fellow—lively, faithful, dependable—was called Cesare and like my faithful Urbino, (whose absence grows thicker every day and about whom I cannot think without tears coming to my eyes) came also from Castel Durante. Well, my faithful Cesare was discovered with the wife of the cook of Monsignor of Forli; the cook himself discovered both of them in bed, and with a kitchen knife he carved them both into a pretty dish: Cesare was stabbed fourteen times and the wife four. So my superintendent departed the pleasures of this world, and I was forced to select his successor at St. Peter's. And I chose Pier Luigi Gaeta because he had served me well on the new Porta Pia and was always grateful (and amusing) that I had managed to extricate him from prison on that matter of the ancient coins.

But the Deputies refused to accord with my choice; they chose instead as superintendent a certain Berto da Fiesole and furthermore they complained to the Pope that everything was going wrong with the Fabbrica because of my workmen. Now I never heard of Berto da Fiesole and if the workmen were making errors that was because they had been hired by Nanni di Baccio Bigio. I knew who was behind this entire thing. So I held firm in my choice of Pier Luigi, and furious at this invasion of my rights, I shouted angrily in the presence of Tomao and Tiberio and Daniele and Antonio my servant and I don't remember who else that if my selection as superintendent was not honored I was going to resign from the works of the Basilica.

Well, that was all my enemies had to hear. Now they felt was the propitious time to substitute Nanni in my place inasmuch as the Old Man, so the rumor went, (and since all Roma is a Cloaca Maxima of rumors swirling round and round so eventually one hears them all. I even know that for the past decade my name is not Michelangiolo but Il Vecchio—the Old Man—or at best Il Buon Vecchio—the good Old Man) since the Old Man has already served notice that he is leaving, obviously because he is not up to handling the heavy duties of the Fabbrica, now is the time to nominate Nanni Bigio in his place.

Well, when this came to my ears, my fury knew no bounds. I charged Daniele da Volterra to charify my attitude to the Bishop Baldo Ferratini who was very influential in the Committee for the Fabbrica.

Daniele returned so lugubrious and so choked up that I had difficulty getting the fellow to open his mouth. No one wants to perform an ungrateful embassy; innocent bearers of bad tidings are frequently clubbed!

"Well, speak up, ragazzo! What did the Bishop say?"

"He said . . . he said . . . O Maestro, it's unspeakable!"

"Speak it anyway."

"Well, it seems the Deputies complain that you don't reveal your building plans to anybody, not even to the Building Commission, and so it's time to nominate a substitute. And then—and then—"

"And then what?"

"And then—the Bishop asked me would I be disposed to serve as superintendent!"

"And what did you reply?"

"I replied that the choice was entirely up to you, Maestro."

So at Tomao's advice—in order not to provoke further conflict with the Deputies, I let it be known that I would accept Daniele as my superintendent in place of Pier Luigi. But meanwhile the Bishop had met with the Committee and proposed not Volterra but Nanni Bigio, and the proof of that was that the Commission declared for Bigio without questioning me at all, and that scoundrel, believing himself finally in charge, immediately set about giving new orders for the Fabbrica, acting as if he considered himself absolute master.

Well, I was in a terrible state. "What shall I do, Tomao? What shall I do?"

"See His Holiness!

"His Holiness! His Holiness has already degraded my office in the Papal household, placing me on the level of the coachmen and the fowlers."

Tomao closed his huge beautiful violet eyes as if in pain. The eyes of that young man I knew thirty years ago are unchanged; incongruously brilliant, youthful they shine forth the twenty-year-old Cavalieri in the drawn bearded face of this old man. He was always soft-spoken, Tomao, but as a Prior of his Confraternity and as a diplomat (he gave away to Cosimo the drawing of a Cleopatra I had made for him!), he speaks sometimes in a whisper especially when he is seeking to mitigate my rage. At those moments I feel younger than he.

"Speak to His Holiness. I assure you he loves you and will guard you against all outrage."

So several days later Tomao accompanied me up to the Campidoglio where the Pope was holding court for a week. Tomao had known this in advance; he knew everything that related to the Campidoglio; he had already seen the preparations for the Pope's sojourn there as soon as he returned from Tivoli; and the Holy Father had promised him that actual work on my project for the reorganization of the Capital would soon get under way. I didn't lend any faith to this, but Tomao did.

The setting was an incongruous mix of Papal splendor and Caesarian wreckage. In the gentle warmth of a June afternoon, the Papal throne had been erected in the open, a few steps away from Marcus Aurelius glinting goldenly on his horse. Christian Pope and Pagan Emperor side by side. Halberds crossed, Swiss guards in their brilliant blue and orange puffed trousers and sleeves, stood guard at the top of the long flight of steps leading to Ara Coeli. There were seats placed for audience, and a plenitude of prelates and their secretaries moving about in front of the wrecked Senate house and Palace of the Conservators. From below, in the Forum, came the mooing of cattle. Swarms of swallows flew dense variable cryptograms against an azure sky behind the white bones of dead antiquities.

It was a day for jubilation, one of those Roman days in June that spreads gladness through one's soul as the linden trees in June permeate with perfume every street of our Fiorenza.

But I was not jubilant. My shouting could be heard all over the Campidoglio. I am almost ninety years old and I don't mind shouting at a Pope. This was only eight months ago. I complained of the selection of a superintendent whom I didn't know. I spat out the name Nanni more than once and with such vehemence that the swallows broke their cryptic circling and sped away to the Palatine. The Swiss guards looked pastier-faced than always. My friend Tomao hung his head in shame at my shouting, ". . . And since obviously the Deputies consider me senile and incapable of the task, I beg your Holiness leave to return to rest in my own city of Fiorenza where the Duke may enjoy whatever talents I still possess and which he has always so desired of me, and I will end my life in my own house; and therefore, I ask your Holiness permission to leave! . . ."

And by this time there was a scurry-ring of prelates listening listening but at a safe distance from my shouting; and the Pope's severe countenance was adamant but he actually reached over and touched me gently (and it was as if Marcus Aurelius had stooped from his bronzen mount). And in order that there be no public scandal, he stepped off his throne and invited me, grumbling still, into his private chambers in the adjacent Palace of the Conservators; there he spoke kind and gentle words inviting me to a more serene colloquy with him. That day began a new relationship between us.

"Be calm, Maestro!" he said, "Do nothing in haste. Come back here after a few days, when I have had some time to investigate the situation. Thursday, Thurs— no, Monday. Come here Monday again. Meanwhile I will convene the Deputies and we will settle the entire matter then."

So the following Monday once again I rode my shuffling easy mule down Macellum Corvorum to the foot of the Campidoglio and dismounted, and for all my years and painful back climbed the long staircase and met the Pope and all the Deputies of the Building Committee in the Palace near Ara Coeli. And I knew at once from the daggers of their eyes that I had won the play. The Holy Father had dispatched his kinsman Gabrio Serbelloni to make a full investigation and Serbelloni (who chaired the meeting) reported that Nanni Bigio must retire from his post. So his brief reign as Superintendent lasted less than a month, but the humiliation of it still rankles me. For though Nanni was removed; so in a sense was I—the Pope himself named in effect as my substitute the architect Francesco da Cortona—although in name I am still the architect of the Basilica.

But I no longer ride there.

I no longer ride anywhere.

I await the horse of the Apocalypse.

❄

Ars Morendi.

I am trying to learn how to die. During his final illness, Urbino, blessèd Urbino, was teaching me the Art of Dying. But I have never really learned. I am still struggling against it, still hammering away in the night, still capable of being stirred by love and hatred, satisfaction and invitation, pride and shame.

When the Duke called on me instead of waiting for me to call on him, I felt a glow of pride and yet I know that pride is a sin. Not too long after I received another loving licking letter from Vasari advising me that the Duke's son Don Francesco was coming to Roma and would be lodged at the Belvedere of the Vatican; Giorgio not undiplomatically suggested that if I were capable of it, I should visit Don Francesco "so that he should not be obliged to come to see you." Obviously Giorgio now is quite engaged in a profession other than the visual arts.

So I mounted my old mule—I find the mule less tempestuous for my aching antique bones—and called on the young man who remained standing with his berretta in hand until I bade him sit down and he hazarded some few remarks so timidly and tenderly that I felt sorry to be unable to make something of my own for him, and so I besought Tomao to find some beautiful bit of antiquity that I might dispatch as a gift to the young man in Fiorenza.

After Don Francesco's departure I found myself chuckling for days at the memory of this princeling nervous in my presence, his blushing girlish complexion and prognathic Medici chin—they are not a handsome tribe.

And again—as at his father's visit—I experienced the warm flush of pride—again—at the very brink!

The sickness of the stone makes it impossible for me to sleep, day or night. So when I am not working on the Deposition I have been drawing, mostly figures of Christ Crucified. I've been using black chalk. I like the cloudiness of the figures, as if you saw them through fog (I see everything through fog) the vagueness of the line, partly because the chalk is soft and crumbles, partly because my hand trembles! For the first time in nine decades my hand now trembles. The calligraphy of my letters (I write very few) now wavers like lines of crooked vines or knotted olive trees staggering downhill.

Notwithstanding the deterioration of this drawing instrument, my Hand, the Pope asked me to prepare some designs for the sepulcher of Iacopo de' Medici, Marchese of Marignano, his brother. They were executed in the Duomo of Milano by the Cavalier Leone Lioni, an Aretine, and apparently it all turned out so much to His Holiness' satisfaction (I never saw it, of course) that Lioni made a medallion in my honor. On one side was my portrait in profile, a good likeness, I must say, although portraiture is not exactly my profession. On the other side he had made a composition after a drawing I had sent him: a blind old man resembling me somewhat, with his dog, groping his way through life. The inscription I wanted came from Psalm 51:13 (which I was still reading in the Italian version, despite the injunction of the Council) but Lioni of course inscribed it in Latin:

DOCEBO INIQUOS VIAS TUAS, ET IMPII AD
TE CONVERTENTUR

I WILL TEACH TRANSGRESSORS THY WAYS
AND SINNERS SHALL BE CONVERTED UNTO THEE

The good fellow sent me four copies of this medallion: two in silver and two in bronze. The silver one, most finely chased, I was to keep "for my love," the others he wanted me to send out as I saw fit. So I sent the other silver one to the Pope, imagining that he might interpret the Psalm to his benefit.

☆

I know that my end is nigh, the end I have so long expected and longed for. But if my body is feeble, I don't like those rumors declaring my mind is feeble as well; and when I recently received a letter from my nephew which seemed to lend credence to such rumors, I dictated an angry reply via Daniele, advising Lionardo not to listen to thieves and liars who are just a pack of scoundrels. And I told him not to worry about how I am tiding and who is taking care of my house, because I couldn't be taken care of better, or more faithfully; and that he needn't fear I'm being robbed because I place complete trust in my servants and friends who are always with me. "Therefore," said I (and I suppose my voice took on an edge because Daniele lifted his eyes as his quill scratched away and a faint smile appeared on his lips) "try to live worthily and don't worry about my affairs, because I know how to take care of myself if I have to, and I'm not an infant. Be well."

That was August, I think; a hot, dry, cricket-chirping month; then the larches lost their leaves, the swallows departed, the winter winds began to blow. Now in rainy February there are few fine days when I can ride a bit as is my wont just before sunset if only around the Forum.

I can't sleep. Can't sleep at all.

The closer I come to the final sleep the less I can sleep here.

So I arise after an hour or so of tossing and seeing my life unroll on the black scroll of insomnia, and shuffle off to my studio as I have done this very night, and chip away here and chip away there and then for an indefinite space of time (or time of space, I don't know which) I just stare into the craggy sketched faces of my Christ and His Mother and try again and stare again. The neighboring campana strikes—. A lovely sound. Bong bong Bebong Bebong. I am alone and teeming. I hear many voices. Is it the rain? Rustle of the rain on the stripped larches.

This afternoon when the rain lifted for a moment, I wanted to ride but Diomede from Siena who now shares with Antonio the government of my household, dissuaded me. My head throbs, I have a steady hissing in the ears (like pumice smoothing marble) and stabbing pains in my head and my legs. ""Lie down, Maestro." But I prefer sitting in the chair near the fire, wrapped in my cloak and hood and I sit there all evening, dozing and waking, and staring at the toothy flames, until the third or fourth hour, chatting with Tommaso and Daniele who never leave my side now, day or night. They are both sleeping here despite my injunctions for Tommaso to attend to his own family. He just smiles, and even after his mouth has stopped smiling, the smile remains in those violet pools of his eyes. And Daniele is the same notwithstanding he has already received orders to commence the painting of britches.

The orders came from the Council of Trent less than two weeks ago and when they came I breathed a sigh of relief that the outrage long contemplated against my work was at last about to be effectuated. For the anticipation of an offense is worse than the offense itself. For more than twenty years—ever since the completion of my Judgement—my picture has been threatened, either with deturpation or total obliteration. So now at last the axe has fallen, and nothing is wanted but a few paltry bits of cloth to cover the shameful parts of what is not at all shameful. And His Holiness is kind enough to permit me to select the deturpator of my fresco. So I chose Daniele who has proved a most loyal and talented assistent (I assigned the equestrian statue of Henry to him, and he has already cast the horse) and he serves as my agent at St. Peter's, so now I ask him to paint britches and he refuses and pounds the table and cries—"*No one has the right!*" and I put my arms around his quivering shoulders and I say "*You* have the right. I give you the right—I bestow it upon you—"

So yesterday I finally convinced him. But he hasn't actually started yet, although emissaries from the Council are exerting pressure that my shameful painting be made as soon as possible if not entirely acceptable at least palatable to good Christians.

And this good Christian doesn't care. I try to convince Daniele of that and he begins to cry—actually cries—that I *should* care. He cares.

I'm certain that he will retouch as little as possible. Within Tridentine limits. The fables of this world.

My head whirls O! Signor mio caro O! I am being O! nailed—Spataf O! I regret Messer my recipe does not dissolve the stones of the kidney. Stones large or small No. bronze the statue I regret your Majesty cannot be done by me given (given!) the precarious state of my body and of my soul However (however!) my most valued assistant Ricciar Besides bronze casting is not my profes Non è la mia professione Tiberio will not touch the head. Fine young Turning up yester—this morn?—and it is raining and I just issuing from the house to take a walk rain or no rain and he: *O Maestro, in this weather?* And I shouting: *What do you want me to do? I don't feel well and I'm unable to sit still!* And that expression of his face. And I apologize. As with Tomao. I apologize. I—

I must—

Donnng. Fifth hour of the night. Donng. Diomede. "Sit by the fire then." Donng.

Marmo. Clean no veins fullmoonwhite Pietà Marmo—No! Bronzo. Bronze Julius. His voice. Whiplash.

When will it be done?

O soon

Soon

Everything will be done
Thy will be done
Il tempo che consuma il tutto
In Manus Tuas

XII

The Homecoming

"Messer, the merchandise has arrived."

"Merchandise? What merchan—? Oh! Where is it?"

"At the customs, Messer. Here is the bill of lading which I was instructed to bring."

Giorgio Vasari glanced swiftly at the red seal. Unbroken. He snapped it with a practiced gesture, fingernail of his thumb: the beautiful movements of a hand that could paint, write, and snap open the seals of letters with speed and ease. He glanced swiftly at the writing, and almost simultaneously, with the aid of his boy who had brought the message, slipped on his doublet and heavy fur-lined Florentine serge cape and was out the door and on his horse galloping through the cold drizzling March weather to the customs house, a small brick building flanking the Porta Romana through which all goods coming from Roma arrived.

The officials of course knew him—everybody in Fiorenza knew messer Giorgio Vasari—chief factotum to the Duke, uomo universale who could perform diplomatic missions or paint (with a horde of assistants) the gold-coffered ceiling of the Hall of the Five Hundred in the Old Palace, or design the U-shaped new Palace of the Offices which was to house the Duke's art collection, or set a Last Judgement within the Cupolone.

Now he was, as any good merchant in a city of merchants, receiving a long awaited shipment of merce about which Lionardo Buonarroti had written him from Roma. The muleteer who had conducted it was stomping about in the customs building, swinging his arms against the cold. Messer Lionardo's servant was sitting on a bench, snoozing, his nose blue-purple, a combination of wine and a wintry journey over the Apennines. The officials bowed and scraped to the great artist as he swept into the warehouse adding a gust of Vasarian wind to the tramontana of March. It was the 11th, a cold day, flecked with snowflakes, everyone at the huge stone gate was stomping and huffing. The guards were gathered round a fire built in the lee of the Porta; the huge ambertoned rustic-stoned structure served as a windbreak. Pigeons nestled shiveringly in the scaffolding holes.

The mules had already been untied; the cart high-heaped with bales of wool stood just inside the wide gate of the customs shed. Wool! Wool! All of Fiorenza's wealth had been built on wool: her very art, thought Giorgio, was an Arte della Lana; no wonder that guild had been among the greatest patrons of the arts.

But this was a special shipment. There had never been a shipment like this before. Buried in that cart, swathed in wool, was a box containing the greatest treasure that had ever been shipped to Fiorenza.

Giorgio signed the necessary papers. Signed them so swiftly his usual meticulous hand was a scrawl. He roused up the snoozing servant and the muleteer.

"Help unload the bales," he ordered.

"That was no part of my commission," grumbled the muleteer. "I was to bring the consignment to the customs house at Fiorenza. And I've brought it." He was tired. Furthermore he didn't like Florentines who had been mocking his accent from the moment he snapped the whips of his arrival. Who did they think they were? He was tired, cold, hungry. For more than two weeks, from the moment that black-garbed solemn Florentine gentleman in Roma had consigned the merchandise to him in the Church of Santissimi Apostoli, and given him strict instructions of what declaration he was to make at the Roma customs guards—Lana. Wool. That's all. Shipment of bales of wool. "Show these papers, they won't inspect the cart. We've arranged all that. Just show them these papers." The papers were sealed with a Cardinal's seal.

It proved as messer Buonarroti had predicted. There was no trouble at the Roma customs. They were practically waved through. But then began the troubles. For more than two weeks he had been fighting cruel winds, icy mountain roads; at Radicofani one mule had slipped and almost carried them all off the cliff. Near Arezzo the storms were so bad they had to remain at an inn for three days. That at least was a respite. There was good Tuscan wine and girls. The girls were even better than the wine and they had already been uncorked. Managg—well tapped. He was tired. And now this burly booming messer Vasari expected him to— "And I'd like to receive the balance of my pay, Messer, and return to a warmer climate—"

"I'll send you to a warmer climate, buffoon,—the warmest—if you don't help unpack this cart! You'll get your pay as soon as that is done."

Muttering fearful imprecations containing many inventive references to the Madonna, the muleteer aided by Lionardo's servant, the customs officials, and Giorgio Vasari himself swiftly lifted off the great bales of wool until the coffin swathed in wool ticking was revealed. Tenderly now, more slowly, the ticking was peeled off, and soon the stark simple wooden coffin was revealed. A hush had fallen on the company. Everyone removed his cap, even the muleteer, and circled around the coffin in the cart; everyone made the sign of the cross.

Michelangiolo Buonarroti had come home to his Fiorenza.

❖

"10 March 1564

"Most Magnificent Messer Leonardo:

"Since I wrote to you eight days ago, your letter of instructions has arrived with the body of that most holy old man, splendor of our arts. I say to you that had you sent this city a great treasure you could not have sent a greater gift than this reliquary so celebrated and so honored. It will, messer Leonardo, be borne on the shoulders of all the Academicians from its present place in the Company of the

Assunta near San Pier Maggiore to Santa Croce, and there it will be buried as you have instructed. I have not wished it to be shaken or touched; I had it sealed at the Customs house yesterday as soon as it arrived, and I have kept His Imperial Excellency the Duke informed of everything . . .

"With regards to having a tomb made for him, the idea pleases me. And since messer Daniele writes me about the statues and marbles in Via Mozza, I have kept His Imperial Excellency informed and he knows that messer Daniele wishes to make a design embodying these; indeed it doesn't seem a bad idea to design one with a statue from Via Mozza, and one without, so that the Duke who perhaps will not want to come to a decision without speaking to me about it, and we will be able to . . ."

Astute, astute, thought Lionardo. This messer Vasari is as wily as the tails of his gigantic painted horses in the Hall of the Five Hundred. Ah, if only my late departed uncle had displayed a similar astuteness. Then the position of us Buonarrotis would be even stronger up at Fiorenza. But even until the end, Zio Michelangiolo managed to offend Duke—no, now Grand Duke Cosimo by Imperial edict.

The first letter Vasari had sent to Lionardo in Roma as soon as he had received news of Buonarroti's death had revealed the Duke's displeasure. Not solely because the great artist had died before Cosimo could make use of his services, but because Michelangiolo had left neither drawings nor large designs nor models. Cosimo was especially irked that in the inventory no drawings were found for the facade of San Lorenzo, family church of the Medici, drawings which Michelangiolo must have possessed since that project— "mirror of all the arts of Italy"—ended, as so many of Zio's projects, in a broken-backed mirror. Oh, the Duke must have been furious to learn from his ambassador in Roma what Lionardo had learned from the servant Antonio—the old man sitting at the fire the last days of his life and tossing into the flames drawings, letters, architectural designs. Oh, Zio Zio, irascible to the end!

What was it, thought Lionardo, seated now in the salotta of the rambling house and trying not to look at the skull on the staircase—a macabre and bad joke—what was it? A final flaring-up of Uncle's republicanism after what seemed these late years to be a reconciliation with the Medici Duke? The Duke of course—like everyone else—had been expecting the old man's death at any moment, and he wasn't especially grieved, beyond the needs of decorum, when it happened. He regretted his death, of course. "The outstanding man in the world in his profession but our regret is increased by his not having left behind any of his designs. To have thrown everything into the fire seems to us an act unworthy of him."

So now when I return, thought Lionardo, there will be need to repair this rent in my relations with the Duke. Vasari's first letter on the 4th of March had been full of good advice in this regard:

"Most Magnificent messer Leonardo:

"With so much unhappiness I've heard the news of the death of my messer Michelangiolo, certainly one who has been a father to me in love, as he has been an uncle to you by blood. and I am especially grieved that you didn't find him alive . . ."

Well, thought Lionardo ruefully, although I did not follow Diomede's advice not to risk riding post on dangerous wintry roads because of my precarious health, I came too late anyway. Besides didn't he say that messer Tommaso de' Cavalieri and messer Daniele and Antonio the servant and himself were in constant attendance and if Uncle is dying, you can't arrive in time anyway. so come immediately but don't put yourself in peril coming, and so I did and arrived three days after Uncle's death and his body already transported to SS. Apostoli, a few blocks from here; and the talk all over Roma that the divine Michelangiolo must be buried in the very St. Peter's he was building and the Pope wanted a suitable monument to be erected for him there. Oh Zio mio, how you complicated all matters, even after your death, making it necessary for me to smuggle your body out to please the Duke at least that much (and to fulfill your dying wish to be buried in your own patria next to your father. And what pleased the Duke had to please the Pope as well for the Duke had made the Pope and so the proper eyes were winked at the 'smuggling' out of the body and the proper instructions given to the customs guards.

And meanwhile Vasari instructed, out of his vast experience in diplomacy, exactly what Lionardo should say to smooth the ruffled feathers of the Duke.

". . . it is clear to me that just as God almighty had lent him to our century as a miracle, both in his rare qualities and talents as in his holiness and manners . . . so as he ornamented the world with his hands, so he will ornament paradise with his soul. And since some details of his Will have come to my ear, although I believe them to be true until I hear otherwise from you, I neither take pleasure or joy in the things I've heard. I must tell you that after your departure, I sent word to your house to madonna Cassandra offering her all my assistence. I advise you that our most Illustrious prince is very eager that the body or, to put it better, the bones, come here to Fiorenza because (as his Excellency writes from Pisa) he wishes to have a statue of Michelangiolo erected in Santa Maria del Fiore.

"Now in my opinion, messer Lionardo mio, it doesn't seem off the mark, should your return be delayed, for you to write a letter to His Excellency expressing your regret for the loss which the city of Fiorenza and his Excellency have suffered from this death, and that you are most sorry that there are no drawings or cartoons or models because you had intended to hand these over to him . . . but since Michelangiolo is gone having left only you, you will be in faith and in service the same as your uncle; and since up here in Fiorenza there are only those pieces in Via

Mozza, whatever they might be, if they please him, they're his; beg him to extend the same patronage to you alive that he had to Michelangiolo before he passed to another life . . . if you will send me this, I will accompany it with a letter of my own . . ."

Good, good, thought Lionardo, with messer Vasari's skillful guidance Zio's brusque departure might be mended. Vasari had also spoken in his first long letter of his plan for solemn obseques which the Academicians had decided to celebrate in San Lorenzo soon after Easter. Meanwhile since Vasari was preparing to reprint within three months a second edition of his *Lives*, would messer Lionardo write down notes for him of all the particulars of Michelangiolo's life from 1550 on, whether concerning the fabbrica of St. Peter's (and the ambassador tells me that Nani Bigio wrote to the Duke the very day Uncle died, asking Cosimo to use his influence to have Nani appointed Chief Architect of St. Peter's, and Cosimo refused) or anything else; also send him any sonnets poems or notes by Michelangiolo as well as "letters from princes and great men . . ."

❖

The day following Michelangiolo's death, even before Lionardo's arrival—the body already removed to SS. Apostoli—an inventory was taken of all his effects in the house at Macel dei Corvi. This was at the instance of Averardo Serristori, Florentine envoy. Immediately after the inventory, the envoy—the 'oratore'— wrote tersely to his Duke that whatever had been in the house was 'little, and (most humiliating) very few designs!' The most important item was a wooden box sealed with several seals which was in Michelangiolo's bedroom, in which box opened by the Governor (sent by the Pope) and in the presence of a chattering Sicilian notary and messer Tommaso de' Cavalieri and maestro Daniele da Volterra, were found seven or eight thousand scudi.

Through all those final days of death and disposition, Tommaso moved like a somnambulist. like all the other close friends he had long—for years, indeed— expected Michelangiolo to die, and yet when the end came it was inexplicable, unacceptable. Death is the supreme inconceivable. For many hours Tomao stood vigil, looking down at the man he had loved as friend, father, Master, counselor, for thirty years and there he was lying in the coffin. He was sleeping. Sleeping in his black damask gown, boots with spurs and a silken hat with a smooth black velvet hanging, sleeping and hence he must awaken (Tommaso *saw* him breathing) but he did not awaken, no he will never—

Before the coffin lid was nailed, Tomao bent down, blind with tears, and kissed the cold forehead—oh, dear God, the greatest maker of monuments had become himself a monument. His forehead was pure white Carrara marble, hard, icy cold. and the coffin was closed and Tommaso and Daniele helped carry it to the Church and covered it with the velvet pall and placed the crucifix on it and lighted the candles. The doing of such tasks, the ceremonial doing of them, seemed to alleviate their wordless grief.

The following day Tomao was present at the inventory. A legalistic affair, he thought, which would have made the Old One chuckle: that chattering little Sicilian notary and the beswathed Governor frozen into his officious dignity, and Cosimo's Ambassador who did not conceal his irritation as the inventory continued and the party walked from room to room, noting down every scrap, the Sicilian busily scratching with his quill, when he was not tickling his nose with the feather; the servants following with long faces (and perhaps some disappointment, thought Tommaso, since the Master had died intestate). Calcagni came and went. Antonio Francese brewed a hot lentil soup for the official party. It took all day. The document, indited in stiff legalistic Latin, began:

Bona et pecunie quondam domini Michaelis Angeli Bonarrote . . .
Goods and money of the former domini Michelangiolo Buonarroti
In Dei nomine, amen. Die sabbati, xix mensis februarii, 1564.

Hoc est inventarium of the goods and furniture and effects found in the house formerly inhabited by Domini, in good memory, Michaelis Angeli Bonerote florentini, most excellent sculptor *dum vixit* (a foolish redundancy thought Tommaso, of course, 'while he lived'!); present domini Angelo Antonis de Amatis assistant at the treasury, sent as factotum by mandate of the most reverend lord Governor, and first;

In the room where he used to sleep:

An iron bed with a straw sacking, three mattresses, two white woolen covers and one of white lambskin. A canopy of fine white canvas and its pomo.
A large credenza, table-size, within which are:
A long old fur coat of foxskin, covered with saglia lionata, frusta.
Another fur coat, half-length, of fox-skin, covered with black cloth (panno)
A cap of fine florentine black cloth, with a lining of black satin inside, almost new . . .
Two hats of black ermesino . . .
Seven white bedsheets . . .

So it went. Somnambulistically Tomao heard the drone of the notary, the scratching of the quill, as the party passed from room to room, annotating, counting, reducing a life to quantifications. It was indeed (the idea flickered in Tommaso's grief-numbed consciousness) a rather poor or, shall one say, austere household for the Divine Michelangiolo. More linens. More shirts. Some old. Some new. Face towels. Body towels. A used bed-sheet. Why did he keep a used bed-sheet? Six napkins. An old box: inside, a large metal mirror and a hand towel. Oh Maestro! Oh Signor Caro Mio. For thirty years you filled my life with radiance. And boxes with old metal mirrors and used towels!

In a lower room, covered with a roof:
A statue commenced representing St. Peter, blocked out and not finished
Another statue commenced representing Christ and another figure with it in one piece, blocked out and not finished (and seven days ago he standing on his feet all day working on this piece, Diomede urging him to rest and he replying angrily *'I cannot rest! What do you want me to do! I cannot rest!* and now dear Maestro you are resting and this Deposition rough and rude as a consumed skeleton is deposed forever and the finished arm of the first draft still incongruously hanging in marmorial space)

Another small statue of Christ with the Cross on his shoulder not finished.

In the Stall: a small chestnut-colored mare (ronzinetto) with saddle, bridles etc . . .
In the cellar: a half cask of vinegar, and a caratello cheese and five large vittine of water, and two schiumarelli and a imbattatore.

In the room of the said messer Michelangiolo:

A box of walnut wood, locked and sealed.
Item a cartoon of two pieces of paper glued together on which is drawn the plan of the fabric of St. Peter's.
Another little cartoon on which is drawn the front of a palace.
Another cartoon on which is drawn a window of St. Peter's.
Another cartoon of pieces glued together on which is drawn the old plan of the said Church of St. Peter considered to be according to the model of Sangallo.
Another cartoon with three sketches of little figures.
Another cartoon with drawing of a window and others.
A large cartoon, on which is drawn a Pietà with nine figures unfinished.
Another large cartoon on which are drawn three large figures and two children.
Another large cartoon on which is drawn a large figure alone.
Another large cartoon on which are sketched the figure of Our Lord Jesus Christ and that of the glorious Virgin Mary, His Mother . . .

"That, Messer," Tommaso injected now firmly, "'belongs to me. That cartoon was given to me by the Maestro a long time ago and it has remained here only because—"

"Messer, we will make a note of it for the final disposition. But for the moment we must continue with the inventory."

"Va bene. Va bene."

In the loggia on the ground floor—La fucina with two little mantici.
A large valise of black curamo . . .

Later, when everything had been duly counted and duly written down, came the ceremony of opening the walnut box. And it was indeed a ceremony (and all this procedure was written down too) that the box had been found in the room where the said messer Michelangiolo slept, that before opening it, it was carefully scrutinized by all, and found to be duly sealed firstly at two different places on bands of paper, that is with five long pieces of white paper sealed at each end; and insofar as might be seen they were unharmed, intact, and immaculate, one of which is the seal of messer Thomeo de' Cavalieri Roman gentleman, present and under oath, tactis scripturis, ita ricognoscente et asserente; and the other is that of messer Diomede Leoni, Sienese, resident in Roma, present, hereby recognized and self-declared under oath, tactis scripturis.

And since it is recognized that originally another seal had been attached to the lock, that is, sealed in the form of a triangle, and that the paper enwrapping the said box and its cover had been removed; he messer Thomeo declared that it had been impressed with his own seal at the request of the aforesaid Antonio seeing the worsening of messer Michelangiolo, and he had it attached by messer Camillo d'Arpino schoolmaster of the said messer Thomeo; and there was present Bonifatio de L'Aquila, servant of the said messer Thomeo, martedi proximo passato the beginning of messer Michelangiolo's illness. And occurring subsequently the death of the said messer Michelangiolo, he messer Thomeo declared that he had broken the seal with his own hand in the presence of the said messer Diomede, and messer Daniele Ricciarelli da Volterra and messer Mario son of the said messer Thomeo and the aforesaid Antonio with the intention of wishing to open the said chest to see how much was within it. However, thinking farther on the matter, everyone agreed that it would be better not to open it, but rather to seal it as they did, and await the arrival of the said messer Michelangiolo's nephew, since he had already written that he was coming; and the key of the said chest remained in messer Thomeo's keeping, the box locked and sealed as before; and now the said box, present the said messer Thomeo and exhibiting the said key, the seal removed in the presence of messer Thomeo, messer Daniele Ricciarelli da Volterra, messer Iacomo Ducis, Sicilian, resident in Roma, witnesses summoned for this purpose etc. etc. with the presence and assistance of the aforesaid messer Angelo Antonio de Amatis, substitute fiscales, et di me notaro etc. etc.

And all the etceteras and etceteras and Latin postcriptum et postquem aperta fuit dicta capsa had, Thomeo noted with gratitude, a certain soporific gauzing effect on the bleeding wounds of his grief and he watched, as from a great distance, the opening of the box and the itemization of its contents:

	Scudi	Baiocchi
In a small white earthenware vase in small coin (paoli, testoni da tre paoli etc.) totalling:	104	20
Item, in a similar smaller vase 60 Julii	6	90
Item, in a big green canvas sack serving as a purse, within a handkerchief, 224 ducats in gold, stamped with the Florentine lily	224	00
Item, in another handkerchief between ducats and Spanish doubloons	119	00
Item, in a small white canvas sack, Hungarian and German money	200	00
Item, in a handkerchief, Venetian ducats	126	00
Item, in a handkerchief, ducats in gold of various coinages	208	00
Item, in the above described green bag, gold ducats of the Camera, within which green bag are contained all the handkerchiefs with the aforesaid ducats	2117	00

Daniele's jaw hit lank-bottom. It was not infrequently lank and during this inventory as the various moneys were counted and set down by the notary, Tomao had noted Daniele's jaw sinking lower and lower until with this last figure it could sink no more. O funny Old Man, thought Tomao. Why did you not bank all this with your friends, the Strozzi? You, who were always complaining about thieving servants . . . why? . . . But messer Angelo's fingers had dipped again into the chest and the voice was droning on:

	Scudi	Baiocchi
Item, in a copper vase, golden ducats of various coinages, numbering	264	00
Item, scudi in gold, Sardinian	194	00
Item, in a broken copper vase, with a handle, in the manner of a bottle, golden ducats and ducats of the Chamber	746	00
Item, in the bottom of the box,		

16 pauls	1	60
Item, in another little white terracotta vase wrapped in paper, 97 gold scudi, with a memorial of one hundred scudi on the account of the Sienese	97	00
Item, in another copper amaccate) vase, ducats in gold of various coinages numbering	3994	00

"Dio mio!" Daniele ejaculated in a hoarse whisper. The notary replaced all the money back in the walnut chest, closing the lid, and a new long reading began in Latin during which time Tomao attempted to sum up round figures as best as he could recall them. But he could not even recall round figures. He knew only that there must be a fortune of liquid cash in that box alone—perhaps nine or ten thousand ducats—(not counting moneys deposited in banks in Roma and in Fiorenza, and numerous properties other than this meanly-furnished house on Macel dei Corvi). And how odd it was for the Old Man! . . . the Old Man so rich in spirit, so rich in art, so generous in gifts to his friends and in anonymous dowries to shopkeepers' and carpenters' daughters and building Saint Peter's for less than Peter's pence, gratis, for his soul's sake and lamenting of his poverty and painting Sistine ceilings only for the honor of his family and to set his brothers up in the wool business.

Michelangiolo mio. Angel divin.

·✳·

So went that day: Tomao's grief steeped and stiffened with legalities. Next afternoon, accompanied by a servant, arrived the Maestro's nephew: haggard after his long wintry ride over the mountains, but Spanish-solemn still as Tomao had first seen him. His jet riding clothes mudsplattered from boots to velvet cap, even his long black beard caked with mud. He must have ridden hard, he had come by post despite Diomede's warning and he was solemn still notwithstanding his weariness and grief at the death of his uncle (whom he loved in his fashion) and concern about the lack of a will.

"There is no written will? Is that possible?"

"None," said Tomao. "Only three phrases pronounced just before his death: that he committed his soul into the hands of God, his body to the earth, and his worldly goods to his nearest relatives

"—Ah."

"—enjoining all of you, that is his family, when your time came, to think upon the sufferings of Jesus Christ. And then he closed his eyes and spoke no more. It was just before sunset, just before the Ave Maria bells."

"I wish I had arrived in time."

"The end came very fast. And peacefully. Take comfort in that, Messer. For the first few days he insisted on sitting up in a chair near the fire. Then we put him to bed. Then, Friday . . ."

After a moment's silence, messer Lionardo said: "The Duke wants the body to be returned to Fiorenza."

"I know. His Oratore, messer Serristori, has already advised us. And the Maestro himself repeated a few days before he died, that he wants to be buried near his father."

I will honor his last wish, thought Tomao, although it will deprive me even of his shell.

"And the Holy Father?"

"There will be no problem. Only everything must be done as unobtrusively as possible, not to stir up the Romans who claim Michelangiolo as their own saying that he spent the last thirty years here, working for the Popes, and that it was a lie that he wished to be buried in Fiorenza and that he should be buried in Saint Peter's itself, and meanwhile he has already received funeral honors in SS. Apostoli, and every artist in Roma has gone to see the coffin. So, I repeat, the body must be removed without noise . . ."

"The inventory?"

"In the hands of the Notary. Incidentally, one of the ten drawings—a pietà—is mine. The Notary would like the Epiphany. The rest are yours—everything—the cash-box too."

"Ah."

That 'Ah', thought Tomao. A sound like an official seal.

·✳·

On March 6th, which would have been Michelangiolo's ninetieth birthday, and as the coffin in the mulecart was still struggling slowly northward over slippery mountain roads, Tomao accompanied messer Lionardo to the bottega of the pharmacist Antonio Martelli to pay off debts incidental to Michelangiolo's final illness and funeral preparations. The total bill amounted to forty-five scudi and one and a half baiocchi, for various syrups, cristers, castor oil, decoctions of thyme isopi, cicory, various liniments of almond oil; porters, candles, torches, and twelve pounds of wax to wax the canvas in which the coffin was wrapped for transport to Fiorenza.

Lionardo paid thirty-eight scudi down, and the pharmacist entered the balance of debt, in a careful hand, on page sixty-two, book B, of his accounts. All these matters,—the re-counting of the moneys in the chest, the checking-off of the inventory against the actual articles in the house, the consultations with the Duke's envoy—all this messer Lionardo performed, Tomao noted, with a kind of stolid unimaginative precision, and it was quite clear that he would not be able to settle his uncle's affairs in Roma for several months at least, and so would unfortunately be absent during Zio's reception in his beloved Fiorenza.

And Tomao wept and not even the comfortings of his wife and sons could comfort him.

·⁘·

And on March 11th, the day after its arrival at the customs house, the coffin was conveyed as unostentatiously as possible to the Oratory of the Assumption in the crypt beneath the staircase of San Pier Maggiore. For more than a week rumors had already been circulating throughout Fiorenza that the corpse of their greatest son was coming home: and now that it had arrived sooner than expected and before proper ceremonial had been prepared, the newly-founded Academicians who were in charge of the matter thought it unwise to permit a stirring up of popular passions without suitable decorum to contain it.

So, by night the mule cart bearing the coffin creaked down Via Romana to Ponte Santa Trinita which had recently been rebuilt by Ammannati after another great flood, and the three graceful swoops of the arches had been suggested and roughly sketched by the man whose corpse was now crossing the river; and then the cart turned right along Lung' Arno, past Ponte Vecchio with its butchers' and blacksmiths' shops and past Ponte Rubaconte until it turned north through narrow stony streets between huge forbidding palaces, and so at last into Michelangiolo's own Quarter of Santa Croce.

And the following day, which was a Sunday, all the painters and sculptors and architects came quietly to the crypt of San Pietro. The coffin and entire bier were covered by a large velvet cloth bordered and embroidered with gold on which had been placed a crucifix. Everyone in the small oratory gathered closely around the coffin. And in that company were Giorgio Vasari silent silent and Angelo Bronzino and Bartolomeo Ammannati who was still executing Michelangiolo's Laurentian Library and whose wife, the poetess Laura Battiferro, was to write a celebratory sonnet for the departed Master, and Benvenuto Cellini, soon to quarrel explosively (as was his wont) with Ammannati about the future obsequies, and Benedetto Varchi who was to deliver the oration, and the Prior of the Innocenti and many others, thirty-two in all.

Then suddenly, about a half hour after dusk, the oldest and most distinguished artists picked up torches, many of which had been brought, and lighted them and all the young men took hold of the bier, and those who could get close enough to place it on their shoulders felt blessed thinking how in times to come they could take glory in having carried the remains of the greatest man who had ever existed in their art. So it was decided that eight torch-bearers should accompany the procession to Santa Croce.

But by this time the word had spread that Michelangiolo Buonarroti had come home at last, and from every street the popolo minuto came running to join this procession of the most famous artists of Fiorenza bearing a coffin accompanied by torch-bearers through the streets of Fiorenza on a Sunday night. By the time it reached Santa Croce, the procession had grown so that it filled the entire huge spaces of the church. With great difficulty, the coffin was carried through the tumultuous crowds into the sacristy, although at first the friars tried to bar its entry because they realized the sacristy could not possibly accommodate such a crowd, agitated and crying out Michelangiolo's name. At this point Don Vincenzo Borghini, Prior of the Innocenti, intervened by right of his office as Vice-President of the Academy and because of his admiration for the genius of the deceased. And observing the universal love manifested toward the dead, and thinking that it would greatly content that throng, and also (as he later confessed) since he wished to see in death one he had not seen in life— or only when he himself was of such tender age that he hardly remembered him at all—he resolved then and there to have the coffin opened.

So it was done.

And Michelangiolo was lying there as if he were asleep. Twenty-two days after his death, more than two weeks drawn in a rocking mule cart over the Apennines, and there he lay, with no visible trace of putrefaction, no odor of death, sleeping peacefully and sweetly in his damask cloak and spurred boots and silken hat with the black velvet hanging, the same features, the same mien except for the slight change of complexion which was that of death, not one limb decayed or revolting.

And everyone who could, touched his head and his cheeks which seemed soft and lifelike as if he had died only a few hours before. And there were those who cried *Miracolo!* as if he were a saint, and others who attributed the preservation of the corpse to the cold season.

❖

David with his sling
and I with my bow . . .

Free lovers, Love, flee those flames . . .

A Yes and No move me . . .

I would want to want O Lord that which I do not want . . .

the fables of the world . . .

The words swam past Tomao's eyes—swam, for he was leafing through a box full of Michelangiolo's poems and the clear beautiful script was wavering through his tears. And when he came upon the last poems, he could hardly read at all, for now the letters wavered of themselves: an old man's hand, *la man che ubbidisce all' intelletto*—the hand that obeys the intellect—trembling, tremulous, the last leaf on the tree:

> Giunto è già 'l corso della vita mia
> Con tempestoso mar, per fragil barca
> Al comun porto . . .

> Arrived at last the journey of my life
> Through seas tempestuous, by fragile bark
> To the common port . . .

PLATE VII

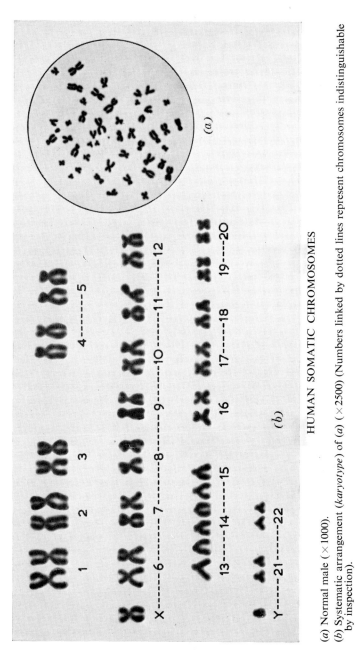

HUMAN SOMATIC CHROMOSOMES

(a) Normal male (×1000).

(b) Systematic arrangement (*karyotype*) of (a) (×2500) (Numbers linked by dotted lines represent chromosomes indistinguishable by inspection).

PLATE VIII

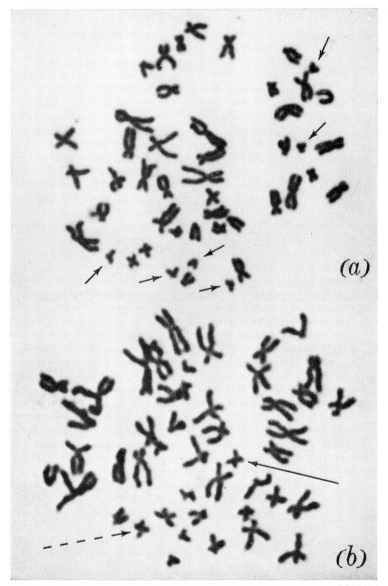

CHROMOSOME ABNORMALITIES ASSOCIATED WITH MONGOLISM

(*a*) Non-disjunctional type: the additional chromosome is either 21 or 22 (*see* Plate VII *b*), thus six of this type of chromosome are visible and these are arrowed (×2400).

(*b*) Translocation type: the chromosome with translocated material is indicated by a solid arrow, the normal homologue by a dotted arrow (×3300).

latter work, scoring was done at metaphase of the second (pollen tube) mitosis and is comparable, therefore, to the method used by Sparrow in *Trillium*.

In addition to confirming the late prophase/metaphase peak of radiation sensitivity, the above studies in *Tradescantia* confirmed the existence of a second peak in the late interphase region of meiosis (pachytene) as well as in mitosis. Thus in both division cycles there appear to be two distinct periods where the chromosomes are exceptionally sensitive to breakage by radiation and the inconsistencies between the results of different researches arose chiefly through differences in experimental techniques.

Having established the differential breakability of chromosomes at different stages of nuclear division it becomes of great interest to determine what mechanisms might be involved; valuable information might be obtained on the nature of chromosome breakage and re-joining.

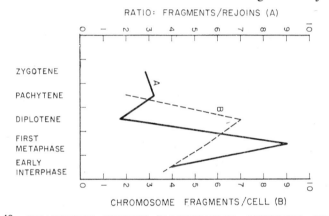

FIG. 49. RELATIONSHIP BETWEEN FRAGMENTATION SENSITIVITY AND THE RATES OF UNJOINED AND RE-JOINED BREAKS DURING MEIOSIS IN *Trillium*

Unfortunately, little is known of the basic biochemical and physical changes that occur in chromosomes during divisions and this limits speculation on the factors underlying differential breakability. Nevertheless, three factors have been considered in a tentative approach to the problem.

One possibility is that the frequency of chromosome breakage does not vary but that differences in the yield of fragments depend upon variable degrees of rejoining. If this were true the ratio of fragments/rejoins should be highest at peak sensitivities for fragmentation and lowest at the least sensitive stages. Later studies by Sparrow and his collaborators supply some evidence in favour of this (Fig. 49). The

ratio is highest at metaphase but on the other hand is lowest at diplotene and relatively high at early interphase, stages of high and low
fragment incidence, respectively. Thus the differential rejoining
hypothesis may in part be correct but is insufficient to explain all the
variations in sensitivity.

The second possibility is that chromosome duplication is implicated
in the process of chromosome breakage. This cannot be involved in
the diplotene-metaphase peak in meiosis since here the chromosomes
are effectively double. Recent studies on the relationship between
DNA synthesis and chromosome replication indicate that these processes occur, in a more or less overlapping manner, at mid-interphase.
Thus the other peak sensitivity period for induced chromosome breakage, i.e. at late interphase, also occurs at a stage remote from chromosome duplication. There is no evidence, therefore, that the processes
of DNA synthesis and chromosome replication influence the rate of
production of breaks in the chromosome thread.

A third factor correlated with relative radiosensitivity is the degree
of condensation of the chromosomes. In the studies on meiosis in
Trillium it was shown that the sensitivity of chromosomes was inversely
related to their length (Fig. 50). Chromosome contraction during

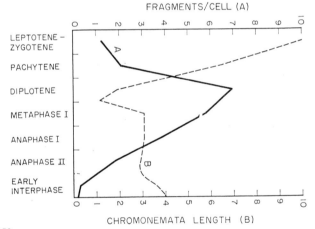

FIG. 50. RELATIONSHIP BETWEEN RADIATION—INDUCED CHROMOSOME
FRAGMENTATION AND THE LENGTH OF THE CHROMOSOMES AT VARIOUS STAGES
OF MEIOSIS IN *Trillium*

division is brought about by coiling of the thread. It is possible that
this coiling is accompanied by chemical and/or physical changes which
facilitate breakage; a satisfactory interpretation of the observed correlation must, however, await further information.

EFFECT OF RADIATION ON DIFFERENT STAGES OF GAMETOGENESIS

Gametogenesis, the development of the germ cells, represents a very remarkable process of cellular change and differentiation. This is especially true in the male, where normal dividing diploid cells develop into spermatozoa with very highly condensed nuclear material and almost no cytoplasm.

It has long been known that radiations are not equally mutagenic to different stages of gametogenesis. In 1928, shortly after Muller's initial discoveries, the mature spermatozoa of *Drosophila* were shown to be much more sensitive than either spermatogonia or oöcytes. Not until recently, however, have these early observations been extended by more intensive studies. Such studies are of importance to the general problem of the basis of the mutagenic process; they are also of use in the evaluation of possible genetic risks that might arise from Man's exposure to radiations.

Research on the induction of mutation in different germ cells has been carried out almost exclusively in *Drosophila* and the following account will be restricted chiefly to these studies.

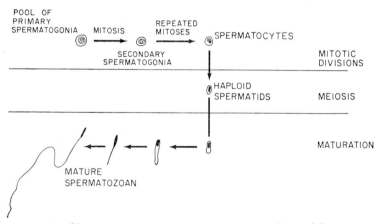

FIG. 51.   THE PROCESS OF SPERMATOGENESIS IN *Drosophila*

During larval development, the spermatogonia divide to produce a pool of spermatocytes which, until pupation, undergo no further development. Meiosis starts in the pupa and on emergence the testes of the flies contain all stages of spermatogenesis up to immature sperm. These rapidly mature and at about 24 hours after hatching the testes contain the full spectrum of germ cell stages. The process of division and maturation (Fig. 51) now continues smoothly and mature sperm is eliminated either by use in mating or by re-absorption or ejaculation in the absence of copulation. Offspring produced in successive mating periods (broods) of irradiated males thus receive sperm which was in progressively earlier stages of gametogenesis at the time of irradiation. Differences in the radiosensitivity of the stages will be reflected in the mutation frequencies observed in various broods. These brood mutation frequency fluctuations are called brood patterns.

In the earliest work, and indeed until recently, broods tended to cover many days and to be rather variable in length. They showed quite conclusively, however, that the earliest sperm used contained many more mutations than that used 14 or more days after irradiation. The use of shorter broods and the establishment of the importance of standardised methods has led to the discovery of radiation sensitivity patterns more complex than the simple contrast between early and late germ cells.

The first intensive studies on the differential sensitivity of germ cells to radiation-induced genetic damage were performed by K. G. Luning in the 1950's. Using a brood interval of three days he demonstrated that the highest frequency of mutation occurred in the third brood, i.e. during the period 7 to 9 days after irradiation. This was true for both recessive lethal mutations and for chromosome breaks, the latter being scored as dominant lethals. Thus in addition to the difference between pre- and post-meiotic germ cells, a difference was also observed between mature and immature post-meiotic stages. These observations have been confirmed and extended by other workers to include aberrations such as translocations and chromosome losses. Slight differences occur in the brood patterns obtained by different workers but these can usually be attributed to slight differences in mating procedure.

Two further changes in the mutagenic sensitivity of spermatozoa have been observed recently, both of which concern the final stages of maturation. First, sperm used in the first 24 hours after irradiation contain more mutations than that used in the next 48 hours and, second, irradiation of spermatozoa in inseminated females results in a still higher mutation frequency. These phenomena have been confirmed for recessive mutations, translocations and for dominant lethals.

Thus two peak periods of mutation sensitivity occur; the higher 7 to 9 days after irradiation, the lower when mature spermatozoa are irradiated in inseminated females. Between these peaks mutation frequency is still high in relation to that found 12 days or more after irradiation. Semi-diagrammatic illustrations of the brood patterns for different types of genetic damage are included in Fig. 52.

The different categories of mutation tend to show a very similar pattern; sensitivity to chromosome breakage is similar to that for reces-

sive mutation. The difference between the stages of high and low sensitivity are most marked, however, for chromosomal aberrations. This
can be explained by the fact that the two hit nature of these changes
results in a greater than linear increase in relation to the increase in
the primary one hit events.

Several attempts have been made to determine in what manner the
germ cell stages present in the testes of the irradiated male are sampled

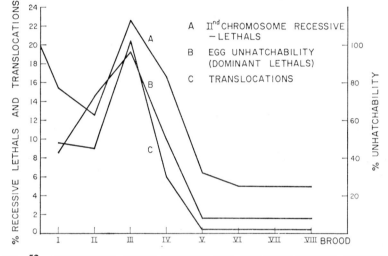

FIG. 52. GENERALISED BROOD PATTERNS FOR RADIATION-INDUCED GENETIC
DAMAGE IN *Drosophila*: BROOD INTERVAL THREE DAYS.
(0 = sperm irradiated in inseminated females)

as spermatozoa in successive broods. Both histological and genetic
methods have been used.

Irradiated males subsequently go through a stage of sterility round
about the fourth brood after irradiation, after which fertility is ultimately recovered. This sterility is not to be confused with that in
earlier broods following a high incidence of dominant lethals. It is
due to a lack of functional sperm and is presumably related to the destruction of part of the germ cell spectrum. By histological examination
of the testes, it has been shown that the cells most sensitive to radiation
killing are spermatogonia which are about to become spermatocytes.
There is some confusion as to the actual change from spermatogonia to
spermatocytes, however, and some observers have claimed that the
destroyed cells were spermatocytes. Nevertheless, it is clear that stages
just prior to meiosis are destroyed by radiation and that this is reflected
in the brood sequence by sterility in the fourth brood. Consequently

it would seem that spermatids at treatment supply sperm predominantly in the third brood and that the peak mutation frequency found here indicates that these cells are most sensitive to the mutagenic action of radiations.   Studies by E. F. Oakberg and others show that a parallel situation exists in mouse testis although, of course, on a different time scale.

In addition to histological methods the first use of sperm from irradiated gonia has been determined in mouse by radioactive tracer studies. Carbon 14 labelled adenine, one of the bases in DNA, appeared in sperm about 30 days after administration.   Adenine is incorporated only during DNA synthesis which is limited to pre-meiotic germ cell stages.

The results of genetic methods for determining the position of irradiated meiotic and gonial cells have largely confirmed the conclusions from histological studies.   Crossing-over, which is normally absent in *Drosophila* males, can be induced by irradiation.   Using this phenomenon, which occurs only in meiotic or earlier germ cell stages, C. Auerbach

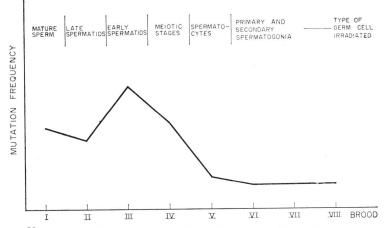

FIG. 53.   RELATIONSHIP BETWEEN BROOD MUTATION FREQUENCIES AND THE TYPES OF GERM CELL ORIGINALLY IRRADIATED

has confirmed that peak mutation sensitivity is reached in the brood pattern before the utilisation of irradiated meiotic stages.   Her data differ from those of other workers in that mutation peaks and sterility arise earlier, in the second and third broods respectively.   This is probably due to the use of an excess of females in matings as compared to the usual practice of mating a treated male to two or three females per brood.   The essential point, that early spermatids are most sensitive to irradiation, is not in dispute. Two other pieces of information are worth noting; first, that clusters of induced mutations arise at the earliest in the fifth brood; these must have arisen in actual dividing cells; second, irradiation of young larvae which contain gonia alone produces only a low mutation frequency. The data on germ cell sensitivity are summarised diagrammatically in Fig. 53.

One possible explanation of the low lethal mutation frequencies obtained after the irradiation of gonial cells is that these cells may be killed by a mutation and thus be incapable of producing lethal bearing spermatozoa. This phenomenon is called *germinal selection* and could operate in the case of sex-linked recessive lethals or dominant lethals. With regard to the former there is conclusive evidence that at least half the induced mutations are lost in this way. This proportion is very far short of that required to explain the difference between pre- and post-meiotic mutation frequencies. In addition, the brood pattern for auto-somal mutations is also characterised by low frequencies in the later broods; recessive mutations other than those on the X-chromosome cannot suffer germinal selection. On the other hand, the almost non-existence of dominant lethals from irradiated spermatogonia can be attributed to germinal selection. The virtual absence of translocations from irradiated gonial cells is probably due to another factor. The chromosomes are far more widely dispersed in gonial cells than in post-meiotic cells; the likelihood that four broken ends will rejoin sym-metrically is therefore small; asymmetrical rejoining results in the pro-duction of dominant lethals.

For the induction of mutations at least, therefore, gonial cells are less sensitive than more mature stages of gametogenesis. An evaluation of the induction of breaks is not possible since they fail to produce viable sperm when induced in gonia. In the post-meiotic stages, how-ever, gross genetic damage has no effect on the viability of the sperm. Variations in sensitivity here, with regard to chromosome breakage as well as to mutation, cannot be produced by selective forces. Two pos-sibilities still exist: either the chromosomes suffer variable degrees of primary damage or they show differential recovery from such damage. Recovery or restitution of breaks can be revealed by a comparative study of the sensitivity of ring as opposed to rod chromosomes. As described earlier, restitution is hampered in the former due possibly to mechanical stresses in the chromosome. Using this approach Luning has tested the hypothesis that variable frequencies of breaks (i.e. domi-nant lethal mutations) depend on variable degrees of restitution. The results showed that the hypothesis was incorrect when applied to the high sensitivity of spermatids since the pattern in the first three broods was the same in ring and rod chromosomes. In considering the high frequency of breaks in the first as compared with the second day after irradiation, however, Luning found that differential recovery did occur. These results stand in sharp contrast, however, to the observation (Chapter 5) that chromosome aberration frequency in *Drosophila* sperm is independent of radiation intensity. On this evidence it was concluded that chromosome breaks induced in spermatozoa remained open until after fertilisation.   More research is obviously required to resolve this apparent paradox.

Oögenesis, the development of the female germ cells, differs quite radically from *spermatogenesis,* the development of the male germ cells. The mature egg cell is relatively normal in appearance having a fairly large nucleus and ample cytoplasm.   It exhibits none of the characters of nuclear and cytoplasmic condensation that are typical of the spermatozoan.   Secondly, as a mature haploid gamete, the egg cell has only a very short life; final maturation occurs only after fertilisation and just prior to the beginning of embryonic development.   Meiosis is blocked in the developing egg cell at first metaphase.   Cells at this stage, the *oöcytes,* may be formed relatively early in the life of the organism and remain for a long period in the ovary without further development. In the mammals it is thought that the oöcytes are in existence during most of post-natal life.   There are, therefore, no stages in females comparable to *spermiogenesis* (post-meiotic spermatogenesis) in the male.

The sensitivity pattern in the *Drosophila* female is consistent with the earlier observation that meiotic metaphase cells are highly sensitive to the mutagenic actions of radiations.   Mutation frequencies drop sharply in those eggs laid later than seven days after irradiation.   Up until this time eggs are sampled that were at metaphase at the time of treatment. Histological examination has shown that eggs sampled later than seven days are young oöcytes with chromosomes in the diffuse stage prior to the meiotic condensation.

Less genetic damage is induced in females than in males when they are given the same dose of irradiation.   This difference is most marked with respect to translocations, for which, in *Drosophila,* the frequency is about 100 times greater in spermatozoa than in mature oöcytes.   In a series of studies on this problem it has been shown by B. Glass that this difference is not due to a differential sensitivity to breakage.   Inversions were only three or four times as frequent in spermatozoa as in oöcytes and for small deletions of the type that produce the *minute* phenotype* (dominant visibles) there was little difference.   This suggests that breakage is at the most only slightly higher in spermatozoa. It has been suggested that the rarity of translocations in females is related

---

* In *Drosophila,* minutes comprise an unspecific group of dominant mutations which all reduce the size of the bristles.

to the improbability of rejoining of broken ends of separate chromosomes in the oöcytes. Chromosome movement is much more limited in these cells than in spermatozoa about to fuse with the female chromosome set of the fertilised egg. Broken ends of the same chromosome stand a greater chance of rejoining; hence inversions are not as rare as translocations in irradiated oöcytes.

Recessive lethal mutations and point mutations detected by the specific locus method are only about twice as frequent in the spermatozoa as in the mature oöcytes. The two stages are not strictly comparable, however, and it seems probable that no difference exists between the mutagenic sensitivity of oöcytes and spermatocytes in meiotic metaphase. Little work has been done on immature oöcytes, but from what has been done, it appears that these cells are very insensitive to radiations. It is again difficult to compare these cells with any counterpart in the male germ line.

Thus although sex may have no fundamental effect on radiation sensitivity, the genetic damage induced in females when exposed to radiations is much less than that in males. This arises through differences between oögenesis and spermatogenesis. Two important aspects both favour less genetic damage in females; first, that the most sensitive stages, spermiogenesis in males, have no counterpart in females, and second, that the least sensitive stage in females, immature oöcytes persist for a very long time relative to the equivalent male stage.

CHEMICAL AND PHYSICAL CONDITIONS WHICH MODIFY RADIATION EFFECTS

The following section deals with factors of an essentially non-biological nature which either increase or decrease radiation effects. Research on such phenomena is chiefly directed at an understanding of the mechanisms of radiation damage. It is to be hoped that this may lead to the discovery of means of protection against radiation damage. Some progress in radiation protection has been achieved but so far this is restricted to somatic effects; i.e. hazards to the individual; protection against genetic effects has yet to be accomplished.

THE INFLUENCE OF OXYGEN IN RADIATION MUTAGENESIS

Several early studies had indicated that organisms were less sensitive to the killing effects of radiation when irradiated under conditions of anoxia. Experiments by J. M. Thoday and J. Read in 1947, demonstrated that this effect was also present in the induction of chromosome breakage by radiations. They observed that approximately one third as many aberrations were induced by X-irradiation of bean root-tip cells when the cells were irradiated in nitrogen rather than in air. Subsequently, they also demonstrated that the effect of α-irradiation was

8

independent of oxygen tension. These results have been confirmed and extended in *Tradescantia* microspores by N. H. Giles and his co-workers, who showed that the effect of oxygen was limited to the period of irradiation; the oxygen tension before or after irradiation had no effect on aberration frequency. In addition, they demonstrated that with increasing amounts of oxygen, the frequency of aberrations increased sharply up to an oxygen tension of about 21 per cent (the same level as in air), after this there was little further increase in aberration frequency up to 100 per cent oxygen tension (Fig. 54). In recent studies

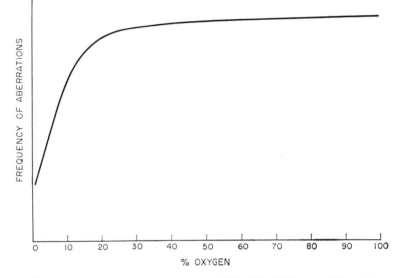

FIG. 54.   EFFECT OF OXYGEN TENSION ON THE PRODUCTION OF CHROMOSOME ABERRATIONS IN X-IRRADIATED *Tradescantia* MICROSPORES

with bacteria, the maximum oxygen effect was attained at oxygen levels very much lower than 21 per cent. It seems probable that oxygen diffusion gradients within the bean root depresses the oxygen effect slope in this tissue. Giles and his collaborators were also able to confirm the dependence of the oxygen effect on LET by demonstrating that neutron irradiation was affected to a degree intermediate between that for X-rays and that for γ-rays. Giles has suggested that oxygen might act by:

(a) Increasing the frequency of breaks;
(b) Changing the sensitivity of chromosomes through metabolic processes;
(c) Influencing the frequency of restitution.

Some evidence is available to support each of these possibilities. They are not in fact mutually exclusive and it seems probable that they all contribute to the oxygen effect. The possibility that has received the strongest support, however, is that the presence of oxygen increases the frequency of breaks. Direct evidence for this comes from the fact that oxygen, to be effective, must be present during the irradiation. If oxygen acted on rejoining, post-treatment should be effective; similarly, pre-treatment should be effective if sensitivity changes arose as a consequence of altered metabolic processes; rapid changes of the latter two types, however, could escape detection. A further point in favour of the breakage hypothesis is that it can be explained on the basis of radiochemical events in irradiated water. The initial effect of radiations in water is to produce ionised molecules which subsequently decompose to produce hydrogen atoms and hydroxyl radicals.

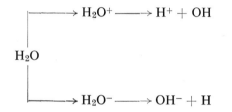

$$H_2O \begin{cases} \longrightarrow H_2O^+ \longrightarrow H^+ + OH \\ \\ \longrightarrow H_2O^- \longrightarrow OH^- + H \end{cases}$$

These may then undergo reaction to produce water or hydrogen peroxide, oxygen and hydrogen:

$$H + OH \longrightarrow H_2O$$
$$OH + OH \longrightarrow H_2O_2$$
$$H + H \longrightarrow H_2$$
$$2H_2O_2 \longrightarrow 2H_2O + O_2$$

If oxygen is present in the water other reactions are possible:

$$H + O_2 \longrightarrow HO_2$$
$$HO_2 + H \longrightarrow H_2O_2$$

Thus oxygen increases the production of hydrogen peroxide, first by direct reaction with hydrogen atoms and second, following the removal of these, by permitting more hydroxyl radicals to react together.

Living tissues contain a large amount of water and evidence presented in Chapter 5 suggested that part of the genetic effect of irradiations were due to indirect action involving H_2O_2. On this basis oxygen would increase mutation frequencies by promoting the indirect effects of radiations. This interpretation is supported by the relationship between oxygen effect and LET. The absence of any oxygen effect in α-ray studies would be due to the fact that a high probability for reaction between OH radicals already exists since they arise in close proximity; further reaction with oxygen would be negligible. It has also been shown that X-rays produce very little H_2O_2 in oxygen free water whereas α-rays do produce H_2O_2 under these conditions. A unified hypothesis can be presented, therefore, to explain the effects of LET, oxygen, and both combined, on the induction of mutations. This may be summarised as follows:

(a) Radiation-induced genetic changes result from direct ionisation within the chromosome and from the indirect mutagenic effect of H_2O_2 produced by radiochemical events;

(b) High density of ionisation favours a high production of H_2O_2 which leads to a high mutagenic effect;

(c) Oxygen increases mutation frequency by promoting the formation of H_2O_2;

(d) Densely ionising radiations respond less to oxygen deprivation since their rate of production of H_2O_2 is not influenced greatly by the presence of oxygen.

THE EFFECT OF TEMPERATURE AND HYDRATION IN RADIATION MUTAGENESIS

Two other factors which modify radiation effects and are closely linked with the action of oxygen are temperature and degree of hydration. Early studies in *Drosophila* had indicated that induced mutation frequencies were higher when irradiation was performed at low temperatures. This effect was demonstrated conclusively in 1939 with respect to chromosome aberrations in *Tradescantia* microspores and in *Drosophila* spermatozoa. More recent work has also confirmed the effect in the induction of recessive lethal mutations in *Drosophila*. Pre- and post-irradiation changes in temperature had no effect on induced genetic change, indicating that the primary effect was on the breakage process. Further confirmation of this also arises from the demonstration that the temperature effect remains constant even when radiation doses are fractionated or given at different intensities. If temperature influenced the rejoining of breaks then it would have relatively little effect if full opportunities already existed for restitution. Furthermore, rejoining of breaks does not occur in spermatozoa yet temperature is still effective in these cells.

Oxygen is more soluble in water at lower temperatures and, since metabolism is retarded under cold conditions, less oxygen will be used by a cell. Both of these factors lead to an increase in the oxygen content of cells which, in itself, must result in an increased sensitivity to radiations. Direct evidence that oxygen is involved in this way comes from the demonstration that the temperature effect is radically changed under conditions of anoxia. In *Drosophila*, temperature has no effect on the induction of mutations in the absence of oxygen, while in *Tradescantia* microspores under such conditions, the temperature effect is actually reversed. Clearly, changes in oxygen tension, which accompany temperature fluctuations, normally mask the effects of temperature itself. Similar increases in mutation frequency with increasing temperature have been found when very low temperature ranges have been studied. Thus from temperatures of $-192°$ C (liquid air temperature) up to $0°$ C, *Tradescantia* pollen grains are progressively more sensitive to the genetic effects of radiation.

The importance of water in radiation effects has been shown by observation on the sensitivity of seeds and spores of various plants irradiated before and after soaking. First indications of an effect of hydration came from experiments by L. J. Stadler, in which he showed that mutations were induced with a far higher frequency in soaked seeds of barley than in dry ones. It remained possible that this was due to a change in the developmental stage of the seed. Later workers have confirmed this result, however, under conditions which preclude this possibility. Furthermore, it has been shown that the effect of hydration is most marked in the presence of oxygen. Obviously these results are in close agreement with the hypothesis that radiation changes partly arise through pathways involving radiochemical events in water.

OTHER MODIFYING FACTORS

Pre-irradiation treatments with cyanide or azide compounds increase the frequency of radiation-induced mutations. The effect of these supplementary treatments also seems likely to be related to an indirect action of radiation. Cyanides and azides inhibit certain enzyme systems which destroy peroxides. It seems possible that their effect arises from an accumulation of radiation-induced peroxides; an additional way in which they might act is to increase the amount of oxygen in cells by depressing the rate of metabolism.

So far in this chapter modifying factors have produced their effects at the time of irradiation, probably by influencing the primary genetic lesions, chromosome breakage or gene mutation. The following account deals with factors which most probably influence the subsequent behaviour of the lesions or, more specifically, the restitution, rejoining or persistence of chromosome breaks. Chromosomal movement is obviously relevant to the likelihood that a break will restitute, remain open or rejoin in combination with a second break; it is not surprising that factors which influence chromosome movement also effect the relative proportions in which these types of effect appear. Thus it is found that centrifugation or application of high frequency vibration leads to an increase in the frequency of open breaks and rearrangements. It is interesting to note, however, that for centrifugation at least, the supplementary treatment is effective only when applied during irradiation. The fact that centrifugation after irradiation is of little consequence might be due to a secondary effect of radiation, the reduction of chromosome movement. The phenomenon does indicate, however, that caution should be applied to the view that modifying factors operating during irradiation alone must act on the breakage process rather than on rejoining.

Certain supplementary treatments reduce induced aberration frequencies. Thus treatments with the alkaloid, colchicine, before irradiation greatly reduces the frequency of chromatid but not chromosome aberrations. Colchicine inhibits chromosomal movement, chiefly at prophase; it is at this stage that chromatid, as opposed to chromosome, aberrations arise. Similarly, ultra-violet treatment before or after irradiation reduces aberration yield, especially that of chromatid breaks and translocations. The effect on iso-chromatid exchanges is less but these arise from breaks that are already close together and restriction of chromosomal movement is not likely to influence their rejoining.

A modifying factor of particular interest is infra-red irradiation. Studies by B. P. Kaufmann in *Drosophila* and by C. P. Swanson in *Tradescantia* showed that infra-red given either before or after X-rays markedly increased the frequency of chromosome aberrations but not that of point mutations. The results from these organisms differed, however, in that breakage frequency was affected in *Tradescantia* but not in *Drosophila*. The *Tradescantia* data suggest that infra-red increases breakage. This interpretation is supported by the fact that post-irradiation treatment with infra-red was effective even when given 18 hours after X-radiation, when the restitutional fate of breaks is supposed to be decided. In this respect it has been postulated that X-rays and infra-red produce metastable states in chromosomes which, in combination but not separately, produce breakage. In support of this it was found that a heat shock, interposed between the infra-red pre-treatment and X-radiation, destroyed the enhancing influence of the infra-red. Contrary to this, the data from *Drosophila* suggested that breakage was not affected. The lack of effect of infra-red in promoting the induction of dominant lethals, in contrast to the marked effect on viable chromosome rearrangement, suggested that infra-red acts by increasing the probability of new rejoining as opposed to restitution. This still involves a metastable state since rejoining occurs some time after irradiation in *Drosophila*. An additional factor of interest is that the nature of aberrations induced in *Tradescantia*, i.e. chromatid versus chromosome types, depends on the time of X-radiation but not on that of infra-red treatment. This tends to support the rejoining hypothesis since with a combined effect on breakage, it would be expected that the first treatment, either X-rays or infra-red, would determine aberration types. It is not yet possible to state conclusively which, if either, of these two hypotheses is correct.

7

GENES IN POPULATIONS

So far we have considered the manner of production of mutations by ionising radiations, their effects on individuals and the frequency with which they arise under given conditions. In the present chapter we shall discuss the subsequent fate of mutations as they are transmitted from generation to generation. This is the study of population genetics. In it we will deal not with individuals but with groups or populations in which they exist. For this purpose a population may be loosely defined as a collection of individuals, in space and in time, which constitutes an interbreeding community.

POPULATION GENETIC THEORY

Populations are made up of individuals, and therefore the nature of a population depends on the nature of the genotypes of individuals comprising it. Population genetics is concerned, therefore, with the probability of the occurrence of individuals of the various possible genotypes and with the factors which affect this probability.

The first of these factors is chance. Most organisms have a great number of gene loci and, even if only two alleles exist at each locus, the theoretically possible number of genotypes is very large. For example, if an organism has only 1000 loci with two alleles at each, the number of possible genotypes is 3^{1000}i.e. 10^{477}, a number that is incomprehensibly large. Thus the number of theoretically possible genotypes is usually far greater than the population size and consequently, the probability that two populations should be alike in their genotypic content is vanishingly small. In other words, for these statistical reasons alone, each population is unique.

Chance apart, there are several factors which are known to play a part in determining the genotypes of individuals. Basically there is, of course, the genotypes in the preceding generation; in addition to this there is the question of the choice of mate, particularly whether related or not, fertility and viability of genotypes, and finally the extent of genetic recombination and mutation.

Theories on the behaviour of genes in cross breeding populations have developed mainly from a consideration of hypothetical models of population structure. In the laboratory we observe such phenomena as gene segregation, mutation, and differences between individuals in viability and fertility; we must suppose that these occur also in natural populations. Mathematical models intended to represent the behaviour of genes in populations have been constructed, and the logical implications of these models have been worked out in detail, notably by J. B. S. Haldane and R. A. Fisher in Great Britain and by Sewall Wright in the U.S.A. But the next step, namely observation of the behaviour of genes in experimental populations subjected to constraints, has in the majority of instances yet to be taken. The reader must therefore constantly bear in mind that the results obtained in the following paragraphs are deductions from theoretical models and that they will be true of natural populations only if the features of the models are true reflections of the features of natural populations. Some certainly are not. In particular, each gene in the model is considered to act in isolation, whereas the genes in natural populations do not since they act through the bodies of individuals which are subject to the action both of other genes and of the environment. Again, in the model there are only two possible alleles at each locus, wild-type and mutant, whereas in nature it is the rule to find more than two alleles. Very little is known about the extent of the error introduced through these and other simplifications since the model is largely untested.

GENE FREQUENCY

Population genetic theory is based on the concept of gene frequency. Consider, for example, a population of N cats and suppose that x of them are heterozygous for the mutant allele P which cause polydactyly. Each cat carries two genes at the P locus and hence there are $2N$ genes in the population, x of which are the mutant allele P. The gene frequency of P is therefore $x/2N$ and, conversely, that of the wild-type allele is $(2N - x)/2N$ or $1 - x/2N$. The two frequencies naturally add up to unity.

CONSTANCY OF GENE FREQUENCY IN THE ABSENCE OF SELECTION

Let us postulate that we have a large population of cats containing x females heterozygous for polydactyly $(P/+)$ and y females and $x + y$ males homozygous for the wild-type allele $(+/+)$. The total population would be $2(x + y)$ and the gene frequency for P is $x/[4(x + y)]$. If each male and female mates once there will be $x + y$ litters, of which x derive from polydactylous females and y from normal-toed females.　In the x litters from $P/+$ females mated to $+/+$ males half the offspring will be $P/+$ and half $+/+$.　Thus if litter size is, on the average, the same for $P/+$ and $+/+$ females, respectively, and if the genotypes $P/+$ and $+/+$ are equally viable, the proportion of $P/+$ in the total offspring will be $\frac{1}{2}x/(x + y)$ and the gene frequency for P will be half this or $x/[4(x + y)]$.　Thus the gene frequency in the off-spring generation is the same as that in the parental.　By an extension of this argument it can be shown that the constancy of the gene fre-quency applies whatever the genotype of the parents.

GENOTYPIC FREQUENCY

Though the frequency of some particular gene tends to remain con-stant from generation to generation it does not follow that frequencies of homozygotes and heterozygotes will necessarily remain constant. This depends on the way that individuals choose mates.　To take an extreme example, in which like mates with like, it can be seen that the frequency of heterozygotes continually diminishes (Fig. 55).　This

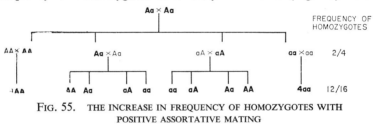

FIG. 55.　THE INCREASE IN FREQUENCY OF HOMOZYGOTES WITH POSITIVE ASSORTATIVE MATING

phenomenon was in fact first shown by Mendel in his studies with the pea, a plant in which self-fertilisation occurs.　Most organisms in nature tend to mate at random; any individual of one sex is equally likely to mate with any individual of the other sex.　This state of affairs is called *panmixia* and a population in which random mating occurs is called *panmictic*.　Mendel's first law states that male and female gametes fuse at random.　Thus in a panmictic population it is clear that random fusion occurs between all the gametes produced in a population.　If the frequency of a mutant allele is p and that of the wild-type allele is q ($p + q = 1$), the probability that the zygote receives two mutant alleles is $p \times p$ or p^2, two wild-type alleles q^2 and one of each $p \times q$, or $q \times p$, i.e. $2pq$.　The proportion of mutant homozygotes, heterozygotes and wild-type homozygotes, respectively, will be:

$$p^2 : 2pq : q^2 \quad (p^2 + 2pq + q^2 = (p + q)^2 = 1)$$

These proportions are dependent solely on gene frequency but, as we have shown that this remains constant in subsequent generations, it follows that the proportions of genotypes also remain constant. This constancy of genotypic equilibrium is called the Hardy-Weinberg law after its discoverers. They did not deduce it in the above way, however, but from a consideration of the frequencies of mating types. Their method is tabulated in Table 4.

TABLE 4. THE CONSTANCY OF GENOTYPIC FREQUENCIES IN SUBSEQUENT GENERATIONS WHERE THE INITIAL FREQUENCIES OF GENES P AND $+$ WERE p AND q, RESPECTIVELY

Parental Genotypes			Offspring Genotypes		
♀	♂	Frequency	$++$	$+P$	PP
$++$	$++$	q^4	q^4		
$++$	$P+$	$2pq^3$	pq^3	pq^3	
$++$	PP	p^2q^2		p^2q^2	
$P+$	$++$	$2pq^3$	pq^3	pq^3	
$P+$	$P+$	$4p^2q^2$	p^2q^2	$2p^2q^2$	p^2q^2
$P+$	PP	$2p^3q$		p^3q	p^3q
PP	$++$	p^2q^2		p^2q^2	
PP	$P+$	$2p^3q$		p^3q	p^3q
PP	PP	p^4			p^4

Offspring Totals

$$
\begin{aligned}
++ \quad & q^4 + 2pq^3 + p^2q^2 \quad & = q^2(q^2 + 2pq + p^2) \\
P+ \quad & 2pq^3 + 4p^2q^2 + 2p^3q \quad & = 2pq(q^2 + 2pq + p^2) \\
PP \quad & p^2q^2 + 2p^3q + p^4 \quad & = p^2(q^2 + 2pq + p^2)
\end{aligned}
$$

GENOTYPIC FREQUENCIES AND INBREEDING

Inbreeding, the mating of close relatives, has long been practised by Man for the improvement of domestic animals. The principle has been to purify and retain "good blood": we will now consider the genetic implications of this.

An offspring from a brother-sister mating has only two grand-parents. In the absence of any mutation any pair of genes at one locus in this individual has arisen by descent from either one or two of the four genes present in the grandparents (Fig. 56). Without implying any allelic relationship let us identify the grandparents' genes as a, b, c and d. If the offspring receives, for example, an a gene from its father it may receive from its mother either a, b, c, or d, each with the same probability. Thus in one case out of four the offspring will receive a second a gene. The same applies to genes b, c, and d, and furthermore, to the genes at each locus in the grandparents. Thus with brother-sister mating, the chance that a particular gene in one of the grandparents will become homozygous in the grandchild is $\frac{1}{4}$. If the gene happens to be a mutant allele with a frequency p in the grandparental generation, the frequency with which homozygotes arise in the above

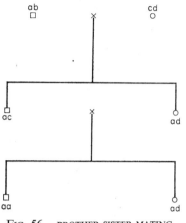

FIG. 56.   BROTHER-SISTER MATING
(Only a few of the possible genotypes shown)

way will be $p/4$.   Homozygotes will also arise, however, by union in the offspring of genes that descended from separate though allelic genes in the grandparents. This is the usual way in which homozygotes arise and we have shown that in a panmictic population the frequency with which they arise is p^2. In brother-sister mating, however, $\frac{1}{4}$ of the offspring's possible gene pairs are homozygous by descent which reduces the frequency of homozygotes by the alternative method to $\frac{3}{4}p^2$. Thus the total probability for homozygosity is $p/4 + 3p^2/4$ which exceeds that under panmixia by $p/4 + 3p^2/4 - p^2 = (p/4)(1-p) = pq/4$.

Thus with inbreeding, the frequency of homozygotes increases, and since gene frequency remains constant, this is balanced by a decrease in frequency of the heterozygotes.   This exemplifies a general rule which applies whatever the degree of inbreeding.

With a more distant relationship between the mates, the decrease in the frequency of heterozygotes becomes progressively less.   With first cousin matings the frequency of the homozygote type is increased by $pq/16$. In absolute terms this amount is small; it is at a maximum when $p = q = \frac{1}{2}$, and then $pq/16 = 1/64$. With this value of p the frequency of mutant homozygotes under panmixia is $p^2 = \frac{1}{4} = 16/64$.   Thus the change from panmixia to first cousin mating throughout the population will at the most increase the frequency of mutant homozygotes from 16/64 to 17/64. If only a part of the population practises cousin mating, say some fraction y, the frequency of mutant homozygotes will be

$$y(p^2 + pq/16) + (1 - y)p^2 = p^2 + ypq/16$$

Thus the increase in the frequency of mutant homozygotes is $pqy/16$, if y and p are small, this increase will be exceedingly small, and almost certainly undetectable. However, we may pose a different question: among mutant homozygotes what proportion have parents who are first cousins? Relative to all mutant homozygotes this proportion is

$$\frac{y(p^2 + pq/16)}{(p^2 + ypq/16)} = \frac{y(16p^2 + pq)}{(16p^2 + ypq)}$$

If p is very small, so that q is very nearly unity and $16p^2$ is negligible compared with y, this expression approaches unity. Thus it will be a characteristic of conditions due to rare recessive genes that there is a very high frequency of consanguinity among the parents of affected individuals, approximating to unity.

Disturbances in genotypic ratios also occur when mating is assortative, that is when like mates with like (positive assortative mating) or with unlike (negative assortative mating). When the criteria for assortative mating are genotypic the effect on genotypic ratios is similar to the effects of inbreeding for positive assortative mating, but opposite in effect for negative assortative mating. Normally, however, assortative criteria are phenotypic and as similar phenotypes frequently arise from different genotypes this has little effect on the ratios of homozygotes and heterozygotes.

FACTORS THAT CHANGE GENE FREQUENCY

Although we have shown that, within the framework of Mendel's first law, gene frequencies in a population remain constant, this is obviously not true in nature. Evolution could not proceed without quite momentous changes in gene frequency. Among the factors which tend to change gene frequency are chance and differential migration. Chance becomes important only when the population size is very small; particular genes tend to be retained or lost by the chance inclusion or exclusion of individuals who carry them. Differential migration is effective where two populations of a species exist in partial separation. Factors which alter the degree of separation will influence the degree of mixing of the two gene pools. While both these factors are of interest in studies of evolution they are not particularly relevant to radiation genetics and will not be considered in detail. Two factors which are of importance, however, are the mutation process itself and selection.   The theoretical implications of these will be considered in the following sections.

MUTATION ACTING ALONE

The effect of mutation acting alone will almost always be to increase the frequency of a rare allele. Consider a rare gene A with a frequency p in a hypothetical population. The wild-type allele mutates to A during each generation with a frequency m (forward mutation) while A mutates to the wild-type allele with a frequency n (reverse mutation). After one generation the frequency of A will be altered by an amount

$$\Delta p = m(1 - p) - np$$

When p is small, $(1 - p)$ will be much greater than p and Δp will be a positive quantity. The frequency of p will increase from generation to generation until Δp becomes equal to zero. If forward or reverse mutation is absent, p becomes equal to 0 or 1, respectively.   Where values exist for both m and n, an equilibrium will be reached when the total forward mutation equals the total reverse mutation

$$m(1 - p) = np \quad \text{or} \quad p = \frac{m}{m + n}$$

If m and n are equal, equilibrium is reached when $p = \frac{1}{2}$. With increasing values of n relative to m, p becomes progressively smaller. Thus the frequency of a gene maintained in a population by a balance of forward and reverse mutation alone will tend to be high unless its forward mutation rate is very much smaller than its reverse mutation rate.   Conversely, if a gene is very rare in a population (e.g. $p < 1$ per cent) there is cause to suspect that some factor other than mutation is affecting its frequency.

SELECTION

Natural selection or survival of the fittest is a process whereby natural populations achieve progress or remain successful in a changing environment.   The number of offspring produced in a generation by any natural species is greater than the number that will become parents for the next generation. There is some loss of potential parents between the time when they are formed, at fertilisation, and the time the next generation is formed.   This loss will involve a greater proportion of those individuals less able to survive and in so far as the disability is genetic, will result in selection against certain genes or genotypes. Conversely, genotypes that confer some advantage over and above the average will tend to be favoured by selection.

The selective advantage of an individual will depend on many factors of an intricate biological nature such as viability, fecundity, ability to choose a mate, and so on. It is very difficult to partition these factors but when considering the effect of selection in a hypothetical population the various causes of loss of potential parents can be lumped together and expressed by a single parameter. Suppose that in a population of cats the net reproductive rate (i.e. the number of young that survive to breed per breeding parent) is lower for a homozygous polydactylous than for a normal cat in the ratio $(1 - s)$ to 1; then $(1 - s)$ is called the *selective value* of the genotype *PP*, and *s* is called the *coefficient of selection* against the genotype *PP*. The coefficient of selection against the heterozygote is usually smaller than that against the corresponding homozygote, so we may write the selective value of the heterozygote *P+* as $(1 - hs)$ where *h* has some value between 0 and 1. Now consider what will happen to the frequency of *P* under panmixia. Suppose the gene frequency of *P* is *p* at the instant of formation of the zygotes of one generation and that the frequency of its normal allele is $q (= 1 - p)$. Then the three types of zygotes, $+ +$, *P+* and *PP*, will occur with the initial frequencies q^2, $2pq$ and p^2, respectively, and they will survive to parenthood in the proportions q^2, $2pq(1 - hs)$ and $p^2(1 - s)$, respectively.

Let us write $W = q^2 + 2pq(1 - hs) + p^2(1 - s)$. The frequency of surviving heterozygotes is $2pq(1 - hs)/W$ and that of surviving *PP* homozygotes is $p^2(1 - s)/W$. The proportion of *P* bearing gametes that they contribute to the next generation is

$$p_1 = [1/W][pq(1 - hs) + p^2(1 - s)]$$

The change in the frequency of the gene *P* will be

$$\Delta p = p_1 - p = [1/W][pq(1 - hs) + p^2(1 - s)] - p$$
$$= [1/W][pq(1 - hs) + p^2(1 - s) - pW]$$
$$= [p/W][q(1 - hs) + p(1 - s) - q^2 - 2pq(1 - hs) - p^2(1 - s)]$$

which by simplification

$$= [p/W][(q + p) - qhs - ps - (q^2 + 2pq + p^2) + 2pqhs + p^2s]$$
$$= -ps/W[qh - 2pqh + p - p^2]$$
$$= -ps/W[qh(1 - 2p) + p(1 - p)]$$
$$= -pqs/W[p + h(1 - 2p)]$$

This equation shows that a deleterious mutant allele will tend to disappear from the population at a rate which depends on the initial gene frequency as well as the coefficients of selection for both homozygotes and heterozygotes. Although still complex the equation is a general one and more specific cases can be fitted to it:—

In the first case, *complete dominance*, $h = 1$. Thus

$$\Delta p = [-pqs/W](1 - p)$$
$$= -pq^2s/W = -pq^2s/[1 - ps(1 + q)]$$

Where P is *completely recessive* $h = 0$. Thus

$$\Delta p = -p^2qs/W = -p^2qs/(1 - p^2s)$$

Where *no dominance* exists $h = \frac{1}{2}$. Thus

$$\Delta p = -\frac{1}{2}pqs/W = -\frac{1}{2}pqs/(1 - ps)$$

Taking the value $s = 0.1$ we can construct graphs (Fig. 57) showing

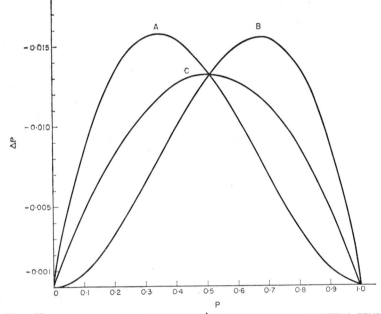

FIG. 57.   CHANGE IN GENE FREQUENCY Δp IN RELATION TO THE INITIAL GENE FREQUENCY p WHERE THE COEFFICIENT OF SELECTION AGAINST THE GENE is $s = 0.1$

A. complete dominance: selection against homozygotes and heterozygotes
B. complete necessivity: selection against homozygotes only
C. no dominance: selection against homozygotes twice that against heterozygotes

the relationship between Δp and p in the above three cases. It can be seen that selection is most effective for intermediate gene frequencies and at gene frequencies below 0.5 selection in heterozygotes is much

more effective than in homozygotes.   Thus when a deleterious fully
recessive gene is rare it suffers little selection.

We may consider next the progressive change in the frequency of a
gene under adverse selection, during the passage of many generations.
From any given starting point on a curve in Fig. 57, the value of *p* after
one generation can be determined.   This new value corresponds to a
new value for Δ*p* which in turn leads to a new value of *p* and so on.
The sum total of such steps required to pass from one value of *p* to
another, represents the number of generations over which this gene
frequency change will occur.   To determine this accurately requires
the application of integral calculus.   The method will not be described
here but curves showing the change in gene frequency in subsequent
generations are shown in Fig. 58.

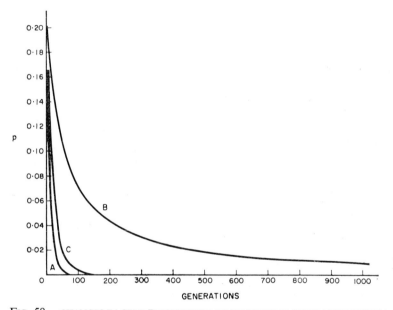

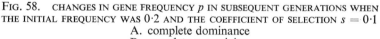

FIG. 58.   CHANGES IN GENE FREQUENCY *p* IN SUBSEQUENT GENERATIONS WHEN
THE INITIAL FREQUENCY WAS 0.2 AND THE COEFFICIENT OF SELECTION $s = 0.1$

A. complete dominance
B. complete necessity
C. no dominance

Under certain conditions selection will fail to bring about any change
in gene frequency.   This will happen if

$$0 = \Delta p = -[pqs/W]\,[h(1 - 2p) + p]$$

9

The equation will be satisfied by:—

$$p = 0, \ q = 0$$

and

$$h(1 - 2p) + p = 0$$

The first two are trivial cases where p or its normal allele are absent from the population. The third is of great interest, it implies:—

$$p = -h/(1 - 2p)$$

Since p can only take positive values between 0 and 1, this solution requires that h shall be negative; in other words, that the heterozygote shall have a greater selective value than either homozygote. Under this condition a stable equilibrium will be reached at which both alleles will remain in the population with a frequency which may be high, despite the selective disadvantage of the two types of homozygote.

Selection operates only through differential reproduction; selection cannot act against genes which express themselves in the post reproductive period and such genes may become common. This leads to a big genetic element in chronic diseases of the elderly.

MUTATION AND SELECTION ACTING SIMULTANEOUSLY

When mutation and selection operate simultaneously in the hypothetical population (as they do in all natural populations) the total change in gene frequency per generation will be the algebraic sum of the changes due to each cause.

$$\Delta p = (mq - np) - [pqs/W] [h(1 - 2p) + p] \qquad (1)$$

When individuals carrying the mutant allele are at a selective disadvantage, the allele will usually have a low frequency in the population. This can be shown in the following way. Suppose the mutant allele was almost absent from the population, so that p is extremely low. Then q, W and $(1 - 2p)$ are all nearly equal to unity and equation (1) reduces to

$$\Delta p = m - ps(h + p) \qquad (2)$$

If p is so small that $ps(h + p)$ is smaller than m, Δp will be positive and therefore p will rise. It will continue to do so in subsequent generations until $\Delta p = 0$, when an equilbrium will be reached in which

$$0 = m - ps(h + p) \qquad (3)$$

$$= sp^2 + shp - m \qquad (3a)$$

Solving this equation:—

$$p = \frac{-hs + \sqrt{h^2s^2 + 4ms}}{2s}$$

$$= \tfrac{1}{2}\left(-h + \sqrt{\frac{h^2s^2 + 4ms}{s^2}}\right)$$

$$= (h/2)\left(-1 + \sqrt{\frac{sh^2 + 4m}{h^2s}}\right)$$

$$= (h/2)\left(-1 + \sqrt{1 + \frac{4m}{h^2s}}\right)$$

If the mutation rate m is of the same order found in normal populations, i.e. 10^{-5} or less, and if neither h^2 nor s is extremely small, $4m/h^2s$ will be less than unity and by the binomial theorem,

$$p = (h/2)\left[-1 + \tfrac{1}{2}\left(\frac{4m}{sh^2}\right) + \dots \text{ smaller terms}\right]$$

which approximates to

$$p = \frac{m}{hs} \qquad (4)$$

Since m is very small compared to unity and we have assumed that h and s are not, it follows that p will be small compared to unity: in other words, a deleterious mutant allele will have a low equilibrium frequency in the population.

If the population is panmictic, the frequency of individuals manifesting the presence of the gene will be

$$2pq + p^2 = p(2 - p) \simeq 2p = 2m/hs \qquad (5)$$

For a fully recessive gene ($h = 0$) eq. 3 becomes

$$0 = m - p^2s$$

Whence
$$p = \sqrt{m/s}$$

Since it is recessive, the presence of the gene will be manifest only in the homozygotes. Their frequency in a panmictic population will be

$$p^2 = m/s \qquad (6)$$

Thus with both dominant and recessive deleterious genes the frequency of the individuals manifesting the presence of the gene will be low and will be directly proportional, at equilibrium, to the mutation rate. This conclusion is of fundamental importance in any consideration of the genetic effects of radiations and other mutagens.

W is called the *average adaptive value* of the population with respect to the allele under consideration. It was defined as

$$W = q^2 + 2pq(1 - hs) + p^2(1 - s)$$
$$= (q^2 + 2pq + p^2) - ps(2qh + p)$$
$$= 1 - ps(2qh + p)$$

Where there is no loss of individuals through selection ($s = 0$), W has the value unity. The term $ps(2qh + p)$ is a measure of the extent to which individuals are lost through the action of selection. But we have seen (eq. 3) that when mutation and selection are in equilibrium

$$0 = m - ps(h + p)$$

i.e.

$$s = \frac{m}{p(h + p)}$$

so that at equilibrium we have

$$W = 1 - \frac{m(2q + p)}{[h(1 - 2p) + p]}$$

Thus at equilibrium the average loss of adaptive value of the population is directly proportional to its mutation rate.

CHANGES IN MUTATION RATE

It has been shown that hypothetical populations in a constant environment settle down to a state of equilibrium at which the frequency of individuals manifesting the presence of deleterious genes, whether dominant or recessive, is directly proportional to the mutation rate and that the average loss of individuals through selection will also be directly proportional to the mutation rate. If the mutation rate is suddenly raised the population is thrown out of equilibrium: Δp ceases to be zero and the frequency of each deleterious gene rises until a new equilibrium point is reached. The increase in the gene frequency in the first generation is simply the change in mutation rate,

$$\Delta p = m_2 - m_1$$

Where m_1 and m_2 are the old and new mutation rates. However, a given absolute change in gene frequency will be much more apparent if the former equilibrium frequency were low than if it were high; a more meaningful measure is, therefore, the relative change. From eq. (4) this is seen to be

$$\Delta p/p = \frac{hs(m_2 - m_1)}{m_1} \qquad (7)$$

for a gene which has some expression in the heterozygote ($h \neq 0$). This shows that the relative change in gene frequency in the first generation is directly proportional to s, the selective disadvantage of the gene; in other words a grossly deleterious allele approaches its new equilibrium frequency more rapidly than does a mildly deleterious allele. Furthermore the initial change in gene frequency is directly proportional to h; in other words a fully dominant gene ($h = 1$) approaches its new equilibrium frequency more rapidly than does one with only a slight degree of expression in the heterozygote ($h < 1$).

For a fully recessive gene eq. (7) is not applicable, as it was derived from eq. (4). With a recessive gene eq. (5) is applicable and we have

$$\Delta p / p = (m_1 - m_2)\, s/m_1 \qquad (8)$$

Here also, the rate of approach to the new equilibrium is seen to be a function of s, but it is proportional to $\sqrt{s}$ rather than to s directly. As with dominant genes, a grossly detrimental recessive will approach its new equilibrium frequency more rapidly than will a mildly detrimental one.

CHANGES IN THE ENVIRONMENT

The selective value of a genotype depends on the environment in which an individual of that genotype lives. If the environment changes the selective value changes. It may happen, therefore, that an allele which was formerly at a selective disadvantage becomes selectively advantageous. If this happens we have as before (eq. 1)

$$\Delta p = (mq - np) - (pqs/W)\,[h(1 - 2p) + p]$$

but s is now negative and therefore the second term on the right hand side is positive. Both terms on the right hand side are then positive; p will increase and continue to increase until the mutant allele has nearly displaced the former normal allele from the population. A new equilibrium will then occur at which selection is counterbalanced by back mutation to the former wild-type allele.

The consequences of the theoretical model of population structure may be summarised;

(1) If environmental conditions and mutation rates remain constant then gene frequencies and phenotypic frequencies also remain constant.

(2) Disadvantageous conditions produced by recessive genes will be rare, and their incidence will be directly proportional to mutation rates; they will also have a high familial incidence.

(3) Disadvantageous conditions produced by dominant genes will be

rare and will arise mainly sporadically by mutation: their incidence will be proportional to mutation rates.

(4) Genes which produce favourable or neutral conditions will tend to have high frequencies which will be independent of mutation rates.

(5) Diseases with a late onset will have a high genetic component since their effects will not be subject to selection.

(6) A deleterious condition produced by a gene that may have favourable effects under some circumstances will tend to have a high incidence which is almost independent of mutation rate.

METRICAL CHARACTERS AND MUTATIONS

We have considered theoretical aspects of changes in the frequencies of alleles that produce contrasting phenotypes; variation in the population was concerned with the expression by an individual of one of two alternative attributes. The straightforward case of the behaviour of two alleles at a single locus was chosen to simplify the mathematical model. The results are applicable, therefore, to the induction of mutations with gross effects since these are almost always deleterious. We have noted, however, that the phenotype is commonly dependent on the combined action of more than one gene. With increasing complexity of this combination of effects the model must become progressively less applicable. The extreme case of multiplicity of gene action is in the determination of phenotypes of a measurable and continuously varying nature. This polygenic control of biometrical characters, which is of paramount importance in population genetic studies, was outlined in Chapter 3. We will now consider this in slightly greater detail before considering the effects of mutation in the system.

It has been noted that polygenes are not detectable individually; each has only a small effect on a character for which the observed phenotypic value is determined by all the genes involved, together with factors of an environmental nature. Polygenic inheritance is thus not amenable to a Mendelian approach and special methods have been devised to study it. These are based on the concept of phenotypic frequencies as opposed to gene frequencies as used in Mendelian studies on populations.

Metrical characters generally show continuous variation. In practice, however, phenotypes are measured in terms of discrete units. For example, stature in Man can be measured in inches in which case we can describe a population as having a frequency of individuals of height between x and $x + 1$ inches, between $x + 1$ and $x + 2$ inches, and so on. The unit of one inch is therefore the *class interval* for which there exists a *class frequency*.   We have observed in Chapter 3 that with progressively smaller class intervals the frequency distribution curve approximates to a smooth curve. Figure 59 depicts a frequency polygon

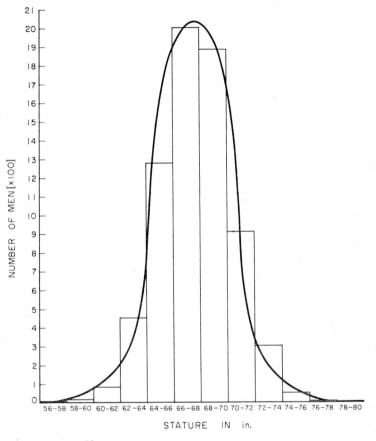

FIG. 59.   STATURE OF FORTY–YEAR OLD MEN FROM
BRITISH SURVEY TAKEN IN 1935

for stature in Man together with the continuous curve as it might be observed with very small class intervals.

This type of bell-shaped curve represents the type of distribution commonly associated with metrical traits in populations. It is a form closely related to a theoretical distribution known as the *normal curve*. A frequency distribution is located on a scale of measurement by the average or mean value of the variable character and its shape is determined by the spread of values on either side of the mean. The latter is an estimate of the degree of variability in a population and is most conveniently measured as the *standard deviation* (σ) which is defined by

$$\sigma = \sqrt{\frac{1}{N} S(x - m)^2}$$

where m is the mean of the variable character x in a sample of N individuals. The standard deviation is the square root of the mean of the squares of all deviations from the population mean. The mean of the squares of all deviations, σ^2, is called the *variance*.

Both means and variances are under the joint control of environmental and genetic factors. The phenotypic value (P) of a character in a population can thus be partitioned into genetic (G) and environmental (E) components, thus

$$P = G + E$$

In a constant environment we can consider that environmental influences acting in opposite directions are equal and that the mean phenotypic value is equal to the mean genotypic value. Thus under the assumption of a constant environment from generation to generation, a degree of simplicity which cannot be achieved, changes in the phenotypic mean imply a change in the genotypic mean value brought about by changes in the gene frequency.

The variance also may be partitioned into genetic and environmental components but in this case the phenotypic variance is the sum of the other two

$$V_P = V_G + V_E$$

Genetic variance is thus a measure of the genetic diversity of individuals within a population. It is a concept basic to the understanding of polygenic inheritance since its value determines the degree of resemblance between relatives. Thus if the genetic variance is zero, the deviation of the phenotype of an individual from the population mean will be determined solely by environment ; there will be no similarity between relatives. Conversely, if environmental variance is zero the resemblance between parent and offspring would be entirely determined by the values of the parents.

The estimates of genetic variance cannot be determined directly since environmental conditions can never be made identical for different individuals. It is possible, however, to obtain genetically very similar individuals, as for example, in highly inbred lines of experimental animals. Thus if one inbred strain of mice is crossed with another, the F_1 individuals are all alike but heterozygous. Following segregation, the F_2 individuals are genetically diverse. The phenotypic variance of the F_1 is thus a measure of V_E, while that of the F_2 is a measure of $V_E + V_G$ (Fig. 60). The difference between the variances of the F_2

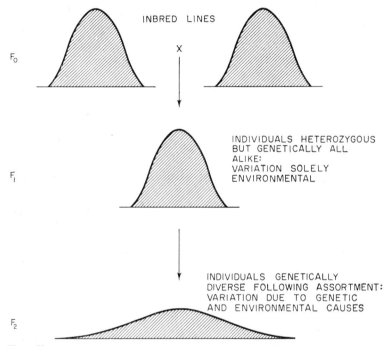

INBRED LINES

X

F_0

INDIVIDUALS HETEROZYGOUS BUT GENETICALLY ALL ALIKE:
VARIATION SOLELY ENVIRONMENTAL

F_1

INDIVIDUALS GENETICALLY DIVERSE FOLLOWING ASSORTMENT: VARIATION DUE TO GENETIC AND ENVIRONMENTAL CAUSES

F_2

FIG. 60. OBSERVATION OF GENETIC VARIANCE FROM FREQUENCY DISTRIBU-
TIONS IN THE F_1 AND F_2 OF A CROSS BETWEEN TWO DIFFERENT INBRED LINES

and the F_1 represents a measure of V_G. The genotypic variance can be partitioned further according to the different modes of gene action. Thus there is an additive genetic component where each gene adds a certain increment to a character, a dominance component concerned with the interaction of alleles and a component concerned with the interaction between loci

$$V_G = V_A + V_D + V_I$$

Each of these contributes to the total genotypic variance of the population but only the additive variance is concerned in the degree of similarity between relatives. The dominance and interaction components are produced by relational balance within the genotype but a parent transmits his genes to his offspring not his genotype. The additive genotypic variance can be determined by the estimation of correlations between relatives. This will not be described here. Another method involves the measurement of the success with which a metric character can be modified by selection.

As we saw in the early part of this chapter, changes in gene frequency can occur under the influence of selection pressure. There we were concerned with selection caused by differences in the fitness of genotypes to survive in a population. For metrical characters we are concerned chiefly with artificial selection whereby certain individuals are chosen on the basis of their phenotypes to be the parents for the next generation. The changes in gene frequencies are conditioned, therefore, by the relationship between genotype and phenotype.

The pressure applied during selection is measured as the deviation of the phenotypic mean of the parents from that of the population from which they were chosen. This is called the *selection differential* (S). Similarly, the difference between the mean of the new population and that of the original is called the *selection response* (R). Clearly the relation between R and S depends on the proportion of the phenotypic variance of the parental population that is due to additive gene action. This proportion, V_A/V_P is called the *heritability* and symbolised as h^2.

Thus

$$R = h^2 S$$

Some values of h^2 for characters in different organisms are given in Table 5.

TABLE 5.   SOME APPROXIMATE VALUES OF HERITABILITY FOR TRAITS
IN EXPERIMENTAL ORGANISMS

Organism	Trait	h^2
Poultry	Egg weight	0·6
	Annual egg production	0·3
	Body weight	0·2
	Susceptibility to certain infectious diseases	0·06
Mice	Body weight at six weeks	0·35
	Size of first litter	0·15
Drosophila	Abdominal bristle number	0·5
	Body size	0·4

RESPONSE TO SELECTION DURING SUCCESSIVE GENERATIONS

Prediction of selection response from the relationship $R = h^2S$ is usually satisfactory for the early generations in a selection programme. When selection is continued for many generations, response to selection begins to fall and may become zero, in which case, the characters under selection are said to have reached a plateaued level. In some cases heritability decreases during selection and diminution in selection response can be attributed to the exhaustion of utilisable variance. When this occurs, the final fixation of favoured alleles prevents response not only to continued selection but also to selection in the reverse direction. More commonly, however, heritability remains high at a plateau level and reverse selection produces a strong and rapid response. Thus during the progress of a selection programme, the genetic determination of a character can change from an additive to a non-additive type.

The underlying causes of the breakdown of the simple model of additive gene action are complex and not fully understood. One aspect that is of marked importance, however, concerns fitness. Attainment of a plateau level for a metrical character is frequently associated with a decrease in fitness in the population. This may be so great that continued selection is impossible due to the low reproductive capacity of the population. If selection is suspended, some recovery of fitness occurs and, at the same time, selection gains are lost. Thus natural selection is working in the opposite direction to artificial selection. This is one way in which selection may be ineffective even in the presence of additive genetic variance; the two forces, artificial and natural selection, balance each other. This explanation seems perfectly reasonable where the character under study represents a major component of fitness, that is, where there is a physiological basis for expecting extreme deviants to be inviable or sterile. In the overwhelming majority of metrical traits that have been studied, a clear cut relationship with fitness is not obvious. In some cases there appears to be no correlation at all. One such example is the number of chaetae (bristles) present on the abdomen in *Drosophila*. The behaviour of this character under selection has been studied extensively by K. Mather, the results of one selection experiment are shown diagrammatically in Fig. 61. The number of chaetae increased rapidly during the first twenty generations of selection but fitness decreased until selection was no longer possible. When selection was suspended, fitness recovered and chaeta number fell. A further process of selection led to an increase in chaeta number without any loss of fitness; the selection gains were not lost following cessation of selection and heritability remained high, as shown by the success of reverse selection. Clearly the mean number of chaetae was not in itself related to fitness; three distinct levels of stability were obtained. Nevertheless, in the initial selection, fitness decreased sharply with increasing chaeta number. In addition to the effect on chaeta number, correlated responses were observed in respect of other bristle systems, mating behaviour, spermatheca number and pigmentation patterns. The explanation put forward by Mather was that chaeta number was determined, in the initial population, by a balanced polygenic system of

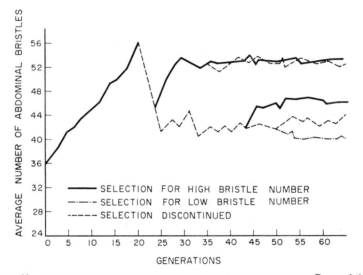

FIG. 61.   SELECTION FOR HIGH ABDOMINAL BRISTLE NUMBER IN *Drosophila*

gene blocks, held together by linkage. Also incorporated into the blocks were genes affecting fertility and other characters. The initial selection upset the balance to produce several correlated responses. During suspension of selection, natural selection and the breakdown of linkage reproduced new balanced systems within which selection was able to induce new stable levels of high chaeta number. The important part of the model is the implication that the polygenic control of metrical characters and fitness are all interrelated and exist in the form of balanced systems. These confer on the individual an optimum range of conditions for all characters but enable a population to undergo slow change should a stimulus be applied. This dual purpose, involving short term stability with long term flexibility, is considered to be due to the selective advantage of heterozygotes. This concept which has been termed *genetic homeostasis* has been described in detail by I. M. Lerner.

MUTATION OF POLYGENES

Experimental studies on mutation in polygenic systems, although sparse, show conclusively that new variation does arise both spontaneously and by radiation treatment. The appearance of new polygenic variation has been demonstrated by increases in genetic variance and by selection progress in metrical traits in populations that were started from inbred, i.e. genetically pure, lines of *Drosophila*. In the first of these studies Mather demonstrated that new variation, in respect of abdominal chaeta number, appeared at a rate of about 0·006 units per generation. In an outbred population the variance was about 5 units and consequently spontaneous polygenic mutation was estimated to produce only about 1/1000 of the normal variation per generation. Put another way, 1000 generations would be required, in the absence of selection, to produce normal variance in a population that originated from a pure line. These observations have been confirmed by G. Clayton and A. Robertson who also studied the effect of radiation on the genetic control of chaeta number. When adults in each generation were given 1800 r of X-rays the average gain in variance per generation, over a

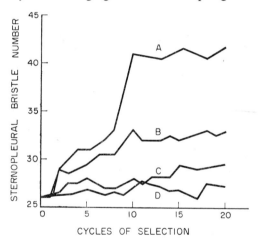

FIG. 62. SELECTION RESPONSE FOR STERNOPLEURAL BRISTLE NUMBER IN *Drosophila* FOLLOWING ALTERNATIVE GENERATIONS OF X-IRRADIATION (3000 r) AND SELECTION
A and B, irradiated lines
D and C, non-irradiated lines

total of 17 generations, was 0·06. This is thus about 10 times the spontaneous rate. One peculiarity, however, was that the response to selection in the irradiated lines, although significant, was much lower than that predicted on the basis of the increased variance. Thus genetic variability for metrical traits arises very slowly by mutation and only a small part of it is utilisable for selection. In fact several attempts to improve selection response by irradiation have proved unsuccessful. An exception to this has been reported by R. E. Scossiroli who irradiated populations of *Drosophila* that had been selected and stabilised for a high sternopleural bristle number. The initial mean level of bristle number was 27 and in two lines in which 3000 r of X-rays and selection were applied in alternate generations, respectively, new mean levels of 41 and 33 bristle numbers were achieved after 20 generations. With continued irradiation and selection the levels became stabilised at 43 and 33 bristles respectively (Fig. 62). In the original plateau population there was still considerable genetic variance. It seems probable that the good response achieved by Scossiroli resulted not from the induction of mutation but by the release of existing non-utilisable genetic variance. Radiation treatment increases the frequency of crossing-over; existing polygenic blocks may have been disrupted, therefore allowing the formation, under selection, of new balanced systems. Other evidence that induced genetic recombination is involved in the response of polygenic systems to irradiation comes from studies reported by T. Komai in which increased variance and selection response arose in an outbred population after irradiation of female but not of male *Drosophila*. Crossing-over in the latter is negligible.

We have seen that mutations detected by Mendelian methods are deleterious in the homozygous condition and when completely recessive are removed from the population only by natural selection acting on the homozygotes. The question of the fitness of polygenic mutations is much more complicated. In the first place fitness is not an innate property of the allele but depends on the balance achieved in the entire genotype. A mutation might push a metrical character in a direction that was favourable in one individual but harmful in another. Even this is too simple an approach since we have seen that, given time, metrical characters can be altered quite radically without adverse effects on fitness; indeed, this facility is an essential part of the theory of genetic homeostasis and evolution would be impossible without it. It would appear, therefore, that polygenic mutation is not necessarily harmful. The incorporation of new mutations cannot be continued indefinitely in a population, however, there must be some equilibrium between gains and losses. If the losses are attributable to natural selection, as with major-gene mutations, the process of mutation must be deleterious. To take a different approach, we may consider the theory, for which there is ample evidence, that polygenic balance is achieved by extensive heterozygosity. This involves the concept that loci are represented by several alleles each present in natural populations at moderately high frequencies. If the different alleles occur with similar frequencies and if mutation from one allele to another is a random event within the allelic group, then the induction of mutation will have no effect on gene frequencies in the population. The disturbance of the balance will be negligible since we have already seen that in this respect recombination is the more powerful agency. On this view induced polygenic mutation would not be deleterious. Several assumptions have been made, however, the most dubious of which concerns the mutability of alleles. Many, possibly the majority, of mutations induced at loci with gross effects involve losses or inactivations of genes. If this were also true for polygenes, non-random changes in gene frequency would occur and equilibrium might be maintained by selection, with the unavoidable implication of deleterious effects. It is obvious that we have too little information in this branch of genetics to predict with any confidence the consequences of induced mutation.

8

MUTATION IN MAN

The study of human genetics cannot be pursued by experimental methods as applied to other organisms. Observations are restricted to events beyond the control of the observer and, in addition, the long generation time in Man represents a serious handicap to the collection of family data. On the other hand, recorded medical data supply an enormous amount of material valuable for analytical studies.

Because of the absence of an experimental approach, human genetics rely to a considerable extent on principles derived from the study of experimental organisms. The basic tenets of genetics are common to all living organisms and their extrapolation to Man requires no special emphasis. This can be safely assumed with respect to the concept of genes, chromosomes, segregation, linkage and recombination, etc. and also to the diversity of genic expression and interrelation. One aspect that cannot be assumed without qualification, and which will be discussed more fully in the next and final chapter, concerns quantitative aspects such as the number of genes in Man and other organisms and their relative mutabilities both spontaneous and induced. In the present chapter we will consider mutation in Man and its consequences in populations; means for determining the rate at which genes mutate spontaneously and the available information on induced genetic changes in populations that have been subjected to radiation exposure.

GENETIC STUDIES IN MAN

The study of human heredity is, of course, intimately associated with medicine and consequently the available data refer chiefly to inherited disease. Thus, in the early days of genetics, effort was directed mainly to the study of family pedigrees within which a high incidence of some spectacular disease or disability was found. These pedigrees were analysed to ascertain the nature of the genetic transmission within the framework of existing Mendelian principles. For example, Fig. 63 shows a pedigree for a condition called *epidermolysis bullosa*. This affliction, typified by extensive blistering of the skin, is obviously determined by a dominant gene. Normal parents produced no affected offspring while affected parents produced 27 affected and 21 non-affected

offspring, a reasonably good fit to the expected 1 : 1 ratio for a dominant condition. A pedigree for a rare recessive trait, Folling's disease
or phenylketonuria, is illustrated in Fig. 64. This disease is characterised

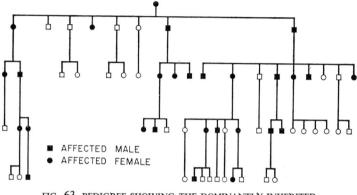

■ AFFECTED MALE
● AFFECTED FEMALE

FIG. 63. PEDIGREE SHOWING THE DOMINANTLY INHERITED
CHARACTER, *Epidermolysis bullosa*

by the excretion of phenylpyruvic acid ($C_6H_5CH_2CO.COOH$) in the
urine (see page 42). In addition to the biochemical effect, the phenotype also comprises a severe form of idiocy. That phenylketonuria is
due to a recessive gene is suggested by the absence of the disease in
parents of affected individuals and by the ratio of four affected to eight
unaffected offspring in the two relevant families. On the basis of
recessive inheritance, each of the four parents would be heterozygous
and the expected ratio of affected to unaffected would be 3 : 9. One

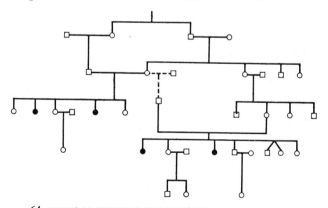

FIG. 64. PEDIGREE SHOWING THE INHERITANCE OF THE RECESSIVE
CHARACTER *Phenylketonuria*

particular point to note in this pedigree is that the parents were cousins in both families which contained affected individuals. Consanguinity is, in fact, frequently found among parents of individuals expressing rare recessive inherited disease (see page 113).

The above examples will suffice to establish the analysis of simple factorial inheritance in Man. Many more pedigrees are available in which can be traced most of the properties of genes that have been recognised through study of experimental organisms. In one important way, however, genetic analysis in Man is less complete than in other organisms. This concerns the specific identity of the genetic basis of an inherited disease; the appearance of similar traits in different families need not be due to the same mutant gene. In experimental animals, allelism tests would quickly resolve this problem but in Man one can only wait for the necessary matings to occur and if the disease is a rare one the likelihood of obtaining such data is very small. Detailed study of pleiotropic effects and analysis of linkage may help to specify a case more completely, but in the majority of instances specific genetical classification of an abnormality can only be assumed.

At the present time, genetic studies in Man have evolved beyond the formal analysis of pedigrees. A much more comprehensive picture of human heredity is rapidly emerging from which many benefits may be obtained. These include the usefulness in medicine of accurate diagnosis and prognosis, the possibility of effecting cure or alleviation of disorders and the reliability of advice on eugenic measures in marriage and procreation problems. A detailed discussion of these topics is beyond the scope of this book, nevertheless, some of the conclusions may be relevant to radiation hazards in Man. If, for example, a complete cure could be effected for some hereditary disease, the possibility that it might arise as a radiation-induced mutation would no longer represent a hazard. This is taking an optimistic view, however; it is more probable that a cure would be partial, in which case another factor enters into the problem. According to the simple model of population structure outlined in the previous chapter, a deleterious gene will be present in a population at an equilibrium frequency determined by the balance of gains through mutation and losses through poor reproductive capacity. Any medical attention which improved the latter would produce an increase in frequency of the deleterious gene. Conversely, if accurate advice could be given to married couples on the desirability of their having children, a decrease in the incidence of inherited disease might be effected. Thus if persons heterozygous for a deleterious recessive gene could be identified by slight dominant effects of the gene, or predicted accurately on the basis of linkage data, their request for advice would lead to more effective selection against a gene; selection would act in the heterozygous as well as in the homozygous state. These points are largely idealistic but nevertheless they might well have a bearing on radiation hazards in the future.

Human genetics can be divided into three broad categories. First, the inheritance of specific disease or disability, e.g. phenylketonuria and blindness; second, the inheritance of biometrical characters, e.g. height and intelligence; third, the inheritance of characters commonly found which have little or no disadvantage on the individual, e.g. hair colour and blood groups. These three categories are not clearly defined nor do they have any biological significance. They are useful, however, in a discussion of radiation hazards. Mutation of genes in the third group is clearly of no significance: gene frequencies for such characters tend to be high and, as explained in the previous chapter, will be affected only slightly by mutation. The different alleles have, in any case, no particular relative disadvantage. Very little is known of the mutation of genes in the second group, but it seems probable that this also will be of minor importance with respect to radiation hazard: frequencies of different alleles are probably relatively high and, as they tend to function as balanced groups, the identity of individual alleles is of little importance. The inheritance of specific disease remains the major known hazard to which Man will be susceptible through the mutagenic properties of ionising radiation. To appreciate the significance of this hazard, it is necessary to know first, the incidence of inherited disease and the rate at which the genes concerned mutate spontaneously and under the influence of radiation; and second, the degree to which Man is exposed to Man-made radiations at the present time or will be so exposed in the future.

THE INCIDENCE OF INHERITED DISEASES

A large number of diseases of a very variable type are known to be inherited. The effects of different loci vary from early embryonic lethality to minor reduction in life span, from completely disabling to only the slightest impairment of health. The total range of inherited defect thus covers a very wide and complex field and the net effect in a human population, that is the social load implied by this, is impossible to determine with any precision. As a rough estimate of the incidence of the straightforward inherited defects, a committee appointed by the National Academy of Sciences, Washington* have suggested a figure of 2 per cent of all live births. This is a disturbingly high figure and it does not include many common traits like mongolism, schizophrenia,

* *The Biological Effects of Atomic Radiations:* Summary Reports (1956) National Academy of Sciences—National Research Council: Washington.

and manic depression, that have a strong, though not straightforward, genetic determination. More recently a survey has been made of the hereditary defects found among births in Northern Ireland. This survey, directed by A. C. Stevenson, covered a period of ten years. The frequencies of different genetic categories are summarised in Table 6. In category A the traits are those which appear to be due to

TABLE 6. THE AT-BIRTH INCIDENCE OF HARMFUL TRAITS THAT
SHOW SOME GENETIC DETERMINATION

Category	*Genetic determination	Number of different traits	Estimated frequency per million births
A	Single mutant	142	34,859
B	Single mutant but with abnormally high incidence	2	864
C	Familial incidence but not single mutant	—	14,115
D	4 special cases	4	7,730
E	Strongly hereditary but also determined environmentally	6	14,800
Total		154	72,368

* A fuller description is given in the text.

the inheritance of a single mutant gene and which have a frequency consistent with the hypothesis that loss of mutants through selection acting against the phenotypes is balanced by fresh mutation.

Category B traits are those that also depend on a single segregating character but have a frequency too high to be consistent with the above hypothesis (an explanation of this phenomenon is discussed more fully in the following pages).

Category C includes a mixture of traits believed to be genetically determined but in a way not yet understood. They are mostly gross congenital abnormalities with rather severe effects.

Category D consists of a small number of traits that do not fit in any of the other groups. The bulk of the cases in this category concern two traits, *Rhesus incompatibility* and *mongolism*. The effect in the former, haemolytic anaemia in the new born, is not produced directly by the genes in the affected individuals. The condition arises in a child before birth as a consequence of a difference between its genotype and that of its mother. The mother develops an immunity against the blood cells of the child which may result in the destruction of the blood of this, or a later, child. The genetics of the Rhesus character is somewhat complicated, three closely linked genes being involved. For simplicity we may assume that there is only one locus. Individuals may be classified as either Rhesus-positive (Rh+) or Rhesus-negative (Rh−); the latter are homozygous for the recessive allele (Rh−Rh−), the former heterozygous (Rh+Rh−) or homozygous (Rh+Rh+) for the dominant allele. The disease may arise in a Rh+ child if the mother is Rh−. Approximately 16 per cent of the population in the United Kingdom are Rh− and among families in which the mother alone is Rh− approximately 4 per cent of the children are affected. Thus the frequency of the disease is about 0·5 per cent of births.

Mongolism is a form of idiocy of high diagnostic specificity; numerous other specific defects in body structure being associated with the mental condition. The trait is relatively frequent having an incidence of about 0·15 per cent at birth. There is, however, a high positive correlation between this incidence and maternal age. The incidence among the offspring born to mothers of about 40 years of age is about 2·5 per cent. This correlation suggests an environmental (uterine) cause, but studies on familial incidence and, more conclusively, on identical twins, has revealed a strong hereditary factor. In recent years the genetical cause of mongolism has been revealed by a series of important discoveries. Cytological examination of chromosomes in Man has demonstrated that in the mongol child there are 47 chromosomes in contrast to the usual chromosome number, 46 (see Plate VIII). The extra chromosome in the mongols is a small autosome and the condition is presumed to arise through non-disjunction in the developing egg cell.

The elucidation of the genetic causes of mongolism rationalises the similar affliction of identical twins but the high familial incidence and the correlation with maternal age are not yet understood. In a small group of mongols, chiefly identified through the young age of the mother, the chromosome number is normal. It has been established, however, that chromosome unbalance is also present in these cases and probably involves the duplication of the same autosome that was found in the former cases. From the appearance of the chromosomes it was concluded that a translocation had occurred between a large and a small chromosome. The breaks were located close to the centromeres and loss of the very small centric fragment would thus lead to the presence of only 46 chromosomes which in fact contain the genetic material of 47. A family has recently been described in which two sibs exhibited this type of mongolism and in which the non-mongoloid grandmother,

mother and third son had only 45 chromosomes. The translocation was thus inherited with no serious consequences but when the small chromosome segregated with its translocated homologue the chromosome unbalance led to mongolism. The familial hereditary disposition of this form of mongolism is thus clear, but these cases represent only a very small minority of affected individuals.

The final category of disorders in Table 6 represent common and often serious traits which although associated with a strong familial incidence, probably depend also on non-genetic factors. Included are such traits as *diabetes mellitus, exophthalmic goitre, idiopathic epilepsy* and the psychotic traits of *manic depression* and *schizophrenia*. These all have high incide ces of 0·1 per cent or over which, as in category B, seem too high to be explained by the balance of mutation and selection. Several attempts have been made to explain their inheritance in terms of single segregating units but these have proved either contradictory or not satisfactory.

It can be seen from Table 6 that the at-birth frequency of illness in which there is some hereditary disposition is 7·2 per cent and that among the living this is reduced by early mortality to 5 per cent. Genetic disease is thus of considerable social importance and this will become more apparent as medicine progresses in the cure or prevention of infectious and otherwise environmentally determined diseases.

A total of 144 apparently single-mutant traits (Table categories A and B) were ascertained in Northern Ireland during the 10-year period. Not all of these traits are gene specific; different mutant genes may produce effects which are clinically indistinguishable. It was estimated, therefore, that about 230 mutant genes were represented in the sample and that these represented a sample of the grand total of about 400 mutant genes which are thought to produce inherited defect or illness in Man.

SPONTANEOUS MUTATION RATE IN MAN

Two methods are available for the estimation of the frequency with which mutations arise in Man. Both are concerned chiefly with mutant genes expressing a marked deleterious effect which are, in consequence, rare in the population. The simplest is the direct method which is employed for dominant and sex-linked recessive mutations. If an individual shows a trait which is known to be dominantly inherited, while his parents do not, it can be concluded that the trait has newly arisen by mutation of the normal gene in one of the two chromosomes that the individual has received from his parents. This mutation may, therefore, have arisen in a germ cell of either of the parents at any time during their life up to conception of the abnormal individual. The frequency of origin of such mutations among all births thus represents twice the mutation frequency (since there are two chromosomes) per generation or twice the mutation rate. As an example we may take the condition called *achondroplasia*, in which the clinical symptoms involve retarded development of the limb bones and many other minor skeletal abnormalities. Several authors have described the incidence of achondroplasia among hospital births. A total of 23 cases have been recorded among 169,935 births. The spontaneous mutation rate is thus

$$\frac{1}{2} \times \frac{23}{169,935}$$

or about 70 per million loci per generation.

The origin of sex-linked recessive mutations can be observed in a similar way but more information is required on the family history of suspected cases The phenotype is, of course, expressed in males since this is the hemizygous sex, but a mutant gene may be present and not observed in the female. Figure 65 shows a pedigree for haemophilia

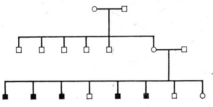

FIG. 65. PEDIGREE FOR A SEX-LINKED TRAIT, HAEMOPHILIA, SHOWING EVIDENCE OF A NEWLY-ARISEN MUTATION

illustrating the sort of evidence from which the occurrence of a mutation may be inferred. The father of five haemophilic sons was normal. Assuming that the haemophilia was the usual type, due to a sex-linked recessive gene, the mother must have been heterozygous for it. It is unlikely that the grandmother was heterozygous for the gene since none of her sons were haemophilic and, consequently, it is more probable that the mutation arose in the germ cells of one of the grandparents.

The second method for estimating mutation rates in Man depends on the principle, described in the previous chapter, that the frequency of a rare gene in a population is determined by its mutation rate and by the relative reproductive capacity of individuals which carry it. Thus it was shown (page 119) that for a dominant gene, the incidence of heterozygotes in a population at equilibrium and under panmixia would be given by:—

$$x = 2m/hs$$

where m is the mutation rate and hs the selective disadvantage of the heterozygote. The latter is usually written as $(1 - f)$ where f is the relative reproductive capacity of the heterozygote.

Thus

$$m = \tfrac{1}{2}(1 - f)x$$

The mutation rate can be estimated, therefore, from data on the incidence of a trait in a population and from the reproductive capacity of the abnormal individuals. For example, in a survey in Denmark, 86 achondroplastic individuals were recorded in a population sample of 3,793,000. The abnormal individuals showed only one tenth the reproductive capacity of the normals hence

$$m = \tfrac{1}{2}(1 - 0 \cdot 1) \times 86/3{,}793{,}000 = 1 \times 10^{-5}$$

It will be noted that this estimate is somewhat lower than that derived from the direct method. This will be discussed later.

For rare sex-linked recessive genes the equation becomes

$$m = 1/3(1 - f)\,x$$

The gene is only detectable in the male, the expectation of homozygous females is negligible, and the gene frequency is thus proportional to one third of the incidence of the trait.

For autosomal recessive genes which are rare in a population the situation is more complex and mutation rate estimates are not very reliable. The frequency of incidence of homozygous recessives in a panmictic population (page 119) was given by

$$p^2 = m/s$$

Expressing s in terms of relative reproductive capacity and given that the incidence of the disease is x,

$$m = (1 - f)\,x$$

We have noted that homozygotes for rare recessive genes arise chiefly from consanguineous marriage. This represents inbreeding and a deviation from the assumption of panmixia, but it does not render the above equation invalid. As long as an equilibrium does exist mutation rate will be proportional to x, the incidence of the disease which, instead of being p^2 as under panmixia, will be $\alpha p + (1 - \alpha)\,p^2$ (page 112) where α represents a coefficient of inbreeding expressing the total effect of all degrees of consanguinity or the probability of homozygosity by descent. Some estimates of spontaneous mutation rates for individual loci in Man are given in Table 7.

There is a considerable degree of variation between the estimates of mutation rates at different loci. There is no doubt that part of this variation represents genuine differences in locus mutability but, on the

TABLE 7. ESTIMATED VALUES OF SPONTANEOUS MUTATION RATES
AT INDIVIDUAL LOCI IN MAN

Trait studied	Estimated mutation rate
Autosomal dominants (direct observation)	
Neurofibromatosis	$1 \cdot 3$ to $2 \cdot 5 \times 10^{-4}$
Achondroplasia	45×10^{-6}
Retinoblastoma	4 to 23×10^{-6}
Epiloia	8×10^{-6}
Microphthalmos	5×10^{-6}
Aniridia	5×10^{-6}
Partial albinism with deafness	4×10^{-6}
Sex-linked recessives (direct)	
Duchenne's type muscular dystrophy	4 to 10×10^{-5}
Haemophilia	3×10^{-5}
Autosomal recessives (indirect)	
True microcephaly	$4 \cdot 9 \times 10^{-5}$
Albinism	$2 \cdot 8 \times 10^{-5}$
Total colour blindness	$2 \cdot 8 \times 10^{-5}$
Phenylketonuria	$2 \cdot 5 \times 10^{-5}$
Amyotonia congenita	$2 \cdot 0 \times 10^{-5}$
Infantile amaurotic idiocy	$1 \cdot 1 \times 10^{-5}$
Ichthyosis congenita	$1 \cdot 1 \times 10^{-5}$

other hand, it is suspected that errors in the estimations may be significant. Many sources of error render the estimates of mutation rates in Man unreliable. These derive from technical difficulties, from faulty genetical assumptions and from inadequate knowledge of demographic trends in Man. The technical errors include first, the difficulties of unbiassed sampling of populations. Thus, in the examples we have included for achondroplasia, the mutation rate estimate based on hospital births was much higher than that from the population at large, this would be expected if pre-natal complications were associated with achondroplasia, since preferential admittance to hospital would be given in such cases. A second technical difficulty concerns the precision of diagnosis. This will naturally vary according to the degree of medical care given to a community, but will also suffer because of the tendency of families or individuals to hide genetic defects, either on cosmetic grounds, or in the mistaken attitude that they represent some general hereditary "taint". The effect of these factors is probably negligible, however, in comparison with errors arising from the lack of knowledge on the genetics of inherited traits in Man.

In order to use the natural incidence of a trait to determine the frequency with which mutations arise at a single locus, the following genetical assumptions must be made:

(1) That the trait is always genetically determined and cannot arise as a phenocopy.

(2) That the presence of the gene always produces the phenotype in question; in other words penetrance and expressivity are always complete.

(3) That the trait is produced by a mutant gene at only one locus.

(4) That recessive genes are completely recessive; they must have no effect in the heterozygote.

In fact, in none of the traits known in Man can all of these assumptions be considered valid. The first can usually be verified in the presence of a familial history but in the case of sporadic occurrence, where the individual leaves few or no offspring, this is not possible. The effect of a deviation from this assumption would be to produce a spuriously large mutation rate; only a proportion of the cases would be of genetic origin. Many defects attributable to dominant mutation, e.g. *retinoblastoma* and *microcephaly* probably fall into this category. A spuriously high estimate also arises if the third assumption does not hold. If two or more mutant genes produce the same phenotype, the

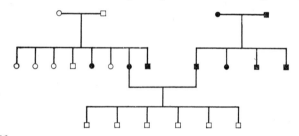

FIG. 66. PEDIGREE FOR HEREDITARY DEAFNESS INDICATING THE EXISTENCE OF TWO DIFFERENT RECESSIVE GENES

estimated mutation rate would be the sum of the rates at each locus. In experimental organisms many instances are known in which two or more genes produce identical phenotypes. In Man one such case, hereditary deafness (Fig. 66), is known for certain and several others, e.g. *chondrodystrophy* are suspected. Likewise the second assumption is known not to hold in many cases in experimental organisms and also in Man. The dominantly inherited trait, *polydactyly*, is one such example. In the pedigree in Fig. 67, several apparently normal individuals must carry the mutant gene since they passed it on to their offspring.

The last of the above assumptions, that recessive genes are completely recessive, is the most dubious, and seriously limits the validity of mutation rate estimates for recessive genes. Whenever the effects of

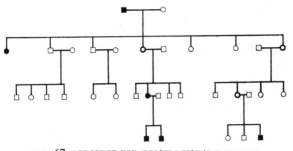

FIG. 67. PEDIGREE FOR POLYDACTYLY SHOWING
IRREGULAR DOMINANCE
(Presumed carriers of the gene are shown in heavy type)

a gene are closely studied it is almost always found that they have some effect in the heterozygote; this is usually, but by no means always, a deleterious effect. As we noted in the previous chapter, heterozygotes for rare recessives are very much more frequent in populations than the homozygotes; consequently they may be subjected to much stronger selection pressures than the homozygotes and this may have a serious influence on the equilibrium gene frequency. An outstanding example of this in Man concerns a disease, largely confined to negroes, called *sickle-cell anaemia*. The name derives from the sickle shape assumed by the blood cells when they collapse in the presence of low oxygen tensions, as for example, in venous blood. Within areas in which sickle-cell anaemia occurs, the blood cells of many non-anaemic individuals also exhibit sickling under suitable *in vitro* conditions. This anomaly is known as *sickle-cell trait* and it has been established that both it and the anaemia are determined by the same mutant gene in the heterozygous and in the homozygous condition respectively. The allele responsible for the sickle-cell character is designated Hb_1^S, and its primary effect is to produce a different type of haemoglobin from that produced by the normal allele Hb_1^A. In this respect the locus shows no dominance; $Hb_1^A Hb_1^S$ individuals have approximately equal amounts of each type of haemoglobin, although, as already stated, they exhibit no anaemia. The sickle-cell anaemia shown by $Hb_1^S Hb_1^S$ individuals is a severely deleterious disease and leads to early death. Consequently, one would expect the gene frequency of Hb_1^S to be very low. This, however, is not the case. Among negroes in America the gene frequency is approximately 0·05 per cent and in certain African tribes it is more than double this. The reason for this high frequency appears to be that $Hb_1^A Hb_1^S$ individuals are resistant to malaria. This was first observed as a correlation between high prevalance of malaria and high gene frequency for Hb_1^S; subsequently, this idea has been confirmed by experimental methods. The gene is thus maintained at a high incidence, irrespective of the deleterious homozygous effect, by the advantage of the heterozygote in areas where there is a high incidence of malaria. The virtual absence of the disease in the majority of human populations indicates that the mutation rate for the sickle-cell gene is very low. In fact, the distribution of the trait among negroes also suggests this. The frequency of the allele Hb_1^S varies very considerably among tribes in Africa and the correlation between high frequency and high incidence of malaria occasionally breaks down. Some areas with endemic malaria have only a very low frequency of the gene. If the mutation rate were high, the distribution of the trait should be more uniformly correlated to malarial incidence. There is evidence that the mutant gene has spread in Africa by both migration and mixture and that mutation has played little part in the present distribution. Clearly, under these conditions, an estimate of mutation rate would be meaningless.

Other recessively inherited diseases are distributed in a manner similar to sickle-cell anaemia. Another severe anaemia, Cooley's disease of *thalassaemia*, although widely distributed, is common predominantly among Mediterranean populations; *amaurotic idiocy* is chiefly restricted to Jews and the inhabitants of certain parts of Sweden; the antigenic character Rhesus-negative is found only in Europeans; *acatalasaemia*, the absence of a catalase enzyme in the blood, is restricted to Japan. There are several other diseases which show similar trends. In the majority of instances no heterozygous advantage can be postulated; the inference, therefore, is that locally high incidences of harmful recessive genes resulted from advantages in the past. The use of an indirect method on the basis of recessive inheritance will, in these cases, lead to over estimates of mutation rates. This is particularly so because of the natural bias introduced by the investigation of populations in which the presence of a particular disease is not too rare.

The final source of error to which recessive mutation rate estimates are subjected concerns the postulate that a population is in genetic equilibrium. It is obvious that this requirement cannot be satisfied by any population at the present time. Human races show marked differences in respect of both biometrical traits and single gene characters. The intermingling of different racial groups, following wars and migration, has occurred throughout history and up to the present time. Similarly, the changing social conditions and environmental circumstances depending on the evolution of the present civilisation, which is far more rapid than biological evolution, must also lead to genetic inequilibrium. While the broad outlines of these factors can be recognised in demographic studies it is not possible to estimate the magnitude of their effects on gene frequencies in populations.

In conclusion, it seems probable that most of the estimated mutation rates for specific loci in Man are too large. It is possible that the lower estimates more nearly represent the true state of affairs.

STUDIES ON INDUCED MUTATION IN MAN

EXPOSURE TO MAN-MADE RADIATION

Some attempts have been made to study the production of mutations directly by observations on groups of individuals who have been exposed to radiations. Four surveys are available on the incidence of various anomalies in the first generation children of:

(a) The survivors of the atomic bomb explosions in Hiroshima and Nagasaki;

(b) Patients in France who were given radiation therapy;

(c) Canadian women who received radiation treatment for sterility;

(d) American radiologists who, by nature of their occupation, were exposed to radiations.

In none of these projects was there any precise knowledge of the dose of radiation given either to individuals or to the population as a whole and in no case were the observations sufficiently numerous for an attempt to be made to determine the incidence of any specific mutation. Nevertheless, it was felt that the studies might give some qualitative indication of the extent of induced mutation.

Records that were taken in these surveys included information on the termination of pregnancies, whether aborted, stillborn or normal, information on the incidence of congenital abnormalities among births and on the sex of the new born. The genetic basis for expecting an induced mutation effect to be revealed by these observations is rather speculative. Lethal mutations that kill before birth are a common category in experimental organisms, indeed they are a major one in *Drosophila*; they have not been observed extensively in Man, however, for obvious reasons. If they do arise in Man it seems possible that they may be revealed by a rise in the incidence of abortions and stillbirths following the exposure of parents prior to conception. Similarly, many congenital abnormalities represent the expression of mutant genes and this is known in Man as well as in experimental organisms. More frequently, however, the inheritance of such effects is not straight-forward and a very large number are probably caused by non-genetic factors. Here again some effect of mutation might be revealed but it is difficult to predict how much.

The data for abnormal terminations and congenital abnormality are summarised in Table 8. It can be seen that there is no obvious effect

TABLE 8. SURVEYS OF BIRTHS FROM IRRADIATED AND NON-IRRADIATED PARENTS

Survey		Dose range in rads	Preg-nancies	Abor-tions %	Births	Still-births %	Births	Con-genital abnor-malaties %
Nagasaki and Hiroshima	Irradiated	8 to 200	—	—	33,181	1·65	33,527	0·89
	Non-irradiated	—	—	—	31,559	1·29	31,904	0·92
French patients	Irradiated	4 to 450	614	11·89	541	2·77	541	2·59
	Non-irradiated	—	996	6·43	932	1·29	932	0·97
Sterility therapy in Canada	Irradiated	50 to 200	513	17·7	513	0·39	513	0·58
	Non-irradiated	—	—	—	—	—	—	—
American radiologists	Irradiated	Not known		7,114	14·62		5,461	6·00
	Non-irradiated	—		5,832	13·08		4,484	4·82

of exposure to radiation. The differences between the controls and irradiated are slight and, in their general trends, are not consistent with each other or with the genetical hypothesis outlined above. Without knowledge of the degree of the genetic determination of these effects, or of the doses of radiation received by the individuals, it is not possible to appraise these results with any confidence. At most it seems probable that they indicate that genes in Man are not exceptionally sensitive to radiation.

The data on sex-ratio are more consistent than those on congenital abnormalities and still births and there is a more elegant genetic hypothesis for anticipating a radiation effect.

The reason for expecting radiation-induced mutation to affect sex-ratio depends on the chromosomal basis of sex determination. In brief, the determination of sex resides in a pair of chromosomes, the X-chromosomes, which are present in the normal diploid condition in females but in the haploid condition in males. In place of the second X-chromosome the male carries an atypical Y-chromosome which contains little or no genetic material. During fertilisation an X-bearing sperm must give rise to a female genotype XX, while a Y-bearing sperm produces the male genotype XY. There is ample evidence from experimental organisms for the existence of dominant and recessive mutations which are lethal to the developing zygote and there is no reason to suspect that they are absent in Man. The production of lethal mutations in the X-chromosome will affect the sex-ratio in different ways according to the sex of the parent exposed to radiation. Thus the recessive mutations induced in the male X-chromosome will not be expressed in the first generation offspring since that chromosome will only be found in the XX female offspring; dominant mutations will express themselves, however, but only in the female offspring; the Y-chromosome carries no genes to mutate. The net effect of the production of mutations by irradiation of the male will be to increase the proportion of male births. Conversely, recessive lethal mutations induced in the maternal X-chromosome will be expressed only in male offspring, while dominant mutations will affect both sexes equally. The effect of the induction of mutation in females would be to reduce the proportion of male births. Thus irradiation of males should lead to an increase, and irradiation of females to a decrease, in the sex-ratio among the offspring in the generation following irradiation.

The data on sex-ratios from the four surveys are summarised in Table 9 and it can be seen that, in general, the trends in the sex-ratio

TABLE 9. SEX-RATIO AMONG OFFSPRING OF PARENTS EXPOSED TO RADIATION

Survey	Estimated Dose in rads	Exposed Parent if Irradiated						Ratio Father to Ratio Mother
		Father			Mother			
		Total Births	Males	Ratio	Total Births	Males	Ratio	
Nagasaki and Hiroshima	0	43,544	22,680	0·5209	As for father			
	8	5,168	2,666	0·5159	19,610	10,193	0·5198	−0·0039
	75	1,226	653	0·5326	3,958	2,036	0·5144	+0·0182
	200	753	397	0·5272	2,268	1,161	0·5119	+0·0153
French patients	0*	696	358	0·5144	236	130	0·5508	−0·0364
	450 to 1,400	405	225	0·5556	136	63	0·4632	+0·0924
Sterility therapy in Canada	50 to 200	—	—	—	407	200	0·4914	
American radiologists	0	4,277	2,198	0·5139	—	—	—	
	Not known	3,491	1,830	0·5242	—	—	—	

* These controls were births prior to treatment.

are in agreement with the genetical hypothesis. Extensive statistical analysis of the data of the two major surveys, those in Hiroshima and Nagasaki, and in France, indicate that these trends are significant. However, it cannot be concluded with certainty that these observations represent the effects of induced mutation; many factors are known to influence sex-ratio, such as paternal age, parity and, more surprisingly, war! Furthermore, recent studies of patients in France who received radiation treatment remote from the gonads, show similar differences in sex-ratio when compared to unirradiated controls. In this case the effect is obviously not due to mutation in the germ cells. In conclusion, therefore, the induction of mutations has not been demonstrated so far by studies of populations that have been exposed to radiations. This negative conclusion does not imply that radiation does not produce mutation in Man; the interpretation of the data is beset with many difficulties not only on genetic grounds but also on problems of exposure doses, population sampling and the availability of appropriate controls. The surveys are of value, however, in indicating that, compared with experimental organisms, Man is not exceptionally sensitive to the mutagenic action of radiations. This indication gives some support to the estimates of radiation hazards to Man that are derived by extrapolation from data on experimental organisms. These will be described in the following chapter.

OTHER METHODS FOR STUDYING INDUCED MUTATION IN MAN

It is possible that continued studies on the offspring of persons given medical radiation treatment will eventually supply more precise data on the induction of mutations in Man. On the other hand, the exposure of individuals to genetically effective doses of radiation (i.e. to the gonads) represents a radiation hazard. Steps which are being taken to reduce this risk, by shielding of the gonads and by improvements in radiological techniques, will make further genetic studies on irradiated populations even more difficult. Other possibilities do exist for long term observation on irradiated populations. Certain areas of the world have exceptionally high levels of background irradiation produced by the presence in the soil of radioactive materials. One such locality, which has been suggested for possible genetic studies, is the Travancore district in India but there are several other districts widely distributed in all continents. The high background radioactivity is produced by the presence of the element thorium which is found in deposits principally composed of the mineral ore *monazite*. This is found in rocks and, by the action of erosion and other physical aspects of weathering, it reaches the sea and becomes washed up as beach sand deposits. Natural thorium is radioactive, emits α- and γ-rays and has a half-life of 1.39×10^{10} years. During disintegration it forms a series of decay products, themselves radioactive, among which is the gas thoron. This diffuses into and contaminates the air and also undergoes further disintegration to non-gaseous decay products which, attached to dust particles, become precipitated on to the earth's surface. The radioactive dust particles may also be retained in the body after inhalation and this constitutes a source of internal radiation.

Some of the monazite areas support fairly large human populations and for the purpose of the genetic survey control populations may be found within the locality but remote from the monazite deposits. Measurements of the background radioactivity in some parts of Travancore have indicated that some individuals may be exposed to γ-ray doses of 2 r or more per year; it has been estimated that populations may be receiving an average of 10 to 30 r per generation of 30 years. By comparison with normal background radiation levels, which are detailed in the following chapter, this is a very high dose rate. Genetic studies on these populations, although of necessity long term, might supply valuable information on induced mutation rates of known genetic markers; in this context it is of importance that medical attention in this area may not be sufficiently advanced to have disturbed the natural balance between mutation rates, gene frequencies and selection.

We have considered in this chapter some of the consequences of mutations in Man, the magnitude of the burden of hereditary disease, means whereby estimates are made of spontaneous mutation rates and some data from direct investigations on the induction of mutation in persons and populations exposed to radiation. None of the latter can lead to satisfactory estimates of genetic hazards to which Man may be exposed now or in the future as a consequence of Man-made or natural radiations. In the next and final chapter we will consider how information derived from experimental animals can be used to deduce such estimates and, from the knowledge of present and possible future exposure levels, the implications this has on the future health of human populations.

11

9
GENETIC RADIATION HAZARDS IN MAN

The expanding utilisation of atomic energy, of radiation therapy and diagnosis in medicine and of radioactive materials in many walks of life must inevitably lead to increases in the amount of radiation received by Man. This raises serious problems with regard to Man's inheritance. To what extent will future generations suffer an increase in inherited disease; will the continued evolution of mankind be affected adversely; and finally, do the benefits derived from the use of the above agents justify an increased load of human suffering? These questions cannot yet be answered with any great conviction; indeed the final question, with its ethical implications, may never be answered. Nevertheless, some estimates can and must be made in order to place the dangers in an approximate perspective to guard against excesses of restraint or negligence in the development and use of atomic energy and radiation.

PRESENT LEVELS OF RADIATION EXPOSURE

Man has always been exposed to ionising radiation arising from natural sources. In addition to this there are, at present, further sources of radiation arising from civil and military uses of atomic energy. Before continuing to describe these sources of irradiation it is necessary to recapitulate briefly one aspect of the genetic consequences of ionising radiation. From the individual's point of view the risk to his descendants following his own exposure to radiation is negligible unless a very severe dose is received accidentally. Where a tragic event has the probability of occurrence of one in a thousand, or one in several thousands, it has little consequence to a family group. The low probability of an event assumes importance, however, when it is concerned with numbers of individuals which, as in human populations, are measured in tens of millions. To anticipate the discussion in the second half of this chapter, we suspect that in an individual the magnitude of the genetic effect of radiations is determined solely by the total dose received by the gonads irrespective of the rate at which it accumulates. From the point of view of the population it follows that the important issue is the total radiation dose that it receives. Thus the significant measure of radiation exposure is the average genetic dose received by individuals in the whole population, the genetic dose being that which is received by the gonads.

150

NATURAL BACKGROUND IRRADIATION

Natural background irradiation results from cosmic radiation arising outside the earth's atmosphere and from radioactive materials present in the soil and rocks. Cosmic rays, primarily high energy protons, impinge directly on the earth's surface but the chief source of direct radiation is produced by their absorption in the atmosphere with the concomitant secondary release of mesons, neutrons and electrons, still of high energy. On the earth's surface there is some variation in intensity but on average the genetic dose from cosmic sources is about 30 mrads* per year. Much greater variation is found at different altitudes, however, because of the absorbing power of the atmosphere. Thus in aircraft at high altitudes individuals may be subjected to a much higher dose rate than that recorded on the earth's surface.

In addition to the production of direct radiation, cosmic rays also produce radioactive elements by interaction with the nuclei of elements in the atmosphere. The chief of these is carbon 14 produced by collision of neutrons with nitrogen nuclei. This radioactive isotope enters the lower atmosphere in the form of carbon dioxide and may then be incorporated into plants during the process of photosynthesis. Subsequently these plants may be ingested by animals. In this way the carbon 14 presents both an external and an internal source of irradiation in Man and indeed in all animals.

Terrestrial sources of irradiation are due only to a small extent to carbon 14; more important are the radioactive isotopes of the heavy metals, uranium and thorium, which are universally distributed in small amounts in rocks and soils. These have long half-lives and in the process of disintegration form several radioactive breakdown products including the gases radon and thoron which can be widely distributed. Different forms of rock or deposit vary in their content of radioactive isotopes. We noted in the previous chapter that in certain parts of the world levels of radiation from thorium amounted to as much as 2 r per year, or more. These are exceptionally high values and background genetic doses normally range from 30 to 100 mrads per year depending on the principle rock formation in any particular locality. Thus the chalk or limestone areas are represented in the lower dose rate categories while the higher dose rates are found in granite areas. Direct measurement of radiation in Britain has revealed quite large local variations: in Aberdeen, a granite city, the mean dose is 104 mrads per year; in Edinburgh the figure is 48·5 mrads per year. This variation makes the estimation of overall mean dose rates difficult, but it is probable that

* Natural doses of irradiation are very small and thus measured in millirads, i.e. 1/1000 rads.

in the United Kingdom the figure for the genetic dose is about 50 mrads per year and it is likely that this does not differ greatly from the world average.

   Radiation exposures also arise from radioactive isotopes incorporated into tissues of the body. Mention has already been made of carbon 14 in this respect. Another and more important source of irradiation is potassium 40—a radioactive isotope of potassium, an essential constituent of living tissue. In addition, the gases radon and thoron and their decay products may be assimilated during breathing. Altogether, internal sources of radiation supply a mean genetic dose of about 25 mrads per year of which about 21 mrads arise from potassium 40. These natural sources of radiation exposure are summarised in Table 10. It can be

TABLE 10.   GONAD DOSES OF IRRADIATION FROM NATURAL SOURCES
IN GREAT BRITAIN

	Source	mrads/year
External	Cosmic radiation Radioactive isotopes—soil and buildings	24 50
Internal	Carbon 14, radon, etc. Potassium 40	4 21
Total		99

seen that the average natural background level is about 100 mrads per year.

CIVILIAN USES OF RADIATION AND ATOMIC ENERGY

   Medical radiology represents the largest contribution to genetic hazards from Man-made radiations. Used for both diagnostic and therapeutic measures, radiations represent an important tool in medicine, but only recently has attention been paid to the undesirable genetical consequences implicit in its use. This delay probably arose from the distinction between the consequences to the individual and to the population with respect to genetic hazards as outlined in the opening pages of this chapter. The benefits to an individual from radiation treatment far outweigh any detrimental aspects. On the other hand, the reverse is not true; suspension of radiological practices would have serious consequences to the health of the population. Awareness of the problem of the genetic hazard has arisen through the efforts of research workers in this field of genetics and has been brought before the public in this country by reports from the Medical Research Council* and, more specifically, by a report from a Government committee under the chairmanship of Lord Adrian†. In the latter, a nation-wide survey of radiological practice showed that the mean genetic dose received in the year 1957–58 was 19·3 mrads. This was made up of 14·1 mrads from diagnostic radiology; 4·5 and 0·5 mrads from radiotherapy of non-malignant and malignant disease respectively; and a minor component of 0·2 mrads from mass-miniature radiography, dental radiology and the medical use of radioactive isotopes. The figure of 19·3 mrads per year is lower than the more speculative estimates for diagnostic radiology alone, presented in the Medical Research Council's first report. While concluding that this low dose rate gave no grounds for curtailment of present radiological practices the Adrian report stressed the desirability of reducing the dose still further. The committee estimated that the implementation of their recommendations could, in fact, reduce the dose to 6 mrads per year, or less, without detriment to the medical use of radiation.

The general public are exposed to radiations from several other minor sources. These include television sets, X-ray shoe fitting apparatus and luminous markings on clocks and watches. Further exposure also arises from the disposal of radioactive waste products from atomic reactors, hospitals, etc., and, in the case of passengers in high-flying aircraft, from the increased cosmic radiation at high altitudes. None of these sources are large and together do not produce an average dose rate of more than 1 mrad per year. Air crews in high flying aircraft will also be exposed to higher than average doses of cosmic rays but for longer periods than passengers. It has been estimated that at 50,000 feet, the increased genetic dose amounts to about 0·5 mrads per hour. Thus even if air crews spent 2,000 hours per year at this altitude they would accumulate only one extra rad per year and this is well below the accepted level for an individual. The contribution made to the dose received by the population does not, of course, differ from that contributed by passengers; it is negligible. Other, and higher, occupational exposures arise in the case of workers at atomic energy sites, radiologists in hospitals, etc. A careful check is kept on the radiation doses received by persons so exposed, by means of film badges worn during working hours. In the United Kingdom this recording is done by the Atomic Energy Authority and by certain hospital departments for their own personnel, respectively. Recording for other individuals is done by the Radiological Protection Service. In 1959 the mean annual dose to the surface

* *Hazards to Man of Nuclear and Allied Radiations*, 1st report 1956; 2nd report 1960.
† *Radiological Hazards to Patients.*

of the body recorded by the Radiological Protection Service varied between about 0·2 and 2·0 rads per year depending upon occupation. The total doses recorded amounted to 7122 rads. Allowing for personnel not monitored, for individuals of an age not likely to reproduce and for the difference between skin and gonad dose, it was estimated that the increased genetic dose totalled 6000 rads and that considering the population as a whole this amounted to an average increase in genetic dose of 0·25 mrads per year. This data excluded occupational exposure received by personnel of The Atomic Energy Authority for which similar data indicated an increased genetic dose of 0·15 mrads per year. Genetic doses from Man-made radiations in civilian use are summarised in Table 11.

TABLE 11. GONAD DOSES FROM THE USE OF RADIATIONS IN INDUSTRY AND MEDICINE

Sources	Dose in mrads/year
Medical radiology	
Diagnostic	14·1
Therapeutic (malignant)	4·5
Therapeutic (non-malignant)	0·5
Miscellaneous	0·2
	19·3
Minor exposures to general public	1·0
Occupational exposure	
Hospital staff	0·25
Atomic Energy Authority	0·15
	1·4
	20·7

RADIATION FROM THE USE OF ATOMIC ENERGY FOR MILITARY PURPOSES

In peacetime, radiation hazards from the military use of atomic weapons arise from the fallout of radioactive debris produced by test explosions. The production and dispersal of this debris, and the hazards it represents to Man, depend on many complex circumstances. Of major importance to distribution is the size and position of the explosion. Low energy explosions of the kiloton range produce dust clouds that are chiefly confined to the lower atmosphere (*troposphere*). Deposition of radioactive material is rapid and may be completed within a few months. If the explosion is near ground level most of the radioactive debris is in the form of coarse particles and these are rapidly deposited over an area to the windward of the explosion. In the case of the megaton range of explosions, however, the violent upsurge of heated air carries a large proportion of the debris into the upper atmosphere (*stratosphere*) from which it may take many years to deposit. This permits a portion of the radioactive isotopes to decay before deposition but also ensures large-scale distribution of the remainder.

The principal agent in the deposition of fission products is rainfall but a small amount of debris reaches the earth by gravitational force and by diffusion. Rain does not occur in the stratosphere and transfer of debris to the troposphere by diffusion is largely restricted by the *tropopause*, the dividing layer between the troposphere and the stratosphere. The stratosphere therefore represents a reservoir for radioactive debris.

Transfer of material into the troposphere occurs by sinking of air in the polar regions during the winter and by diffusion and precipitation through gaps in the tropopause that exist in temperate latitudes. This implies that the pattern of fallout from megaton weapons will depend on the latitude and also upon the season in which they were exploded. This is reflected in the fallout pattern observed during the years 1954 to 1960. In the United Kingdom the fallout rate remained constant, with the exception of seasonal varation, until the begining of 1958 and then

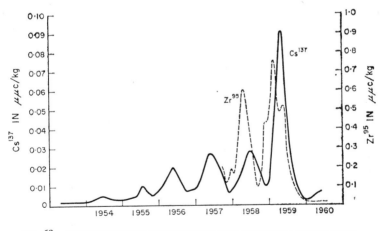

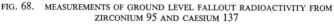

FIG. 68. MEASUREMENTS OF GROUND LEVEL FALLOUT RADIOACTIVITY FROM ZIRCONIUM 95 AND CAESIUM 137

increased threefold during 1958 and 1959. The early tests of weapons were mostly carried out in, or near, equatorial regions and the radioactive debris introduced into the stratosphere from these explosions could not immediately enter the troposphere. After the autumn of 1956, however, tests were carried out on a larger scale and mostly occurred in northern latitudes where transfer is more rapid.

Figure 68 shows the seasonal and annual pattern of fallout in the United Kingdom and it can be seen that the effect of the change in weapon testing in 1956 was associated with a rise in fallout about one year later. These observations are also supported by estimates of the age of the debris reaching the earth's surface. In 1959 this was six to thirteen months while in earlier years it ranged up to a few years.

BIOLOGICAL HAZARDS OF FALLOUT

Many different isotopes are formed during a nuclear explosion but only a small number contribute to biological hazards. The great majority of fission products are very short-lived and decay before they reach the earth. Others, with half-lives of under a few weeks, only present a hazard when deposited rapidly; those with half-lives of many years continue to represent a hazard even though they remain in the stratosphere for years. Two other factors of importance are the biological properties of an isotope and the type of radiation it emits upon decay. An isotope of an element which is a normal constituent of living tissue may be accumulated in the body but if it produces only weakly penetrating radiations, the hazard may be restricted to certain tissues

Of chief importance to human hazards are the isotopes zirconium 95 and niobium 95 with moderately short half-lives, caesium 137 and strontium 90 with half-lives of about 30 years, and carbon 14 with a half-life of about 5700 years. The first two have become important following the rapid fallout from weapons that were tested after 1956. Measurement of ground radiation in Great Britain showed a sharp rise in dose rate in 1958 and 1959 and this resulted chiefly from isotopes like zirconium 95 and niobium 95. Particularly high dose rates were recorded, ranging up to 30 per cent of the normal background. These exist for only short periods of time, however, and when due allowance is made for the shielding effect of buildings and overlying tissues, the estimated gonad dose rose from 0·4 mrads per year for 1956 to 1·8 mrads and 4·2 mrads per year in 1958 and 1959 respectively, and fell to 1·5 mrads per year in 1960. None of the isotopes are accumulated in living tissues and in the absence of further weapon tests would cease to represent a hazard in future years.*

Caesium 137 and strontium 90 are the principle sources of fallout hazards to Man. They have long half-lives and, more important, they

* This chapter was completed before the beginning of the 1961 series of Russian test explosions. A brief report on the effects of this series is included on page 165.

are incorporated into living tissue. Strontium 90 is accumulated in bone; as a beta ray emitter, it contributes very little to genetic hazards. Caesium 137, on the other hand, is more generally distributed and emits highly penetrating gamma rays. These can be detected outside the body; by direct measurement the mean genetic dose during 1958 and 1959 was estimated to be between 1 and 1·5 mrads per year. In addition, caesium 137 outside the body represents a source of external irradiation which, in 1959, was estimated to contribute a genetic dose of about 1 mrad per year. Caesium 137 is taken into the body mainly by ingestion of contaminated food. It has been found that the isotope enters the plants mainly from the superficial deposits on the surfaces of the leaves; once in the soil, caesium 137 is no longer available for plant use. For this reason the hazard to Man from ingested caesium 137 depends on the fallout rate and not on the accumulation of fallout.

We have already noted that carbon 14 arises from the interaction between cosmic radiation and nitrogen in the atmosphere. In a similar way, the neutrons from a nuclear explosion also produce carbon 14 and, like the naturally occurring isotope, this is rapidly oxidised to carbon dioxide which becomes available to all living organisms. This radio-active carbon source is present initially in greatest quantities in the stratosphere. It subsequently diffuses into the troposphere and is then transferred to the earth's surface to become incorporated into plants or dissolved in the oceans. In this way the carbon 14 produced by nuclear explosions will persist for thousands of years, slowly decreasing in quantity as it is absorbed in ocean waters or fixed in soils. Estimations of the total carbon 14 produced by nuclear explosions up to 1959, indi-cate that the total *per capita* dose of radiation from this source will be about 110 mrads spread over many thousands of years. In the current 30-year period beginning in 1960 the extra dose will average about 9 mrads with the dose being approximately halved in subsequent 30-year periods.

An additional mechanism exists by which carbon 14 may produce mutations. Carbon is one of the basic constituents of living tissue and, more specifically, it is an important element in the genetic material DNA. During decay a carbon 14 atom undergoes transmutation to a nitrogen atom. If the carbon 14 atom was part of the DNA molecule its replace-ment by the chemically different nitrogen atom would have profound effects. Little research has been devoted to this aspect of radiation genetics as yet, but some results indicate that the mutagenic effect of the transmutation process is about equal in magnitude to that of the direct radiation from carbon 14.

The genetically effective doses of radiation received from fallout and allied sources are summarised in Table 12. Included are estimates of the total doses received in 1959; doses received in subsequent 30-year periods under the assumption that no further tests of nuclear weapons

TABLE 12.   GONAD DOSES FROM FALLOUT IN 1959 AND ESTIMATES OF 30-YEAR DOSES

			Gonad Radiation Dose in mrads		
	Sources	1959	Current 30–year period	Second 30–year period	Equilibrium value mrads/year
External	Short lived isotopes	4·2	—	—	5
	Caesium 137	1·2	25	12	2·5
Internal	Carbon 14	0·4	9	5	3·5
	Caesium 137	1·0	20	10	2·5
	Total	6·8	54	27	13·5

(On the assumption that there are no more tests and estimates for equilibrium values assuming that tests continue at the same rate as in the period 1956 to 1959)

take place; and the equilibrium doses anticipated in the event that tests continue at the same rate as during 1956 to 1959. The total doses of radiation received by persons in the United Kingdom are summarised in Table 13.

TABLE 13.   TOTAL AVERAGE GONAD DOSES OF RADIATION FROM ALL SOURCES IN THE UNITED KINGDOM

	Dose in mrads	
	During 1959	*Current 30-year period
Natural sources	99	2,970
Medical radiology	19·3	579
Occupational exposure	1·4	42
Fallout	6·8	54
Total	126·5	3,645

ESTIMATION OF THE GENETIC CONSEQUENCES OF HUMAN EXPOSURE TO RADIATIONS

Mutant genes with individually recognisable effects are almost always harmful to the individual.   Although Man has improved domestic

* On the expectation of no further testing of nuclear weapons and no further increase in medical or occupational exposures.

animals and plants by the utilisation of desirable mutant genes, the advantage only persists while the organisms are under domestication; in the wild, domesticated animals and plants would be at a serious disadvantage. The principle that all major mutant genes are harmful is also in agreement with the principles of evolution. Since, by natural selection a population comprises the fittest genotypes, any major change must be detrimental. It will be noted that in this paragraph we have specified individually recognisable or major genes; in that part of the genotype concerned with polygenic inheritance there can be no distinction between mutant and wild-type alleles since they are not individually recognisable and have no value *per se* in the genotype.

No one doubts that ionising radiations produce mutation in Man but as yet they have not been detected by direct observation. There is no direct evidence, therefore, of the type of mutation that might be expected nor of the rate at which they might appear under given conditions of radiation. The only approach to these problems at present is to consider in what way the observed effects of radiation on other organisms can be applied to Man.

TYPES OF MUTATION CONSTITUTING THE RADIATION HAZARD

The first part of the problem, what types of mutation can be expected, is relatively straightforward. Living organisms are exposed to radiations from natural sources and there is no reason to suspect that this has not been so since the beginning of evolution. It follows, therefore, that all the possible types of radiation-induced mutation have occurred at some time or other and that no novel types will arise from exposure to artificial or Man-made radiations. Individual induced mutations will therefore be of types that are found to occur naturally. This does not necessarily mean that the spectrum of induced mutations will be the same as the spectrum of spontaneous mutation. Natural background levels of radiation are far too low to account for the spontaneous mutation rates that are observed in experimental organisms. Other processes contribute the greater part of these rates and there is no *a priori* reason for expecting them to lead to effects similar to radiations. Nevertheless, no great distinction has been observed between spontaneous and induced mutations in experimental organisms. It may be concluded, though only tentatively, that the effect of radiations in Man will be to produce an increase in existing natural mutation rates without the appearance of any new types of mutation. Thus the observed variety of inherited diseases and disabilities provides a reference to what may be anticipated in the genetic hazards of radiation exposure.

The second part of the problem, the measurement of the magnitude of the hazard from radiation-induced mutation, is beset by many difficulties, not least of which is the absence of any data directly bearing on induced mutation in Man. Several ways are open, however, for estimating expected increases in hereditary disability in Man on the basis of observations in other organisms. Although these estimates can only be considered tentative, in that they involve many assumptions and simplifications, they do indicate limits within which the true state of affairs is confidently thought to exist.

THE EFFECT OF DOSE

Human beings are exposed on the average to genetic doses of radiation of the order of 150 mrads a year. Thus in the 30-year generation time, individuals receive an average of about 4·5 rads. This low radiation exposure is far below anything yet reported in experimental studies*. The radiation dose is received chiefly from continuous exposure to very low intensity radiation; only in the case of medical radiology does the radiation intensity come within the range that has been employed in experimental research. Early work in radiation genetics established the principle that the frequency of induced mutation was directly proportional to dose and independent of the rate at which it was accumulated. As described at the end of chapter 5, an exception to this rule has been discovered in relation to the induction of mutations in immature germ cells. In these cells, low intensity irradiation was less effective, per unit dose, than high intensity irradiation. Since most of Man's exposure to radiation comes within the scope of low intensity irradiation, and since the germ cells which receive the long term irradiation are predominantly in immature stages, it would appear reasonable to assess human hazards on the basis of the lower effectiveness of low intensity radiation.

In the studies on the mouse, low intensity radiation (0·01 r/min) was only about $\frac{1}{4}$ as effective as higher intensities. This figure is only approximate and the possibility that the intensity effect is even greater at progressively lower radiation intensities is not known; it is suspected, however, that this is not the case. It must be emphasised that this implies that a linear dose response still exists below the low radiation intensities. The postulate may thus be framed that below a small range of radiation intensities the mutagenic effect is only one quarter of that above this range. Human exposure falls in the first category, experimental work mostly in the second.

* A study has been reported of the genetic effects of radiation doses of 5 r given to *Drosophila* males and females; the data support the principle that mutation frequency is simply proportional to dose.

THE DOUBLING DOSE

One of the most straightforward approaches to the question of mutation rates in Man concerns the concept of the *doubling dose* which is defined as the dose of radiation required to induce a mutation rate equal to the spontaneous rate. The mutagenic effects of radiation depend quantitatively on many biological factors. Different organisms differ in their sensitivity to radiations and so also do different cells and different loci within any particular organism. If there is a correlation between spontaneous and induced mutation rates then these variables will not affect the magnitude of the doubling dose which should be similar for all organisms. If experimental evidence supported this conjecture the doubling dose could be used to estimate the rate of mutation in Man on the basis of human spontaneous mutation rates.

Doubling doses for several organisms under various conditions of irradiation are summarised in Table 14. It can be seen that there is

TABLE 14. SOME EXAMPLES OF DOUBLING DOSES IN
EXPERIMENTAL ORGANISMS

Organism	Mutations	Irradiated cells	Doubling dose in rads
Zea mais	4 recessive visibles	Pollen	28
Oenothera	Self-incompatability	Pollen	60
Drosophila	Sex-linked recessive lethals	Post-meiotic germ cells	50 to 100
	Autosomal recessive lethals	Pre-meiotic germ cells	300
	Sex-linked recessive lethals	Oöcytes and oögonia	390
	Autosomal recessive lethals	During spermatogenesis	70
Mouse	7 recessive lethals	Spermatogonia	80
Escherichia coli	3 biochemical mutants		68 to 186

considerable diversity but that this is mainly due to the very high doubling doses in immature cells in *Drosophila*. The conditions underlying the doubling dose estimates for these cells, however, are unrepresentative of germ cells as a whole. They are the least sensitive germ cells in *Drosophila*, and as far as genetic effects are concerned they have a relatively short life before undergoing meiosis. The spontaneous mutation rate comprises the sum total of effects during the entire cycle of spermatogenesis. It is to be expected that this rate is determined to the greatest extent by mutation in post-meiotic stages which are known to be the most sensitive stages to radiations and also to most chemical mutagens. It follows, therefore, that in *Drosophila* a comparison of spontaneous with induced spermatogonial mutation rates will give a very high doubling dose estimate. Apart from this the remaining doubling doses in the table cluster within the range of 30 to 100 rads. Clearly the most significant comparison would be between spontaneous rates and induced rates following continuous radiation exposure of the whole developmental cycle of the germ cells. This has only been done for autosomal lethals in the male germ line of *Drosophila* but the continuous irradiation of spermatogonia in the mouse probably represents a fair approximation to these conditions; spermatogonia represent by far the longest developmental stage in mammalian spermatogenesis. The doubling doses under these conditions occupy an intermediate position in the range but more important, they derive from chronic irradiation at low intensities and may thus be considered most nearly related to conditions in Man. On these grounds the doubling dose appears to be about 70 rads but in view of the tenuous nature of the above arguments it is perhaps safer to consider that it most probably lies somewhere between 30 and 100 rads. If we accept this range for the doubling dose it follows that in the current 30-year period natural background irradiation will contribute between 3 and 10 per cent of the spontaneous mutation rate and that medical radiology will increase this by between 0·6 and 2·0 per cent; fallout from nuclear test explosions up to 1959 will produce a further increase of between 0·06 and 0·2 per cent.

GENETIC LOAD ASSOCIATED WITH PRESUMED INCREASES IN MUTATION
     RATES

We obtained a rough estimate of the rate at which mutation may occur in Man under the action of radiations. It now remains to interpret these estimates in terms of the future frequency of inherited disease or ill-health.

The frequency of existing hereditary abnormalities in human populations was discussed in the previous chapter. From the comprehensive survey in Northern Ireland it appeared that inherited abnormalities are present in about 7 per cent of all births. Just over half this frequency was made up of conditions with complex underlying genetic causes, not fully understood, but not involving single mutations. One

of these conditions, mongolism, is associated with chromosome unbalance and translocation. It seems unlikely that this results from
radiation-induced chromosome breakage; the probability of two breaks
arising sufficiently near to one another in time to undergo exchange
is extremely small and it seems improbable that an increase in
mutation rate will affect the frequency of mongolism. The same conclusion can be applied tentatively to the other conditions with complex
causes. It may well be that they are determined by unfortunate com-
binations of several genes which separately have no disadvantage to an
individual; the frequency of these would be largely independent of
mutation rates.

The conditions determined by single mutant genes represent the most
tangible way in which an increased mutation rate will be harmful. Of
the 3·6 per cent incidence of such traits in Northern Ireland, 3·3 per
cent were due to dominant genes. 107 specific traits were ascertained
which, since they are not necessarily gene specific, probably represent
about 180 loci. Accepting that the most likely average spontaneous
mutation rate for dominant genes is 14×10^{-6}, the number of new
mutations of natural origin appearing per million births would be
$180 \times 14 = 2520$. Medical radiology would increase this by between
15 and 50 mutations and fallout radiation by between 2 and 5 mutations.

Under the present conditions then, it may be estimated that
during the next generation the incidence of dominantly inherited
defects will rise from about 33,000 cases per million births to, on the
worst estimate, 33,055. With reduced exposure to Man-made radiation
the figure would rapidly revert to its original magnitude but with con-
tinuation or increase in the amount of radiation it would remain at the
higher rate or increase rapidly. It is obvious that compared with
natural frequencies, the additional induced frequencies are low. The
reason for this is that the majority of dominant conditions are very mild
and a large number have no detectable effect on viability or fertility.
They occur, therefore, with high frequencies relative to the mutation
rates of the genes concerned.

The recessive traits affected 0·15 per cent of births and were probably
represented by about 50 loci; all were severely detrimental. The
estimated spontaneous mutation rates for recessive genes were shown
to be much larger than those for dominant genes, although numerous
factors combined to make them of doubtful validity. If one accepts the
average rate of about 24×10^{-6}, though it is almost certainly too high,
the number of mutations arising from present exposure to Man-made
ionising radiations will be between 8 and 27 per million loci. These will,
of course, only produce the disease when in the homozygous condition,

and the increase in the frequency of the traits will be the summation of the squares of the increase *in the frequency at each locus*. It is perhaps easier to consider one particular trait. Phenylketonuria is found in about 100 cases per million births. This incidence equals the square of the gene frequency which is thus 0·01; one mutant allele per hundred genes. The mutation rate from Man-made sources of irradiation will be, at the highest estimate, 2·2 per cent of the spontaneous rate of 24×10^{-6} or one mutation in two million normal alleles. Thus the gene frequency will change from 0·01 to 0·0100005. This will obviously have a negligible effect on the frequency of the disease in one generation. Nevertheless, according to the basic principles of population genetics, deleterious mutations entering a population through mutation must eventually leave it through selection. Mutations induced by Man-made radiations will eventually express themselves in direct proportion to their rate of production even though this may be very many generations removed from their origin. If the spontaneous mutation rate for a recessive gene is raised permanently by a factor of 0·022 the incidence of the disease will eventually be increased by this factor (see page 119).

The mutations dealt with so far determine specific inherited diseases or disabilities; they may be compared with the visible mutations found in experimental organisms. In *Drosophila*, the organism for which most data are available on this point, visible mutations represent only a small part of the total induced mutation frequencies. Recessive lethals are about ten times more frequent than visibles, and detrimentals forty or fifty times more frequent. Can it be assumed that similar categories of mutations arise in a similar way in Man? No answer to this question can yet be given but an indirect appraisal is possible. Studies on the litter size in the offspring from mice backcrossed to their irradiated fathers indicated that lethal mutations are induced at a rate which is about fifteen times as great as that in *Drosophila*. A similar figure has been obtained by comparing the rates of induction of specific locus visible mutations in *Drosophila* and mouse; consequently it may be deduced that the relative frequencies of induced visibles and lethals are the same in *Drosophila* and mouse; hence they may be representative also for Man. This is a rather tenuous argument and, in any case, the estimates of induced lethal frequencies in mouse cannot be accepted with great confidence. If one does assume that lethal mutations are frequent in Man, however, the genetic hazard need not be considered serious. Pre-natal death of an embryo does not have the same unfortunate social implications as post-natal death or disability. It is also unlikely that it would affect fecundity since family size in Man is usually restricted by "family planning" and is not correlated to potential fertility: if both parents carry the same recessive lethal gene in the heterozygous condition this will only result in a 25 per cent reduction in potential fertility.

The question of deleterious recessive mutation is more important in an assessment of human radiation risks. These mutants will express themselves in individuals and result in personal unhappiness and adverse social complications. It is not at all possible, however, to estimate the magnitude of their relevance to human radiation hazards. Some idea of the significance of deleterious mutants in human populations has recently been achieved by an analysis of surveys on life span of off-spring from cousin marriages. Their offspring, as explained in Chapter 7, will tend to carry more genes in the homozygous condition than offspring from unrelated parents; deleterious recessives would thus render the former offspring slightly less fit than the average. The statistical examinations have been expressed in terms of *lethal equivalents*, that is, the number of full recessive lethals that would represent the same total average reduction in life span in a population. On this basis it has been estimated that individuals carry an average of about three lethal equivalents in the heterozygous condition. It is not yet possible to carry this sort of analysis further to determine the numbers and effectiveness of individual loci but this obviously remains an important branch of genetics in future research.

To conclude, the increased exposure of human populations to radiation is not likely to produce new, bizarre genetic effects but is expected to increase the frequency of those types of hereditary disability that are already known. The magnitude of this increase under present levels of exposure to Man-made radiation can only be deduced by extrapolation from data on experimental organisms; no data from direct observations on Man are, as yet, conclusive. It seems probable that the increased mutation frequency will be only a small fraction of that which arises spontaneously, but that it will definitely produce a small increase in the frequency of individuals showing some hereditary illness. Should tests of nuclear weapons be continued, the frequency of affected individuals will rise until an equilibrium point is reached between production and decay of radioisotopes and origin and removal, by selection, of disadvantageous mutations. It appears improbable that the increased levels of radiation exposure would have any effect on biometrical characters such as stature and intelligence but here, most of all, the state of knowledge is too imperfect to allow more than very cautious conclusions to be drawn.

RECENT ATMOSPHERIC TESTS OF NUCLEAR WEAPONS

As explained earlier in this chapter, the deposition of radioactive

12

debris from nuclear explosions follows a seasonal pattern determined largely by the downward movement of air from the atmosphere during winter months. Maximum deposition of fallout is thus recorded in the spring and the effects of the nuclear explosions carried out by the U.S.S.R. in the autmun of 1961 will not become apparent until the spring of 1962. Some indication of the extent of fallout can be deduced, however, by comparing this series of tests with the 1958 series which was also carried out in the U.S.S.R.

The production of radioactive isotopes comes from the fission of Uranium 235 in the atomic primer of a nuclear explosion. The relevant comparison, therefore, is between the fission yields of the 1958 and 1961 series respectively. The 1961 series was remarkable in that, compared with the total yield of about 120 megatons, the fission yield was only 25 megatons. In all tests up to and including the 1958 series, the total yield comprised 170 megatons of which 92 megatons represented fission yield. In the 1958 series, the fission yield totaled 15 megatons and it has been estimated that this produced about 70 per cent of the fallout observed during 1959. If conditions in 1958 and 1961 were identical, the additional fallout in 1962 would be approximately $0.7 \times 25/15$ or 1.2 times the total amount in 1959. In one important respect, however, the tests in 1961 differed from those in 1958. In the former, a large proportion of the total yield came from very large explosions of the 30 and 60 megaton weapons. It is possible that the enormous upsurge of air following these explosions carried radioactive debris to a far greater height in the stratosphere than hitherto. In this case it is possible that some of the debris will remain in the stratosphere far longer than usual and not be precipitated as fallout in 1962. If an arbitrary figure of 15 per cent is given for this delayed fallout, it follows that fallout in 1962 will be increased by an amount approximately equal to that observed in 1959. The long term effects, as represented in terms of fallout during 30 year periods, will be increased approximately in proportion to the ratio between the fission yield of the 1961 tests and the fission yield from all earlier tests; in other words, by a factor of about one quarter.

Since carbon 14 arises from the bombardment of nitrogen nuclei by neutrons, its production is dependent on the total yield from nuclear weapons testing. In this case, the 1961 series may be expected to increase the carbon 14 component of fallout by a factor of about $120/170$ or 0.7.

The effect of the 1961 test explosions on the genetically effective doses of radiation received by Man may be estimated by applying these calculations to the data in Table 12. The results are summarised in Table 15.

TABLE 15. ESTIMATES OF GONAD DOSES OF RADIATION ARISING FROM
FALLOUT FROM NUCLEAR WEAPON TESTING UP TO AND INCLUDING THE
1961 SERIES. (See also Table 12)

		Gonad Radiation Dose in mrads				
				Estimates for		
	Sources	1959	1962	*Current 30–Year Period*	*Second 30–Year Period*	*Equilibrium Value mrads/year*
External	Short lived iso-topes	4.2	4.2	—	—	5.0
	Caesium 137	1.2	2.0	31	15	2.5
Internal	Carbon 14	0.4	0.6	15	8	3.5
	Caesium 137	1.0	1.8	25	12	2.5
Total		6.8	8.6	71	35	13.5

The calculations used here are necessarily very speculative. More
decisive conclusions must await the collection and analysis of fallout
data during 1962.

FURTHER READING

PHYSICS
Radiological Physics, J. K. Robertson, 1956. Macmillan, London.

GENETICS
Principles of Genetics, E. W. Sinnott, L. C. Dunn and T. Dobzhansky, 5th Ed. 1958. McGraw-Hill, New York.
Genetics of Micro-organisms, D. G. Catcheside, 1951. Pitman, London.
The Genetics of the Mouse, H. Gruneberg, 2nd ed. 1952. Martinus Nijhoff, The Hague.

CYTOLOGY
Cytology and Cytogenetics, C. P. Swanson, 1957. Prentiss-Hall, Engelwood Cliffs.
The Handling of Chromosomes, C. D. Darlington and L. F. La Cour, 3rd ed. 1960. George Allen & Unwin, London.

POPULATION GENETICS
Population Genetics, C. C. Li, 1955. University of Chicago Press.
The Genetic Basis of Selection, I. M. Lerner, 1958. John Wiley, New York.

HUMAN GENETICS
Principles of Human Genetics, C. Stern, 2nd ed. 1960. W. H. Freeman, San Francisco.

RADIATION GENETICS AND CYTOGENETICS
Action of Radiations on Living Cells, D. E. Lea, 2nd Ed. 1956. Cambridge University Press.
Radiation Biology, Vol. 1. Ed. A. Hollaender, 1954. McGraw-Hill, New York.
Mechanisms in Radiobiology (2 Vols.) Ed. M. Errera and A. Forssberg, 1961. Academic Press, New York.
Radiation Biology of Vicia. J. Read, 1959. Blackwell Scientific Publication, Oxford.
Chromosome Aberrations Induced by Ionising Radiations, H. J. Evans, 1962. International Review of Cytology. Vol. 13. Academic Press, New York.
Immediate and Low Level Effects of Ionizing Radiations, Ed. A. A. Buzzati-Traverso, 1960. Supplement to International Journal of Radiation Biology. Taylor & Francis, London.

OFFICIAL REPORTS
The Hazards to Man of Nuclear and Allied Radiations, Medical Research Council 1st Report 1956. Cmd 9780. 2nd Report 1960. Cmd 1225. H.M. Stationery Office, London.
The Biological Effects of Atomic Radiations, Summary Report 1956 and 1960. National Academy of Sciences, National Research Council, Washington.
Report of the United Nations Scientific Committee on the *Effects of Atomic Radiation*, 1958. United Nations, New York.
Radiological Hazards to Patients, 2nd Report, 1960. Ministry of Health, Department of Health for Scotland. H.M. Stationery Office, London.

INDEX

169